BE LIKE THE BEST

BE LIKE THE BEST

A GUIDE TO REACHING THE TOP IN THE FITNESS PROFESSION

ANTHONY RENNA

ON TARGET PUBLICATIONS, APTOS, CALIFORNIA

Be Like the Best
A Guide to Reaching the Top of the Fitness Profession

Anthony Renna

ISBN-13: 978-1-931046-37-4, paperback
ISBN-13: 978-1-931046-33-6, epub

First printing October 2019

On Target Publications
P. O. Box 1335
Aptos, California 95001 USA
otpbooks.com

LCCN 2019036479

Library of Congress Cataloging-in-Publication Data was not ready before print date, but is available upon request.

CONTENTS

INTRODUCTION

"It's said that a wise person learns from his mistakes. A wiser one learns from others' mistakes. But the wisest person of all learns from others' successes."
~ John C. Maxwell

In today's "Age of Information," it's so easy to be inundated with shortcuts, tricks and schemes to "make it." It's simple to start following the way one person does things and then get sidetracked and change course when we see what others are doing. We get information overload and then we get paralyzed. It's called "paralysis by analysis" and it stops us from taking action.

This book is a collection of interviews with some of the top fitness professionals in the world. I picked a mix of people from different sections of the profession—personal trainers, physical therapists, strength and conditioning coaches, gym owners, chiropractors, entrepreneurs, professors and business coaches—to gain different perspectives on the success journey.

During the last 12 years of interviewing hundreds of strength coaches, fitness professionals, physical therapists and gym owners as the founder and host of *The Strength Coach Podcast* as well as *Strength Coach TV,* I have accumulated a rolodex of "The Best of the Best" in the fitness profession.

I picked the people in this book that I not only consider to be masters of their craft, but who are also accessible. These are people who have given endless hours to not only help their clients and patients, but to other professionals they encounter at conferences, workshops, through social media and podcasts.

I love the quote, "No one cares how much you know until they know how much you care." I have a personal relationship with every person I interviewed in this book and I can tell you it's a group of the most caring people you've ever met. These are professionals who really care about making an impact in the world and in their profession.

You'll learn how they evolved in their careers, what habits and traits they believe made them successful, their goal setting processes, how they get through hard times and even some books to read and people they recommend following.

After each interview, I have included what I call a "Be Like."

What the heck is a "Be Like?"

It's a challenge or action step based on a takeaway from each interview. They're designed to encourage you to make the necessary changes and habits to Be Like the Best on your journey to dominating this profession.

For example, during the Mike Boyle interview, he said, "I believe my success coincided directly with writing and speaking." Hence, the "Be Like Mike" challenge gives you action steps and ideas to start writing and to eventually turn that into a presentation to use to get in front of everyone you can.

While there are many takeaways in each interview, the specific "Be Like" for each person was something that stood out to me. Many of the "Be Likes" in the book come from my own experience having top-level coaches and I've used them with great success.

I promise you that if you pick the "Be Likes" that match an area where you need improvement or change, you'll absolutely be on your way to being among the best in the fitness profession.

But you can't go at this half-heartedly. When you decide you will do a "Be Like," you have to give it everything you have, with complete focus and a commitment to stay the course.

It's the only way you'll make a change!

Don't just read the interviews and not take action on what they're suggesting. One of the biggest differences between the most successful people and those who are on the border is that the most successful people take the action steps needed.

Be Like the Best and make a commitment to yourself that you're the kind of person who takes action…and does so immediately.

How to Read this Book

Any way you like!

You can read it cover to cover or you can pick some people who you want to Be Like and read their interviews. You can also look at the Be Like index and find the areas you need to address and get after it.

As a fitness professional, you're already making an impact in your clients, athletes and patients. This book will help you stand out in a crowded field and help you stay on the road to success.

Good luck in your journey!

Anthony Renna

John Berardi is a Canadian-American entrepreneur best known as the co-founder of Precision Nutrition, the world's largest nutrition coaching, education and software company. He's also the founder of Change Maker Academy, devoted to helping would-be change makers turn their passion for health and fitness into a powerful purpose and a wildly successful career. Over the last 15 years, he's advised Apple, Equinox, Nike and Titleist, as well as the San Antonio Spurs, Carolina Panthers, US Open Champ Sloane Stephens and two-division UFC Champ Georges St. Pierre. He has also been named one of the 20 smartest coaches in the world and 100 most influential people in health and fitness. His book, Change Maker, comes out in the fall of 2019. Check out more at changemakeracademy.com.

You've reached such a high level of success in so many areas, as an athlete, professor and entrepreneur. The Precision Nutrition certification has helped more than 100,000 health and fitness professionals. Your mission is to help people continue on that journey. But how you do you define success?

I come at this from a different angle—defining words can get esoteric and less concrete. If I were to describe someone I thought was successful, what criterion would I use to determine that? For me, it's a triangulating of different areas. Certainly, there are external validations associated with the amount of money people make or the kind of company they've grown; one part is going to be financial. But stopping there is a fairly large mistake.

I'd look at the work. Is it work that has both personal meaning and makes some kind of contribution? It doesn't have to—as Steve Jobs said—make a dent in the universe, but is it meaningful to them personally and to the people they serve?

It goes another step further because someone who has a lot of money and is doing personally meaningful work is not always a successful person. That's when other things come in—things like having a great life perspective or having a great social and family balance. Another element is self-care. Do they take care of themselves? And that's not just the proactive steps of exercising, but also includes recovery and recharging.

I triangulate the idea of success as "having your shit together." That's a phrase everyone understands. That's how I'd describe a successful person: someone who has reached a certain amount of financial wealth, has done meaningful work, and has great perspective and wisdom.

Successful people make time for social and family life and take care of themselves, although you don't need all of those to be a personal success. And people get to define this on their own terms, but that's something I hope to achieve personally and that I'm impressed by in others.

Some people say you can't create a work–life balance, but trying to have your shit together in that respect is certainly a meaningful goal. When did you feel you were starting to get your shit together?

I learned a valuable lesson about this when, early in my life, I looked to external validations for success. One of my famous stories is when I worked hard through academia early in my career. I did an undergrad, then a master's, then a PhD, and at the end of the PhD road, you should feel academically successful. You've achieved something that only a small percentage of the world has accomplished.

The dissertation defense is the last stage of the PhD accomplishment. You're in a room with four or five professors to grill you and not only determine whether you're worthy of the degree, but also humble you in important ways—you're smart, but not at their level.

I remember walking out of the room after they'd given me a handshake and said, "You've passed your PhD requirements." I remember looking around and the hallway was empty. I went home and fixed dinner like I would have any other night of the week. There was no parade in my honor; there were no people calling me up exclaiming, "It's so awesome!" It was a strange, anticlimactic moment when I'd achieved an external validation of success, but didn't feel any different. In fact, there was a major letdown because I believed there were certain accompaniments to "success" that weren't there.

Another example is when I wanted to publish my first book. My brother and I went home for Christmas and visited a bookstore and I said, "Within two years, I'm going to have a book in this bookstore." That goal meant way more than having a book in the bookstore, but I didn't know it at the time. Two years later, it was true. We went home for Christmas, went to the same bookstore and I said, "Remember what I told you two years ago? There's my book."

It was objectively true, I had accomplished that goal, but what I didn't realize was that I'd expected that to mean I'd be rich and famous and have a big house on the hill and everyone in the store would want my autograph. What ended up happening? Nothing. The conditions were the same as two years earlier, except I had a book on the shelf.

Early in my career, I set out to be a millionaire by the age of 35 and I accomplished that. It was almost the same feeling as the PhD story. I had a million dollars of net worth by age 35, and there was no parade or party in my honor.

You start to realize after accumulating a few of these experiences that if you define success by external validations, you're going to be consistently let down. Almost every successful person talks about this.

The idea of becoming a success started to center around meaningful work, self-care, wisdom, social and family balance…having your shit together. When you look at it in those terms, you realize no one wakes up that way. You don't wake up in the morning and say, "I'm not lazy. I'm a great communicator. I have wisdom. I'm going to spend every minute with my family. I'm also going to do meaningful work."

You don't wake up like that. You wake up *unlike* that—and it's a practice every day because you wake up sucking at things and then work on accomplishing them. You don't just become a great communicator or a great parent or become great at taking care of yourself. You actually wake up bad at it every single day.

And you don't fix the problem and then you're set for life. This is mindfulness and other intangibles. You wake up and you're bad at them.

That's how I feel about the idea of being a success and striving toward that.

There isn't a day when you just accomplish it and you're done, when you can stop worrying about being a success because you've accomplished it and now it's a success cloak you can wear for the rest of your life. No! It's like bathing. You get dirty every day and have to wash the dirt off.

It's the same with mindfulness, meditation, success and self-care. You get worse over time and you need a bath or the equivalent to recharge yourself. That's how I think about success and my own relationship with it. I wake up every day and work at it.

You've devoted your career to making health and fitness achievable and attainable for everyone in all walks of life. Is that what gets you out of bed and motivates you from a business or a fitness perspective?

There are two major things that drive me professionally. I grew up in an immigrant family. My parents came from a really poor part of Italy, post-World War II, where there weren't many resources. When they came to the States, they had no education and they didn't speak English, but they were hardworking people. This was embedded in my DNA and in how I was raised. I realized early on that I was going to work hard at whatever I did. It didn't matter what it was, I don't have it in me not to put out the effort. All the examples I had were that—working tirelessly, working hard and not complaining about it.

I decided that if I'm going to work hard no matter what I'm working on, it would be cool if when I was ready to retire or was on my deathbed, I'd have chosen something that was meaningful. If I worked hard and didn't complain about something that was meaningless, that's fine. But it would be cool if I was working hard on something I knew was worth the effort.

Due to circumstances, I was on the wrong track during my teenage years, but someone got me on the right track through exercise. It made me want to do my hard work in this field.

That person and the fitness and health profession in general saved my life in some metaphorical but also concrete ways. This is why I want to be in this field. I have a clear definition when I die or retire: I would like to know that my work helped the people working in health and fitness see their clients differently.

When I came up in health and fitness, we saw clients as fundamentally lazy people who were broken, who were missing this fitness thing we had. We thought we had to change them, to turn them into fitness people like us.

I'm hoping through my work and through the work of others who come after me that we'll have made a dent in that, to help people working in our field see their clients fundamentally different—as independent, autonomous people with superpowers they use in other areas of their lives, turning those superpowers toward the things they can use to propel their health and fitness. I want people who work in our profession to see their work differently—rather than, "I'm a personal trainer," or "I'm a nurse," or "I'm a physical therapist," but more that, "I'm a concierge for transformative change."

That's what gets me motivated—seeing the health and fitness profession change, the people working in this field seeing their clients and their role in the world differently. We've accomplished some of that, but we still have lots of work to do.

Precision Nutrition has become a great company that's making a big difference. I have a meta-goal there too, which is that we want to become the first billion-dollar company that works remotely using a totally different management system. Precision Nutrition is about a $200 million company now. We work remotely; we don't have a head office. We help people set up home offices wherever they want to live.

Some people live in different places throughout the year, and we use a distributed authority system. The term of the method we use is called "wholeocracy." Knowledge workers don't thrive in an environment where they have to check in, work for a certain number of hours every week and have bosses. They generally work well when they're given a lot of independence to be creative, but with a certain degree of structure—what we call an "independent authority." That's the meta-goal.

I'd love to lead Precision Nutrition to become that size company and be the first to do it remotely using a distributed authority system with knowledge workers because it hasn't been done before. I believe it'll be a transformative thing for the business world to see that the old structures don't have to be used anymore. Those are my professional motivators.

One of the things I've always loved about your message is when we thought we were going to hear you talk about nutrition…and ended up learning about the behavior of change. You made us think—you're always so ahead of the curve. Talk to us about that process. Do you have a morning routine?

We have four children, so a lot of my schedule is determined by the other things in my life. When I get up, I roll out to the kitchen. and cook breakfast for the family.

I help the kids with breakfast and usually leave mine in the oven to stay warm until I ship them out. Amanda takes them to school and at that point, I put in a solid 8:30AM until 2:30PM workday. I work straight through and then I pick up the kids from school, bring them home and we all hang out until bedtime. That's when I grab my workout—when everyone's in bed.

I think a lot about the goal of my life. What's the goal of my work? What's the goal of my week? My month? My year? This particular day? I do a prioritization filter. I know my goal for work—it's already been pre-established through collective planning. I know the objectives and strategy for the year. I know what we're trying to do each month.

We can do 100 things, but not in a day and not in a week. I have an importance filter I run each day. Sometimes there are 20 things I could do. There are probably 30 things people asked me to do the day before, but I can only do three. How do I prioritize so the three I do actually matter? There could be someone working 14 hours in the next building, but if they're doing 10 things that don't matter and I do three that do, I win every time.

Everyone who has a job and thinks their work is meaningful and wants to make a difference knows it's anxiety-producing to have 30 things on your to-do list. How do you eliminate the anxiety?

I've already established my goal. Not this morning, but in a moment of clear thinking when I wasn't in the midst of problems and challenges. I took time away and in a clear-thinking moment or day or strategy session, I decided the goal. I'm just holding myself to that decision. I do the hard work of saying that of these 30 things, I can do only three today. These are the most important things.

There was a phase in my career when I had five or 10 things on my to-do list and at the end of almost every day, they wouldn't be done. Even if I finished four out of five, I'd still feel tremendous anxiety because I hadn't finished my work list. It would take me a couple of hours to relax and some nights I'd never get out of that headspace. That's when

I realized this magical thing happens when you only put three things on your list, things you know you can accomplish. If I put three things on my list and accomplish them, I feel great for the rest of the day.

I'm going to commit each day to less than I know I'm capable of so I can finish and feel satisfied. If there's time for one more, that's a bonus because in the other scenario, I ticked more items off the checklist, but I still felt bad. It's not just what you accomplish, but how you set things up so you can feel good about what you've done.

John, you're mentioning goals, but is there a formal process where you set goals? Give us a look into that process.

When I was younger, it was important to me. The mentor who saved my life brought me into the fitness profession. He was big on personal development, so he introduced me to Zig Ziglar, Stephen Covey, Tony Robbins and that group of what used to be called "motivational speakers." From them, I picked up the goal-setting practice. When I was young, I used to do a lot of it.

I now do very little goal setting. It's a tiny fraction of my life because I have the framework of how we teach curriculum development. This is how we teach fitness—that goals have almost no traction because just you saying what you want.

That's important, but for a tiny microsecond. Skills are required. You don't achieve goals you've never accomplished without building new skills, and you don't build new skills without practicing things.

Classic examples are learning a language or to play an instrument. Part of that is boring because just like in the gym, you have to build new neural connections and muscle connections. When you're practicing scales on a piano, you're building new neural networks. It's generally boring work, but you have to do it daily so you can build the skills that lead to the goal of being able to play Beethoven. Most of my time is spent figuring out what skills I need next and what daily practices I need to accomplish those skills to get a goal. Goal setting is still valuable, but it's a tiny percent of my life. Most of what I'm doing day to day is after that singular thing has been defined.

A professional goal example might be having the first billion-dollar company to work remotely with distributed authority. How do you do that? You start working backward. I can't think my way to a billion-dollar company; I have to actually sell stuff. How many coaching clients will I have to get? How many certifications would I have to sell? How many software users would we have to have? Here are the numbers, and then you wonder, what industries would we get those from?

We're getting a certain number from fitness, but fitness isn't big enough to support those numbers. Would we go to physicians? Would we go to yoga practitioners? You start breaking things down; for example, we'd need to get so many new yoga practitioners using our programs, so many new physicians, new nurses, new fitness people.

But as a company, we don't have the skills to do that yet. I don't know how to speak to integrative medicine practitioners or what conferences they attend. How do we build the skills and what practices will we need to get good at? We have a downloadable worksheet on the site because it's how I approach everything.

Here's another example. My daughter takes gymnastics; instead of sitting on the side with all the parents while she's exercising, I asked the owner if I could get a private lesson. Now I work out while my daughter's working out and I can build some new skills. I brought my funny little chart to my new coach and told her it was partly just about being active, but that I'd also love to learn to do a back flip and a front flip and other stuff. Could she help me fill out the chart? If my goal was back flipping, what skills would I need to do a back flip? What things should I practice first and which should I practice next?

At first, people are a bit weirded out; they think it's too "systems thinking." But this is the way humans develop goals. It's something I use in every aspect of my life. It takes two seconds to determine a goal—although, longer if you're not sure or when there are competing goals. But once the goal is settled, there's a lot of work to do on skills and practices.

That's brilliant. It really brings new meaning to reverse engineering a goal by bringing in the skills and practices. You have a huge company and you have a lot going on. How do you stay organized?

I have different types of days in a week, specific days for specific things. Generally, Mondays and Tuesdays are meeting-free days. Those are for creative work, writing or just thinking. If I'm in the "What goals should I go after?" stage, those days are just for thinking and drafting ideas. Wednesdays and Thursdays are meetings and on Fridays, I generally work half a day. The first half of that is for media and podcasts. The second half, I'll either do quiet reading or sometimes even take the day off to take the kids out of school and do something fun.

How do you recharge after all this work?

The key for me is getting enough sleep. I'm a natural-born introvert and I believe I need more quiet time than many other people. With four children and a business, I get much less quiet time than I want. But I still get more than most people because either they don't find it important or don't prioritize it. Quiet time is an important recharging time—that may be reading a book, sitting quietly or just ideating on something.

Hiking and getting outdoors is important to me. I try to do that at least once a week. That's one of my most restorative activities—just getting out on a trail in the woods. We live by some amazing hiking in the "waterfall capital of the world." There are a few hundred waterfalls close by and I get out there often.

The other side of this is proactive: I don't let myself get uncharged, which is like prioritizing my work week and focusing on the big things and only tackling three things a day. I'll never run myself to the point where I badly need time off because we don't get many weeks off during the year. We take vacations as a family, but anyone with four kids knows you're not chilling on a beach relaxing when you go on a family vacation. It's actually much more work than our regular daily lives.

I don't get a lot of "go on vacation to recharge" time. That's a blessing because it's forced me not to wait until vacation to recharge, but to build it in to my life. I could complain and say, "I never get to recharge because even vacations are stressful," or I could say, "I need to recharge, so how do I do that in small ways in the context of my life?"

It's made me better at this and works better than if I waited for my annual vacation weeks.

Do you have any rules other than working Monday through Friday? What are those rules that keep those barriers up?

I generally try not to work at all in the evenings and on the weekends. Saturdays we do fun things and often on Sundays we do the same. For example, our five-year-old is into BMX racing and we go as a family or I'll take him for open track. Before they actually have races, there are two hours where you get to ride the tracks. I get a bike and ride too.

At pickup from school and on the weekends, I try not to do any work, but that's not a hard-and-fast rule. Sometimes things will heat up at Precision Nutrition and we'll be working on something ambitious, something's coming to fruition and I need to be more present. In that case, I ask my family if that's okay: "For the next month, we're working on something pretty big at work, which may mean some evenings I need to go in my office for an hour or two, or maybe on a Sunday, I might need to spend half the day working. Is that okay, and how can I make it up to you during the time we do get to spend together?"

I try to respect that they're active participants in my life and try to find ways to make it okay when I need to spend time away from them at work.

We see so many parents sitting on the sidelines. I love that idea of you doing what your kids are doing.

It's a blast. What's the alternative? I can tell you what it is because nearly every other parent is doing it: sitting on the sidelines on their phones if they're by themselves, sitting there chatting with other parents, sitting in the car reading or running errands. I don't judge anyone else's choice because I don't know what's going on in their lives, but I have the opportunity to be there and be present and what's more present than being participatory?

I also get to have a workout. I get to go out on the gymnastics floor with our three-year-old and participate in this class every Saturday, which is one of my favorite days of the week. It's a blast. It keeps me active, and it prevents me from doing things I don't want to be doing, like scrolling on my phone.

It's fun for the kids and provides a deeper connection with them. John, it's not always the best of times, so how do you push through those tough times?

For me, there are three things. One option is counseling—I'm a huge believer in counseling. I run a coaching business, so for me to sell coaching and not actually get coaching is hypocritical. Counseling has been an important part of my life as a proactive step.

When I was considering getting married to Amanda, we got a marriage counselor before we were married because we didn't want to need one later. I wanted to get one early so I could build strategies and do the equivalent of self-care in advance for our relationship.

When we started thinking about having children, we did the same. Let's get a family counselor and figure out in advance how to do this before there are problems. When you have a relationship pre-established and things aren't going well, you have a trusted person you can talk to.

At PN, we have a counseling budget for our team members—especially our coaches. It's a funny conversation to have when they join the team, "Welcome to PN. Here's your budget for getting therapy." Everyone who works in the counseling field knows you need a therapist to help offload things you're experiencing when you're working as a therapist. Every coach should have this.

That's important for me. I did an informal experiment a few years ago, looking at all the people I felt really had their shit together and I asked, one by one, "Have you ever been through therapy or counseling?" A surprisingly high number of the people I most respected had, which sealed the deal for me. If success leaves clues, this is a great clue, and it's one most people don't openly talk about because they're worried about being judged.

I talk about it as much as I can. Counseling is something the people we admire the most invest in heavily. Let's not keep that a secret anymore. There's real value to it. Even if you're not hurting right now, it's a proactive measure to build the skills you'll need for another stage of your life.

Then, when the hard times are acute, I get out my bike and ride hard. There have been many times when we're doing a launch of a product and the technology goes down or everyone's freaking out. The number one thing I do in the midst of a storm is get out my bike and ride as hard as I can until I'm exhausted. When I come back, my head is clear. I can get back to work on solving the problem. There's something magical about physical exertion in times like that.

The third thing is not forgetting to do the things that helped during the good times. People fail to do this all the time. When times get tough, they stop working out; they stop eating well. They used to do yoga once a week and now they don't. They used to practice gratitude; they used to spend time with family and friends. When times get hard, they give up all the things that made their life meaningful during good times, and it becomes this crazy downward spiral.

You want to consistently remind yourself to not forget to do the things that kept you healthy and happy during the good times because these are the things that will help you during the hard times.

You said success leaves clues. Who are three people from any field we should follow?

The idea of following people has always been uncomfortable to me. It places an undue focus on celebrity. I'll give you a couple people who are good, but what I really like to do is encourage students to meet people in their communities. That could be your proximal community—the people where you live—or it could be at events and seminars in your field in so you can empty your cup. It doesn't matter if the people are famous or successful.

There's an old parable in which a teacher starts pouring tea into a cup and it gets full and she keeps pouring. The students ask, "Why do you keep pouring once the cup's already full?" The teacher answers, "This is like you. You have so many ideas in your head and you think you know so many things. If I try to teach you, it'll just spill out because your cup's already full."

The idea is to go into scenarios where you meet people—even if they're not people you think you can learn from—empty your cup…have no opinions, impressions or ideas, and figure out what you can learn. Very specifically, by asking pointed questions, figure out each person's passion. Discover what people are good at, figure out what's unique about them and then just ask questions. This has been one of the greatest gifts in my life.

Growing up an introvert, I never did this when I was younger. I was afraid of being awkward talking to people and eventually I realized I had to have a system for talking to people or I'd never do it. It started with asking questions, but I discovered that asking people mundane questions just made for a boring conversation. I hated it. That gave me no motivation to talk to people—I had to ask better questions. I started doing that and if I asked really good questions, not only would we have a good conversation, I could learn things instead of trying to teach something.

How can I learn from everyone everywhere—the person I sit next to on an airplane, the mom at school, the teacher, someone at music, someone at gymnastics? That's my best advice. There are people who are doing great stuff; don't just follow famous people. I've learned more from asking great questions of people and being open to learning. Almost everyone has something they're good at and that means they have a system for being passionate and good at it. Even if it's not something I'm into, I can learn from that and bring it into my world.

Independent of that advice, there are people I turn to time and time again. Ray Dalio is one person who's getting a lot of press. He's a billionaire hedge fund manager who's a personal mentor to Phil and me at Precision Nutrition. He wrote a book called *Principles*, which is phenomenal. He's a tremendous thinker. His principles are based on the idea of seeing the world for what it is, calling it out, and then operating in accord with reality. Ray's an amazing person to learn from.

Maria Montessori is another person who would be unconventional to suggest because she's not even alive anymore. Most people are familiar with her educational system; there are Montessori schools around the world. I got hooked on her teachings as a method for understanding learning. If you want to talk about someone who didn't see barriers to her success, she's the person. In the 1800s, she had ideas for educational materials and at the time, women couldn't get patents. She made up an alter-ego as a man and filed hundreds of educational tools and patents under that name. She was a no-barriers person. Her philosophy about respect and dignity for children and the learning process translates to learning everything. I'm super enamored of her work.

The last person people don't listen to enough is themselves. This is kind of clichéd, but the number of people who have no "plugged-in-ness" to their inner wishes and their own inner voice is staggering. Sometimes people ask how I'd know the right decision in a certain scenario. My response is that my inner voice knows. I call it my "soul yes" or my "soul no." I can rationalize any decision, but there's a part of me just screaming yes to everything it wants to do and no to everything it doesn't want to do.

I ask people about their "soul yes" and "soul no" and they don't seem to hear it very often, maybe because they're too busy following other people and not plugging into themselves.

That's a long answer, but some people have some great ideas that are all meaningless until you know how to get ideas from everyone, including yourself.

Everybody should be following you because you're an inspiration. You're making such a huge impact on not just the fitness field, but also the world. Thank you for talking about your journey through life and your successes.

BE LIKE JOHN

"You don't achieve goals you've never accomplished without building new skills, and you don't build new skills without practicing things. Classic examples are learning a language or to play an instrument. Most of my time is spent figuring out what skills I need next and what particular daily practices I need to accomplish to get the goal."

FROM GOAL TO ACTION

The first step is to pick a goal. It could be anything—write it down on the top of a sheet of paper.

Next, write down all of skills you will need to accomplish that goal. Who will you need to meet or learn from? What course can you take? What books can help? What videos can you watch?

Learning about those skills will not automatically achieve the goal.

One of the reasons John has been such a successful coach is he that gets people to put new skills into some kind of a practice, ideally daily.

Ask yourself, "What particular daily practices do I need to accomplish in those skills to get to the goal?"

In the Precision Nutrition coaching program, when assigning a new habit, they ask "On a scale of one to ten, one being 'there's no way' and ten being 'no problem, I can do it,' how likely are you able to fit this into a daily habit?" If you can't answer a nine or ten, you need to dial things down and start smaller.

If learning the guitar is a goal and learning scales and chords are the skills you need, how much practice do you need to become proficient?

Can you practice five hours a day? If the answer is no way, give yourself a one.

Can you practice one hour a day? If it's sometimes—give yourself a six.

Can you do 20 minutes a day? Yes, absolutely. Give yourself a nine or a ten.

That's how to start. Schedule 20 minutes a day to practice the skills you need to become the guitar player you want to be.

Try this with a single goal and see how it works.

You can download a worksheet from *PrecisionNutrition.com* to go deeper into this exercise.

Mark is an international speaker, consultant and entrepreneur. He is a co-founder of Business for Unicorns and Mark Fisher Fitness. MFF was recognized as #312 on the 2015 Inc. 500 fastest-growing companies in America and is among Men's Health's "Top 20 Gyms in America." Catch up with Mark via businessforunicorns.com.

Mark, you've accomplished so much in a short period of time. I'd like to know how you define success.

That's such a good question; it's really *the* question. There are two things I want to do with my life: be a student and be a servant. I'm happiest when I'm learning and developing myself and skills that make other people's lives better and will allow me to be a more effective servant to all the communities in my life. That includes not just the Ninjas, Mark Fisher Fitness and our Unicorn lovers and Business for Unicorns, but also our team, my wife, my friends and anybody in the world who would benefit by me continuing to become a better version of myself.

There's a great Earl Nightingale quote I quite like that says, "Happiness is the progressive realization of a worthy goal or idea." That really sums it up.

I want a feeling of forward momentum that I'm moving toward my goals. Any worthy goal or idea, ideally almost inevitably, is a mission that articulates how you hope to impact the other people in your life. For me, that's success.

There's a lot of science behind happiness and the idea of slow progression toward improvement. It's an idea of "better every day."

There's a great book if anyone wants to dig into one well-known psychologist's current stance on this: *Flourish,* by Martin Seligman, who wrote a book called *Learned Optimism,* a seminal work in psychology.

Seligman was part of the first generation of psychologists who studied happiness. I highly recommend listening to the audiobook because he's kind of a curmudgeon and it's hilarious. He's a cantankerous fellow—the expert on happiness. There's a lot of value in his paradigm because he's specific. He says the word "happiness" is hard to define and instead, he refers to what he calls "wellbeing."

He says wellbeing has five elements; he uses an acronym PERMA. We have positive emotion, which is what many of us refer to as happiness. Positive emotion is a physical sensation that research suggests is up to 50 percent genetics. You can't change a lot of your positive emotions.

Admittedly, I'm one of those people who is pathologically stoked almost all the time in a way that's borderline obnoxious and I'm ashamed of it sometimes. Since it's partly genetic, one might argue it's one of the least important parts.

Next, we have engagement, which is being fully immersed in your work—flow states for those familiar with Mihaly Csikszentmihalyi's work.

Then we have "R," which is relationships. Do you have a feeling of belonging? Relatedness? Do you have the opportunity to truly care for others, and in turn feel truly cared for?

The next is meaning—does my life have purpose? Am I contributing to something larger than myself in a meaningful way?

And then finally: achievement. Achievement speaks to the concept of progression. Are we seeing intimate, incremental progression toward our goals?

It's success when you have those five elements—PERMA, those elements of wellbeing.

When I give seminars, I sometimes use that Earl Nightingale quote to show how that's reflective of the things we now consider to be reasonably evidenced-based elements of what it means to live a happy, moral and ethical life.

Many people don't think about having a purpose. If you don't work on understanding it, it can be hard to get a true sense of goals. In turn, you won't know how you're progressing. Understanding purpose makes the process clearer and it's easier to identify the progression. When did you start to consider things progressing in the right direction to where you were feeling successful?

I have trouble identifying a particular moment when I felt successful because, speaking candidly, I didn't feel very successful for much of my 20s. There was a lot of anxiety and a constant sub-text saying, "Is it going to be okay? Am I going to be all right?"

On some level, I was always aware of that question. I, by all accounts, was a happy guy; no one who knew me in my 20s would have thought of me as morose. But I had anxiety around the questions, "Am I going to impact the world in the way I want? Will I really live a life of meaning?" I might not have articulated that then, but there was a little existential anxiety throughout my 20s.

Another reason I am pathologically happy is, to steal a phrase of a brilliant author named Robert Wright, I'm what I call a "grim optimist." I'm an optimist, but I'm grim and don't expect much for the universe. I'm generally delighted on a day-to-day basis that there's a semblance of society and that it's not a bunch of marauding, looting and pillaging, raping pirates and Vikings.

I haven't talked about this much, but I did a lot of useful self-work in my late 20s—I jokingly say I mind-washed myself. I became obsessive about reading a lot of what now, frankly, is almost embarrassing "self-helpy" literature. I reframed a lot of things and started cultivating powerful disciplined gratitude practices. That's ultimately why I started to perceive myself as a success.

I don't know that my external circumstances warranted it at the time. But because my mindset changed, I started perceiving myself as somebody who was successful and I was so grateful for any good thing that happened in my life. That was the tipping point.

I'm not articulating a particular moment when that happened, but it was certainly around the time Mark Fisher Fitness became a thing. I started not just feeling it, but seeing proof that I have certain skills that can help people in a meaningful way. Most importantly for me, I've been able to create a tribe—this core community at Mark Fisher Fitness—who together have these super powers.

When you make a conscious effort to have gratitude for the simple things in life, you don't need as much of the external input. I start every morning reading from or

listening to a few minutes of a recording I made of all the things I'm grateful for. I start with things we take for granted: I'm grateful I can walk; I'm grateful I can run; I'm grateful I can walk upstairs…that I can hear music. I'm grateful I can see the beautiful world around me. I try to go through the senses, then notice my relationships and experiences. I try to remember basic things that are so amazing. It's been a game changer.

Two of my friends have this hilarious but perfect saying, "Holy shit, we're alive," which has become sort of a credo. There's something to be said for learning how to appreciate that kind of thing. I feel blessed because for better or for worse, I'm drawn to the most painful, uncomfortable truths. I really want to dance with the potentially meaninglessness of all existence.

The flip side, weirdly, is that I'm excited about everything. Several times a week, I find myself talking to my wife and literally crying because I'm so grateful for our life and my relationship with her and for our beautiful home and for what I do professionally…and for our dog.

My life is an embarrassment of riches. I'd be excited regardless, but perhaps more so because I feel entitled to nothing. I feel quite lucky to be a part of civilization.

You have that effect on people—an energy that comes across when you talk. What is it exactly that's getting you out of bed in the morning? What's your "it"?

I love my work so much. I love the people I spend time with. I very rarely have anything I need to do professionally that I'm not excited to do. Like everyone, I certainly have moments where it's not something I'd choose to do that second, but the reality is, I've continued to curate the exact work and life I want. At this point, I have autonomy and freedom in my schedule.

The thing that gets me out of bed is knowing that what awaits me is a day of things I love: hanging out with my wife and playing with my dog, writing articles and creating courses, eating a healthy lunch and getting to work out. I usually spend afternoons in meetings with people on my team whom I really love. I have a great opportunity to challenge them and be challenged by them and we continue to move the ball forward. Often, evenings are spent with a robust community of friends from all walks of New York City life.

I'm also very happy with the current balance of things I get to do. I know that will change, but at the moment, I have the perfect menu of things that fill me up and keep me interested by providing variety in my day.

Do you normally wake up early and what do you do when you wake up? Is there a specific morning routine?

I actually don't get up very early by entrepreneurial standards. I wish that I could, but my wife is a Broadway performer. She often doesn't walk in the door until late. I like to see her because I like spending time with her. I'm also a stickler for eight hours of sleep.

More often than not, when I get up, I first meditate for 20 minutes. I practice a form of transcendental meditation called Vedic meditation. Then I usually have several hours of a term I stole from my pal Craig Ballantyne called "Magic Time" where I work on high-leverage key priorities. These are key tasks that are both cognitively challenging and that will really move the ball forward. That's always working on projects, writing content for Business for Unicorns or Mark Fisher Fitness or developing courses, which tends to be higher-level work.

There's a quote Craig uses from Gustave Flaubert, "Be regular and orderly in your life so you may be violent and original in your work." I have found that to be reflective of my best life.

I'll usually do that first, then work out mid-morning because after a couple of hours, my brain needs a break. I'm a creature of habit and won't bore you with the rest of it, but my days tend to be pretty consistent day to day.

Do less to achieve more. If you can do that, you get better balance and have energy for the things that matter. Mark, how do you set goals?

If I'm looking for a turning point in my life, I'd go back to August of 2010. I'd always been a big reader before that, but it was then that two things happened. Number one, I decided to start reading two books a week, which I've kept up and surpassed most weeks. Based on Mike Boyle's Recommended Reading page on *StrengthCoach.com,* I read Brian Tracy's *Goals* and I took up a serious, regimented goal-setting process. It's now something we work on with some of our Business for Unicorns clients because most people benefit from developing a rigorous goal-setting process.

I have an elaborate process and a simple one. Every three months, I do a quarterly goal-setting process. I also do one-year and five-year plans, using the best practices of goal setting, which is to write in the present tense. I personally prefer to write in a goal-setting notebook, where I go into painstaking detail, visioning everything about my dream life and my dream day and how I'm spending my week and how much money I'm making and what's going on in my personal life. For example, I fully described the NoLita two-bedroom apartment with a terrace overlooking the city, which eventually came to pass. I've found that level of rigor to be very important. Interestingly—and this is a bit of departure from traditional goal-setting processes—I don't usually refer to the notebook much after I do it.

In fact, occasionally I flip through my old quarterly goals after I've written new ones and found myself thinking, "Oh man, I'm making less money than I set in my goal-setting process!" There's validity in keeping it top of mind. Some people make a "goals card" to keep in their wallets. Vision boards can be very powerful and a useful tool, but it isn't something I've used.

I try to turn this tactical, where you turn your dreams into goals and then turn your goals into skill sets and finally, skill set acquisition into habits. That's a beautiful way of describing this process of creating ambitious and inspiring dreams that turn you on and fill you with energy but…"When you pray, move your feet."

How do we work that back and what do we need to do today? For me, that's usually educational practice. The most useful questions I pose to myself when looking at a five-year vision of my life are who I want to be and how I want to serve my communities. What does that mean for me now, as a student? What skills do I need to become world class at? Where do I need to focus my educational energies to become the person I need to be to create that life and to be worthy and deserving of that life? Those are the questions I find myself asking.

People often get caught up in the "how" too early in the process, but the "how" is second. First, figure out "what" and then worry about "how."

Some people have a greater propensity for visioning and other people are better at the day-to-day tactical work. This seems in keeping with a lot of things we know about the brain, about these inversely correlated cognitive systems.

Almost invariably, the people who are successful at big dreams and visions have nothing when they get to the day-to-day effort. Conversely, there are a lot of people who are truly excellent and meticulous with daily work—they crush their day to day, but don't look up from the computer to think about where their lives are headed. We need both.

Goal setting is a skill and something people get better at. Often, when people do it the first couple times, they're not good at it. When people don't have a background in it, it's harder to vision in painstaking detail everything about a life.

The first time you do it, you probably won't be good at the goal-setting process, but every master was once a disaster. You might find it frustrating. Lean into that discomfort because like anything you do, practice and you'll get good at it.

Last year I decided I needed help and went to Michael Hyatt's *Your Best Year Ever* goal-setting workshop to immerse myself in the process. It's been a work in progress. You're very organized and get a lot done. What do you do to stay organized?

I use a regular notebook, which is yet another thing I stole from Mike Boyle. My friends sometimes jokingly refer to me as the "Tax Man" because *True Detective* Matthew McConaughey always had a notebook with him. I always have my notebook in hand because if a thought strikes me or something happens, I write it down.

I'm a fan of David Allen's *Getting Things Done* methodology. He said, "Your brains are for having ideas, not for remembering them." The most important piece of my time management system is getting ideas out of my head, on paper and into a place where I can later process them and make a to-do list.

It's a simple system and isn't particularly sexy. When I open up the notebook, each two-page spread is a given day in a week. I usually list the days a week to three weeks in advance. Based on how much space I have for "Magic Time" in a day, I assign both discrete tasks and blocks of time for various projects.

I also have a system of different types of to-do lists. One is a meeting list where I curate the things I need to talk about to various people so I'm not barraging them with email. I also have an ongoing project list where I keep track of what I'm working on—writing a sales page or creating content for Business for Unicorns or a course or going to a presentation.

Finally, I have a "someday list," more accurately "not going to do this right now." These are ideas I want to remember, but I'm purposely not doing them now. If I just get them out of my brain, I stop thinking about them. I trust those things to live in the system.

I use my notebook the night before to look at the various to-do items and then create a meticulous, almost minute-by-minute schedule of how I'll use that time to accomplish the various tasks and projects I need to get done.

Do you have rules as to when you'll answer email, texts and correspondence so you have fewer distractions?

I have my phone on "do not disturb" at all times. My phone does not buzz. My team knows if something is really an emergency, if the Club House is on fire, if it's truly urgent, they can call me. But it's never truly urgent.

If you need a response within the next hour or two, text me and I'll get back to you. But it won't buzz or beep because I don't ever want anything to take me out of a flow if I'm in deep work time. I like my phone being my servant, not the other way around.

Part of the ethical challenges we're having right now with personal tech is that it's designed like a slot machine to take advantage of our natural selection, the way the brain is developed to be prone to become addicted to dopamine hits. The good news is that if you're able to get around that, it's a competitive advantage. Most people are becoming completely unable to focus for long stretches as required to do deep work. This becomes a huge opportunity for people who master their tech.

I'm lucky because at Mark Fisher Fitness, I don't personally have to follow up on leads anymore; we've got a team now. If you're working in customer service, you unfortunately almost have to invert that to where you're mostly available.

The way I've set up my life, I'm mostly never available, but then I have a few periods where I'm super available. I try to check email three and no more than four times a day. I'm certainly not perfect—sometimes I backslide, but I tend to never check my email until after my Magic Time. Since doing email means being responsive, I want to schedule my cognitively challenging high-level work while I'm crisp. I can do email later in the day. Once my brain is a bit fatigued, I can still answer email, but I won't be as effective at important creative work.

I still get to inbox zero every four to six hours. I haven't found that to be a missed expectation for most people. However, this is where people need to use their intuition based on the profession or job expectations.

You might in some cases to have to educate some people. You might have a situation where a manager emails you at 5:35PM and then emails again the next morning, railing about not getting back sooner. This takes finesse.

If you master your communication flow, you'll have freedom of mind to do deep work. That doesn't mean you can't also be incredibly responsive. I'm one of the more responsive people ever. I often say the only reason I've had such success in my life is because I'm hyper responsive to email, and I'm warm and personable and concise and to the point.

If you don't hear back from me in less than 24 hours after an email, you can assume I'm dead. You should call my wife. Something terrible has happened.

Let's talk about recharging. We talk about it a lot our clients, but it's something we often neglect for ourselves.

I have certainly found that my meditation practice is a big part of that. This year, I've gotten very good about taking at least one full day off each week, which is tough because I love my work. In many ways, it's almost harder because my work often can be re-energizing, but I try to be predisposed about taking one day mostly off—I might catch up on email during the day. I also try to travel on a semi-regular basis.

Weird perhaps, but my goal-setting process and certain types of what could fall under the categories of business education I find to be renewing. For people who want to go deep into this, it's part of the "Time Ninja Time Management" curriculum. The brilliant Dr. Richard Boyatzis has a course called *Leading with Emotional Intelligence,* and he's written a couple of excellent books including *Primal Leadership* and *Resonant Leadership.* Dr. Boyatzis has done a lot of research getting biometric data on what he calls "psychological renewal." Importantly, he makes the distinction that psychological renewal is distinct from physiological rest.

For rest, you can sleep; you can take time and physically not be moving around much. Certainly, there are other physiological inputs that are useful, including but not limited to eating well, being active…all the things we know from fitness.

With psychological renewal, they categorize it into four different strata paradigm. The four pieces are *compassion,* which is feeling, caring for other people and feeling cared for. Then there's *mindfulness,* which could be meditation or prayer or if you subscribe to a wisdom tradition, it could be spending time in nature. Then we have *hope,* which is spending time being inspired by a beautiful vision of what life could be in your future. And finally, there's *play*—that could be silliness, humor, laughing.

These four elements of self-renewal are things I think about seriously. When I work with people, I often help them get clarity about which of the four are most effective, because each of us will get more or less inspired by different self-renewal activities.

Another takeaway from Boyatzis's work studies the way we either flare up the sympathetic nervous system or use activities to get parasympathetic and chill down the nervous system. Boyatzis makes the point that this can't be saved up for the weekend; it becomes another time-management issue. Can you justify going to a coffee shop in the middle of the afternoon to research vacations in the middle of a busy work day? Honestly, you can.

You might do more effective work if you get serious about committing to renewal strategies in a disciplined way.

Hemingway and others used a practice of shutting things down while still in a flow of writing. When you're in the middle of writing—it's going well and you feel in the flow—just stop. Put it aside until the next day. There's something to stopping during then that prepares you for the following day so you won't be staring at a blank page.

That reminds me of the Pomodoro technique—doing discrete work chunks of 25 minutes at a time with a five-minute dedicated rest in between.

We can often take what we've learned from human physiology and apply it to mental and brainwork. The brain is a physiological system. It can respond to certain physiological inputs; I'm very excited to see this becoming a part of the conversation for high achievers.

Not only do I think it will help people be happier and calmer and enjoy their lives more, but ultimately, the more people creating awesome work, the better our world is. These are exciting times.

Although you're innately a positive person, there are times when we're down and wonder why we're doing this work. How do you push through those times?

Not unlike fitness, it's often to just stupidly and blindly doing the work. Just do the things I know I need to do.

Like most entrepreneurs, at times I've definitely struggled—I don't know if it would be clinical depression, but I've had times when I was sad and bummed. I've been so lethargic I could barely work and I found that physiological inputs can help. Once I start doing something, I've got some momentum.

A meditation practice is also helpful. I tend to feel more secular in the way I do meditation. It seems obvious in my studies and practice of Vedic meditation that it's an experience I physiologically feel.

I get space around my emotions and things that are bumming me out; I just care less. The problems are less of an issue and interestingly enough, if I'm finding myself in a place of low energy and lethargy, after I meditate I actually have more energy.

Ultimately, if I'm going through a hard time, it's because I'm resisting some reality of my life—my feelings are hurt or maybe I have anxiety around someone being frustrated with me. I sometimes struggle with being such a people pleaser.

If someone is upset with me, it's hard to let that go and do my work. I've found both physical activity and meditation are useful strategies to get back in the game.

I burn really hot; sometimes I get mad about things. Sometimes I get my feelings hurt and I feel bad about myself, particularly if I didn't meet up to my standards. The older I get, I'm getting better at compassion toward myself, knowing it's okay to not be okay at times.

Life is not all rainbows and butterflies, even for a happy guy like me.

Be patient and realize sometimes you're going to be bummed—you're human. It's useful to develop the skill to learn how to nurture yourself. It's not uncommon for me to use self-talk in those situations to try to get to "the wise advocate" and think, "It's okay. You're kind of bummed about stuff right now. It's totally normal."

I coach myself up. It doesn't always work. Sometimes you're sad. Try to make it not last too long.

Mark, this might be a hard question for you. What are three non fitness–related books everyone should read?

It is truly, wonderfully impossible to name only three.

You can go five.

The Moral Animal by Robert Wright is an analysis of evolutionary psychology. It was a complete game changer for the way I look at everything.

Sapiens is certainly the "it" book of the moment—the industrial thought leader and well warranted. It's an excellent, though brief, history of all of humankind that will echo many things from *The Moral Animal*.

Ray Dalio's book *Principles* is amazing to help us think more clearly, which at the end of the day is what we're looking to do. If looking at books outside the fitness space that are going to make us more successful in life, we really want to learn how to think better. We're learning how to debug our emotional algorithms and the cognitive shortcuts that sometimes lead us to make ineffective decisions.

Influence by Robert Cialdini is the best book on marketing. Whenever people ask me what to read for marketing, I tell them to just read that over and over and over.

I found *Antifragile* to be another important book and a good counterpoint for my rational optimism and a reminder that ultimately, we're never more than a really poor choice away from a nuclear holocaust and the end of all things.

Now give us three people we can all learn from.

It's hard not to just go right with those authors—they've been very inspiring to me. I would add Robert Wright, who wrote *The Moral Animal* and also the equally excellent *Nonzero, the Logic of Human Destiny* and most recently *Why Buddhism is True*, which is a masterpiece, a super excellent book. I'd definitely recommend following Robert Wright.

Follow Ray Dalio, who wrote *Principles*. He continues to set the bar for how brilliant people should think.

This choice is maybe a little out there, but—it's so cliché—someone like Elon Musk continues to remind us, "Here's how to think big." He isn't someone whose work is easily consumable, so maybe we should sub him out for Kevin Kelly, who wrote incredible book called *Inevitable*. Of all the people thinking deeply about how tech is changing everything, he thinks cogently.

Thinking deeply about what's happening in tech—and not just industrial and professional, but also the moral and ethical ramifications—is a very good thing to spend time on. Things are happening so quickly and they're going to keep happening faster; there are a lot of serious changes we're going to see in the next couple of decades. The more people have thought through the base moral, ethical and philosophical considerations of what it means to live a life of value and what it means to be an ethical human, the better off our entire society will be. There are some really crazy things coming down the pike.

Mark, you're truly one of the great success stories in fitness. Thanks for continuing to inspire trainers from all over the world and thanks so much for sharing your journey.

BE LIKE MARK

"I fully describe the NoLita two-bedroom apartment with a terrace overlooking the city."

VISION YOUR LIFE IN FULL DETAIL

Mark describes in painstaking detail the place where he wants to live. He knows the location (NoLita–North of Little Italy in Manhattan), how many bedrooms, having a terrace and what his view will look like.

When he's describing it, he can picture what the furniture looks like, where his favorite chair is and who he's with.

Write on paper with as much detail as you can:

Where do you live? What does your house or apartment look like?

Do you have a vacation home?

Who are you with—do you have a spouse, kids?

What job do you have?

Do you own your own business or businesses? What kind of money are you making?

Is there a specific car in your garage?

What charity do you work with and contribute to? What kind of volunteering do you do?

What is your ideal bodyweight?

What makes up your exercise?

What does your free time look like? What activities and hobbies do you do regularly?

What "toys" do you have?

Where do you travel?

Who do you spend time with?

Keep writing; expand on these questions and add to them.

This is a work in progress—try it again the following week and then a month later. You'll start to refine your thinking and get a clearer picture of your future.

Extra credit

Make a story out of this. Write it down as if it has already happened. For example, "I live in a penthouse apartment by Central Park" as opposed to "I will be living in a penthouse apartment in Central Park." To go deeper, record and listen to it as part of your morning routine.

Sue is the owner and founder of Structure and Function Education and Falsone Consulting. She's an Associate Professor of Athletic Training Programs, Arizona School of Health Sciences at A.T. Still University and is the author of Bridging the Gap from Rehab to Performance. Sue is a consultant to professional athletes and professional sport organizations and her website is suefalsone.com.

Sue, you've had success on many levels, not only as Vice President of Performance Physical Therapy for EXOS,® but also as the first female head athletic trainer in American professional sports. Through your company, Structure and Function, you're teaching all over the world. How do you define success?

My definition of success has changed over time—we continue to evolve. I remember being in physical therapy school and thinking about all the letters I wanted after my name, all the certifications I wanted. I thought if I had all the certifications and things I want to study and do, I'd be successful.

I got all those and then realized I still didn't feel like I knew everything. I wanted to continue to get better, to become the best possible physical therapist I could be. I wanted to be the best athletic trainer and strength coach I could be, and to integrate all those things. I'm always on that path and it probably doesn't have an ending.

As soon as you think you've become the best, you should probably retire because you're not going to have the desire to continue to get better. We can always get better no matter how much experience we have.

I'm trying to find some semblance of balance between work and life and combining those two. There's no balance, just a combination of work and home life. How do you cultivate and grow your professional relationships, as well as cultivate and grow your personal relationships? How do you marry those different sides of a person? That's how I'm defining success, which I know is not a solid definition. But it's one of those things we continue to constantly strive for.

If your question had been, "Do you think you're successful?" My answer would be no.

That is my next question. When did you start to feel you were doing things right? You were at Athletes' Performance where you were working with the top athletes in the world. You worked with the Los Angeles Dodgers and held the distinction of being the first female head athletic trainer. That's a pretty significant accomplishment.

You're on too many boards to mention and people are calling on you for advice all the time. You have to have a bit of the feeling that, "I'm getting this right." Was there a time when you started to feel, "Maybe now I can write my book because I know a little of what I'm talking about?"

During those last few years I was with Athletes' Performance and working with the Dodgers at the same time, I guess I was hitting my stride. I was teaching, managing other people, mentoring younger clinicians and helping athletes feel and become better. It was during that time that I thought, "I'm on a good path. It's a tough path and a difficult task, but it's my path and I love it."

Those final years I was with Athletes' Performance, looking back and seeing what we built, how we built it and feeling like we did it right—that was one of those times in my life when I stepped back and thought, "I've been able to do some pretty cool stuff."

We look at your resume and think, "She's helping top athletes. She's a role model for women. But also, she's helping other companies and other clinicians." With such a diverse portfolio, what is it that drives you with your mission?

Again, those have changed entirely over the years. Right now, it's education and mentoring other clinicians. It's being able to spread that message and share whatever message of success I've had, whether it's as a woman in professional sports, how I connect with athletes or how I clinically help get athletes better.

I'm not the best physical therapist in the world. Sometimes you put things together in a certain way that makes you unique—that's what makes me a good clinician. I enjoy being able to share that message with younger clinicians and people who are trying to find a path in the field.

The word "mentor" is funny, but if I can be that to other people, I'll have a broader reach. I can only treat so many athletes; even on our busiest days, we can touch only so many people. But when we reach other clinicians and they go out and start touching patients, it grows exponentially.

I have a wider reach now with the education company. Being able to be more of an educator and mentor people gets me fired up in the morning.

With all you've done, you were doing a lot of other things at the same time, like lecturing and educating. People say these are not sacrifices—they're choices. But they're sacrifices because you're giving up something. Did you feel you made sacrifices to push to where you are now?

Some of the things I'm trying to rectify at this point in my life are my personal relationships. When I was with Athletes' Performance and with the Dodgers at the same time, it was a crazy season in my life. I was constantly working and many of my personal relationships suffered. I missed weddings and funerals. I missed high school reunions. I missed lunch dates with girlfriends…and boyfriends, for that matter.

You make personal sacrifices for your profession. The people who are left standing understand that, and they're there for you on the other side. But I've had to make some difficult choices, where often I chose work over family and friends. I had to do it at the time, but those are the things I'm trying to work on now.

I'd like to believe I'm not 43 and single because I'm a total weirdo. But the last 20 years I've focused on my career and didn't focus on the personal aspects of my life.

"I'm not weird. I was working." I'm sure it was hard during those times when you weren't with family or didn't have more personal relationships when you were travelling so much. How did you push through those tough times?

You need a network of people you can trust—people who are going to be there on the other end of it no matter what. But they're also willing to call you out on your crap when it needs to be called out.

Having those people who are willing to call you out in a loving and supportive way is huge. Whether that network is one person or five people doesn't matter. My mom is a huge support in that way. She doesn't understand our profession whatsoever, but she's been through the ringer with me, starting in physical therapy school when it was a four-year undergraduate degree.

It's been a long road and my mom is my sounding board. I can call her to talk about whatever success I'm having and whatever is exciting. Sometimes I'll send her something and say, "You're the only one I can send this to without seeming like I'm patting myself on the back." At the same time, she's the first person I'm going to call when I'm crying about some sucky thing that's happening.

You have to create a network of people who will be there for you.

To get to your level, you had to have dedication and discipline. You have to develop habits that will be crucial to being consistent. Let's talk about some of your habits. Do you have a routine you go through every morning to set you up for the day?

Because I'm doing so many different things, I don't have too many days that look the same. I might be out on the road or at home. When I'm home, I get to work from home, which is nice. But it's tough; you have to have discipline to work from home because it can easily turn into a low-grade work from 9:00AM to 9:00PM, but not get anything done except answer email. It can turn into, "Sure. I can go to lunch," or maybe deciding to clean the house. Before you know it, nothing gets done.

I try to set up my week so Mondays and Tuesdays are meeting days. My Wednesdays are open for writing. On Thursdays, I usually travel and I'm often teaching on the weekends. I try to leave one or two days a week where I don't schedule meetings, and it's rare I let something infiltrate those days.

I also set a time limit on email. I'll check it first thing in the morning and in the evening for about an hour each time—and that's it. If I don't schedule it like that, I'll send two email messages and three come in and I'll send three more and four come in…and I'll never catch up. I'll waste my whole day just checking email.

It's the same with social media. I do social media for maybe 30 minutes in the morning and I recheck it at the end of the day—that's it. I put limits on when meetings are scheduled and limits on email and social media.

I schedule my creative time and map that out weekly based on my travel schedule.

Michael Hyatt sets up his days in a similar fashion. He always asks, "What kind of a day is this—a front-stage day (speaking, webinars, seeing clients), a backstage day (working on things that will help the front-stage), or an off-stage day (rest and recovery)?" If you set your week up like that and stay true to it, it can be tremendously productive.

It's good to have our time scheduled, especially down times. The time can get sabotaged in a heartbeat. When you start opening up time slots, before you know it, the time is gone and now your mental health is flagging. You have to be careful about people sabotaging your time—and you letting them.

Talk to us about goals. Do you have a formal process with goals?

I need to get better at that, which is a bit ironic because I am a physical therapist and everything is about short- and long-term goals for our patients.

We tell athletes, "You want to return to football? Excellent. That means you have to be able to walk. You have to be able to run. You have to be able to cut. You have to be able to decelerate. You have to be able to do all of these short-term goals to achieve your long-term goal."

You would think in my world, I'd have the same thing set up for myself, but I don't. I need to do a better job of that. I have a lot of different interests. A couple of years ago, there were a lot of things going on and I spread myself thin. I'm interested in so many things: education, business, working with athletes, working with patients, speaking and traveling and before you know it, I'm doing some of all of them.

But I'm not headed to an endgame or a goal or the next version of things. That's something I want and need to get better at, that short- and long-term goal setting—having those different time periods during the year.

Without that, all I do is grind and before you know it, it's the holidays and the year is over.

Another thing we're always preaching to our clients is about recovering and recharging. Talk to us about how you recharge.

My morning time with Richard the Wiener Dog, a cup of coffee and a book is my daily recharge. Once that time is gone, it's insanity the rest of the day. I try to put "weekend time" into my week. Most weeks, I'm normally teaching on the weekends, which means I can easily work Monday through Wednesday, travel on Thursday or Friday, teach all weekend, and then I'm right back in the grind on Monday.

I try to make sure I have a day during the week where I permit myself not to work a whole heck of a lot. I go to the store or lie around and watch Netflix. I try to have that time to recharge, even if it's only a half day.

I need to connect with a friend during that day, either talk to someone on the phone for an hour or meeting for dinner. That sounds ridiculous, but it can easily become that I haven't been to dinner with a friend in a month because I've been on the road. I try to make a weekly personal connection time.

I've gotten into wine in an entirely super nerdy way—when you start looking into it, it's so science-y and very chemistry-based. It's about farming and how the soil impacts the aromas, what the wine is and how the annual weather affects the grape and so on. So, I always end up tacking on time when I travel. I had some business I needed to do in New Zealand, so I planned to stay an extra five days to go for wine-tasting events.

The same thing in Spain—I spoke at a conference there, then tacked on four days to do wine tasting. I want to experience the country or city where I'm working. As much as I can, I plan some of those trips on an annual basis. It's good for me; it's fun and I enjoy it.

I like it when my friends join me, but I like traveling and learning alone, too.

I know you have a stack of books by your couch. What are some books you recommend for our readers?

Right now I'm reading two, and it's funny because they're about the same thing. One is *You're a Badass: How to Stop Doubting Your Greatness and Start Living an Awesome Life*. I know I'm probably late to the party on that one because people have been talking about it. But I've never read it, so that's in my pile.

The other is a small book I've almost finished entitled *Get Your Shit Together*. It's about how to stop worrying about what you should do so you can finish what you need to do and start doing what you want to do.

Those are the two books in my to-be-read pile, along with, from a technical or treatment standpoint, the newest Luigi Stucco fascia book, which is also sitting in front of me—*Atlas of Physiology of the Muscular Fascia*.

Name some people you follow from whom we can learn.

I'm following many wine people right now, which is not great for most of your readers.

Lindsay Becker is a personal friend of mine. I adore her. She was named one of the top golf fitness and performance instructors by *Golf Digest*. She does a great job on social media, sharing what she does with her junior golfers—she works with professional people as well. She does a great job of showing videos of how she's looking at things. She's clinically applicable and super fun to follow.

From a research standpoint, Phil Page is another great friend; your readers can find him on social media too. Phil is a PhD athletic trainer and physical therapist. He does a great job of making research clinically applicable—showing us why we should care about certain things and why we shouldn't care about others. Because something was published doesn't necessarily mean it's good information. He's trying to teach people how to discern between good and bad research. That's important, especially for clinicians.

I'm a clinician and researcher; it's tough—I'm not a PhD. Navigating research can be difficult. Phil does an excellent job at breaking things down, making data clinically applicable to people like me who don't always understand statistical analyses of different factors.

Lindsey and Phil would be my two people who deserve a shout-out.

It's been so great to follow your career and see all of your success. Thanks so much for sharing it with us.

BE LIKE SUE

"I also set a time limit on email. I'll check it first thing in the morning and in the evening for about an hour each time, and that's it. If I don't schedule it like that, I'll send two email messages and three come in and I'll send three more and four come in…and I'll never catch up. I'll waste my whole day just checking email.

"It's the same with social media. I do social media for maybe 30 minutes in the morning and I recheck it at the end of the day, and that's it. I give myself limits on when meetings are scheduled and limits on email and social media."

LIMIT EMAIL AND SOCIAL MEDIA

If you want to be really productive, you need to be in control of your time. We've all experienced times when we go on social media and end up down a rabbit hole two hours later watching random funny videos. When we're inattentive, it can be a real time suck.

If you have a cell phone, click on "Settings" and then "Battery." It will show you how much time you spent on each app. Seeing how much time you spend on Instagram or Twitter can be an eye opener.

Pick some timeslots during the day and block them out on your schedule (see Nick Winkelman's Be Like) as the only times you will check and return email or go on social media.

Don't make the mistake of doing email first thing in the morning or the last thing before bed.

Sue does email twice a day, but that might be hard at first. In the beginning, try only checking mail three to four times a day. Be strategic about when you do.

Ideally, it's after your morning routine (see Allistair McCaw's and Craig Ballantyne's Be Likes)—maybe before lunch and then as part of your evening work shutdown (see Alwyn Cosgrove's Be Like).

Take social media apps off your phone so you won't be tempted to check all the time.

Try a free version of RescueTime, which will let you know when you spend more time than you want on social media.

Darcy has worked for more than 20 years in the human performance industry in multiple director positions. His past 10 years have primarily been focused on creating and implementing methodologies, applied data, building strategic relations, hiring, training and managing medical, rehab, fitness, nutrition, psychology and sport science staff at the highest level. Having lived and worked in four countries with scores of invitations for speaking engagements around the world, Darcy's professional relationships and networking span the globe in all sports. Get in touch with Darcy via darcynormanconsulting.com.

You've been around a lot of success and have been extremely successful in your career. How do you define success?

Success happens in the small, magic moments you can never plan or predict. It's like doing something for someone that you didn't realize had a positive impact, where you're a part of something bigger than yourself.

Success is about relationships. It's about the interactions I have with people and trying to be better myself, as well as to better the people around me.

When did you start to consider yourself successful?

My dad was a self-made guy. He had a 10th grade education; he provided for his family and he was money-driven. Money was his definition of success.

As I took jobs that made more money, I found myself thinking, "I'm not happy. I'm making money, but I don't feel successful." That prompted me to realize, "Money's not that important to me. Otherwise, I'd be happy and feel successful." Instead, when I've had a positive impact on someone, I feel I've been successful, and that happens in more of the day to day.

I didn't set a goal to be on a team that won a World Cup or even to be a trainer for that matter. It just happened—one thing led to another. The next thing that came up seemed more interesting and challenging than what I was previously doing so I took it on. That's how I've lived my life. I don't know if I've "made it" yet.

Twelve years ago in my first interaction with you, you were teaching at the Athletes' Performance mentorship. You got to the highest level at Athletes' Performance and you've won a World Cup. You're a success, but the journey doesn't end.

When you have the title "Director of Performance," people imagine what it means—it sounds important. But I go to work and try to help people improve their performance just like everybody else who does this work.

Whether we're talking about the equipment techs, the nutritionist or the physios—we're all pitching in so we can win. The World Cup piece was interesting because there was a huge buildup. You train; you go into the tournament; you play super intensive every three days for six weeks—you make it to the end; you win and there's a massive party. We flew back to Germany and joined another massive party with the country. We came out of the Brandenburg Gate to what seemed like millions of people waiting there, heads as far as we could see. And then we walked off the stage and down the stairs and everyone got in their respective cars or buses and it was over; just like a puff of smoke…finished.

I went back to Truckee, where I was living at the time. I'd show up somewhere and someone would say, "Darce, I haven't seen you in a while. What have you been doing?"

And I'd say, "Just working." A success only means something if it means something to you. It's an interesting philosophical thing.

It might mean the achievement of a lifelong dream or just that you've taken the next step to your ultimate goal. That's a good segue into your "it." What is it that gets you out of bed in the morning?

My family is my "it." I am trying to do what they need me to do, providing for and helping them. There are also people who rely on me being at work and the athletes I try to help. People relying on me is what gets me going.

Speaking of getting up, are you an early riser? Is there a morning routine?

It's contingent on when I go to bed. I need my sleep; that's one thing I've learned about myself. I don't function well if I don't sleep well. The culture in Italy, where I currently am, is a late one. People here don't eat dinner until later, which means I'm not getting to bed until midnight or later, which has limited my early-riser ability.

With this job, some days you train in the morning, some times in the afternoon, and we're traveling so much. Routines are difficult. If I want to accomplish something, it has to happen first thing in the morning when I've got the full energy commitment. As the day wanes and my energy starts to dissipate, it makes it harder to execute difficult things.

How do you recharge on a daily or weekly basis?

Recharging is tough because my current role is pretty much a seven-day-a-week gig. I find nature is my best way of recharging—getting out in the mountains and trees, walking trails or mountain biking…skiing.

I have a hard time finding day-to-day balance or even week-to-week balance. My next step is to try to execute a better year-to-year balance, so once the season's over, I can unplug and recharge with my family and friends.

I made training a priority. I'm doing that for myself, which I'm happy about because I didn't used to do that as much. I've now gotten back to that; I'm slowly trying to check off the boxes.

Working and living in a foreign country with a foreign language, my brain gets tired pretty fast. If I'm having a bad day in a foreign country—which is way worse than just having a bad day—I have a motto, "Go to bed." I get some sleep, start over fresh the next day and retackle things in the morning.

What are some of the traits that have helped you become successful?

I would say just showing up. Showing up on time and being present—trying to bring the best energy to whatever it is I'm doing. I've learned to manage the expectations of others. But what got me here is being consistent, honest and empathetic.

It was part of my upbringing that I don't pretend to have all the answers. At times when I think I know the answer and am a little bull-headed then realize I didn't have the answer after all, it feeds the notion that I don't have the answers to anything. There are a lot of ways to do things—I try to be open to that.

Another thing I've learned is to take responsibility for what you've done or are doing. Even if it's failing, own it and that's okay. Life will move on. You might get in trouble for failing or for taking responsibility for something you've done poorly, but in the long run, you'll learn from it and people will respect you more.

My wife says I always give people the time of day. Anyone who's ever wanted to chat or who has a question, I'm always happy to take the time to answer and converse if I can and that's paid dividends for me.

I can't tell you how many times I've answered an email and that ended up down the road turning into something valuable. That's happened several times, which reinforces the idea that we should take time for conversations and walk through as many doors as possible for experiences.

I had to learn to say "no" more often, but I try to do it in a polite way. If somebody asks for advice, I'll be honest and say, "I'd love to sit down, but I can't make that happen. Maybe in the future."

Do you set goals? Do you write them down? Do you review them?

They're typically in my head; I'm trying to get better at writing them down. Because English was not my best subject and I always had a hard time getting thoughts out of my head and onto paper, I'd just keep them in my head. I'm learning that I need to get them on paper. Otherwise, they keep rolling around in my head, which doesn't help anybody.

About 10 years ago, my wife and I used a bar napkin to write out what we wanted to do in our lives. When we were moving to Italy, we found the box containing that napkin. We'd done 90 percent of the things on the napkin.

That's something we try to do regularly—make a list of thinking huge, like discussing what you want to do before you die. Let's see if we can make those things happen.

What are you doing to stay organized?

There's a great book, *Getting Things Done* by David Allen, about continuing to review your task list. He says if you can't get something done, it's because you didn't write a small enough goal. There are micro tasks to those tasks you can't get done—you're not making chores small enough to tackle them. That stuck with me. When I have more challenging things that keep going from one list to the next list for months on end, I need to figure out how to break it down so I can get it done.

What are some of the sacrifices you've made to get to where you are today?

There are definitely sacrifices because you must be willing to go an extra mile. Sometimes people will say some version of, "Darce, can you get me a job at EXOS?"

And I respond, "I can talk to some people—they have an opening in LA."

And they say, "I don't want to live in LA."

"I guess you don't get the job."

You have to be willing to make sacrifices. If you want something badly enough, you'll make the sacrifice; if you don't, you won't. You can use that as a reflection tool.

With all the traveling I've done, one of the sacrifices is not being able to share it with my family. Relationships are built from memories—you have to work to create memories. If you want to build strong relationships, you have to have memories, and the only way to get those is by doing things together. Those are things we're trying to do more of as a family, to create those memories.

Sometimes people forget it's important that goals be in line with their spouse's goals. If you always wanted to live in Italy and your wife didn't, it wouldn't work.

In taking this role in Italy, it was a family group decision. It sounds cool to say, "We're moving to Italy. We're living in Rome. It's going to be amazing." And it has been amazing, but it's also been difficult at times.

As long as you're all on board, it's easier to deal with the difficult times. If one person doesn't want to do it and the other does, it becomes more ammunition during an argument and probably won't end well.

You hit the nail on the head: Everyone has to be in.

Tell me a mistake you've made in your career.

The first thing that comes to mind would be advice I've given patients or athletes. Now that I know better, I would have changed a rehab plan or changed training that might have caused overtraining or created tendonitis.

I make mistakes using the wrong words in conversations. There are also those tough conversations you have with athletes and 20 minutes later when it's all done and you're on your way home, you think, "I wish I would've…" Those are things I wish I could take back and redo.

Was there a time when you wanted to give up but didn't? And what did you do instead of giving up?

You have to keep reassessing why you're doing what you're doing and why you got in it in the first place, because there are times when your motivation changes. Your goals change; you learn new things—you want to do different work.

When I was seeing physical therapy patients eight hours a day, every 30 minutes, it sucked the life out of me at times. I began to think, "I don't want to do this anymore."

I loved helping people, but going through the process was draining. At times, you feel like you can't give your best because you're too exhausted. You have to refocus and accept where you are and start problem-solving how you can reassign yourself to something that gives you motivation and drives you forward.

I need to feel mentally stimulated in what I'm doing, and if that's happening, I'm typically happy. If I start to lose mental stimulation, it's time for a change. I need to reassess my scenario to see if I can't either change my current position or review the position to find more stimulation in it.

The other thing is to accept the fact that you're going to have hard times—it's normal; it's okay to have hard times. Reframing those hard times is difficult because you're frustrated at not getting what you want from your current situation.

If you're not getting what you want, you have to change what you're doing. If you look at it more like a puzzle, you can reframe the challenge and carry on. There have been a lot of tough times in my current position—being in a foreign culture, country and language—where I've thought, "I don't know if I can keep going with this. This is tough." You have to keep putting one foot in front of the other and start reframing.

Sir Edmund Hillary was part of the first team who climbed Mount Everest back in the 1950s when they didn't have all the gear we have now. When he came off the mountain, someone asked, "How was it—what did you learn from the experience?" He answered, "It's not about climbing the mountain; it's about conquering yourself."

My wife and I once climbed Mount Shasta. It was the most mentally challenging thing— it's 14,000 feet. I was so miserable going up that damn thing. I was in my head, feeling as though I was putting one foot in front of the other, but I wasn't getting anywhere. Though I was going as fast as I could, it wasn't fast enough and I was thinking, "Who does this? This is stupid."

When we finished, I couldn't believe how mentally caught up I'd been in the whole thing. I realized at that point that I needed to gain some mental toughness and needed to take on some challenges. Put one foot in front of the other and eventually, you'll make it. Mountaineering is a great analogy for life.

Darcy, I know you read and listen to a lot of books. Give us three non fitness–related books everyone should read.

A couple phenomenal books I've read recently: *Resilience* and a similar book called *The Obstacle is the Way*. *Ego is the Enemy* is another book from Ryan Holiday and finally, *Black Box Thinking*, which is about accepting failure.

Success leaves clues. Who are three people we can all learn from?

First, I'd have to say one of my mentors, Mark Verstegen. He's an amazing guy. He's not on social media, which is one of the things that impresses the hell out of me. You don't find him on Facebook, Twitter…or anywhere. You'll find his company, EXOS, but not him personally.

Next would be Michael Gervais, a sports psych guy who works for the Seattle Seahawks with Pete Carroll. Check out his podcast called *Finding Mastery*, which is phenomenal.

Finally, I'm going to give you a topic and a person: Complex systems thinking is the topic and the guy's name is Russell Ackoff. There are a few YouTube videos from 1990s that blew my mind. He was talking about complex systems thinking and reframing our thinking. It's brilliant material.

Thanks for those suggestions and for being a big part of my development and thank you for sharing your journey, which is obviously not over as you continue toward even greater success.

BE LIKE DARCY

"About 10 years ago, my wife and I used a bar napkin to write out what we wanted to do in our lives. When we were moving to Italy, we found the box containing that napkin. We'd done 90 percent of the things on the napkin.

"That's something we try to do regularly—make a list of thinking huge, like discussing what you want to do before you die. Let's see if we can make those things happen."

THE BUCKET LIST

This will be a little different from the "Find Your Mission" exercise (see Christa Doran's Be Like), Vision Your Life in Full Detail (see Mark Fisher's Be Like) and Goal Setting (see Todd Durkin's Be Like).

This is more of a bucket list of things you want to experience, places you want to visit and things you want to achieve in your life.

Set aside a quiet time to do this. Give yourself at least 30 minutes.

On a piece of paper, write out time frames. For example: "Before I die," "Before I'm 50," "Before I'm 40," "This Year."

Under each time frame, write "Places I Want to Visit" (Italy, Alaska, Boston), "Things I Want to Accomplish" (Get a massage license; Get my masters), "Things I Want to Learn" (Learn to speak Spanish; Learn to play a guitar), "Things I Want to Do" (Climb Mt. Shasta; Go to a Super Bowl). Add whatever topics you want (People I want to meet).

Just keep writing under each topic. Think big and don't hold back—just get it all on paper.

Organize the topics into a checklist you can print and reference periodically like you do your goals.

Check things off when you complete them…and make sure you celebrate (see Dan John's Be Like).

Think about adding some of the bucket-list items to a vision board (see Nikki Metzger's Be Like).

Don't be afraid to change things.

Keep doing the exercise. It will evolve as you do.

Todd is the founder of Fitness Quest 10 (San Diego, CA). He's the Lead Training Advisor for Under Armour and was listed multiple times in the Top 100 Most Influential People in Health and Fitness. He conducts mastermind groups for fitness professionals desiring business, training and personal mastery. You can learn more about Todd at todddurkin.com.

Your facility, Fitness Quest 10, has achieved an amazing level of success. With your personal training and your motivational speaking, you get everybody fired up. You've had success in many areas. Talk to us about how you define success.

I define success as literally maximizing your potential and while doing that, motivating and inspiring others to reach theirs. You've got to tap into your best self, your best potential within. What do you do with that? For me, it's motivating and inspiring other people to reach their potential.

It's apparent that success evolves over time. When did you start realizing what you were doing was working?

There still are days when I feel I haven't gotten to where I want to go. There were times in my 18 years of having a brick and mortar shop—in the beginning, it was downright scary. I had no clients, no money, no business plan. I didn't know if the brick and mortar thing would work.

It was the year 2000 when I opened it and back then, small studios didn't really exist. The landscape at the time was large health clubs. Having a business based on people paying for personal training and not a membership was atypical.

The first time I realized things were working was when I became a sports massage therapist for the San Diego Chargers. Soon after, I became the trainer and coach of LaDainian Tomlinson; I worked with him for nine years. That was the first time I realized, "Maybe I've got something going on here." Having a special client after years of being in the trenches and grinding 50 hours a week might have been my first break. I thought of that as a success moment.

You've had such a well-rounded career. You were a massage therapist, a personal trainer, a strength and speed and conditioning coach. Some people who have heard you speak might not even know you're a trainer because you're so energetic and inspiring—they might think you're a motivational speaker. What is it that drives you?

Someone is depending on my words. That's what I think about; it's one thing to think about my own purpose because I'm designed to motivate people to greatness.

A video or an Instagram story or a Facebook post or something I'm going to say throughout the day drives me now—even knowing that Fitness Quest 10 is going to make a difference in someone's day. When you read the *Five Languages of Love*, you learn what type of language you are. I'm a guy of affirmation; I like feedback.

When someone drops me an email or a Facebook post and says, "Your words made a difference in my life," it fuels me. That's what makes me get up in the morning because I'm fulfilling my purpose—knowing someone is depending on my words.

I want to take a different twist here because many people might look at you and think, "I can't do what Todd does. I don't have that personality." Talk to us about the habits or traits you weren't born with but you developed, traits other people can develop to help on their path to success.

Success is a habit, doing things over and over. It's not just one moment that's going to make you successful. It's the old adage of "it only took me 10 years to become an overnight success." The habits develop over time.

It takes consistency. You have to work your tail off; you have to have grit; you have to sacrifice. It takes all of these things on a regular basis to be successful. For me, it's a habit to be disciplined in doing the little things it takes to be my best self.

You may say, "Todd's always full of energy." No, I'm not—there are times when I'm not. But it's when I'm not that I do my best practices, like making sure I do my early morning routine, which fuels my fire.

This morning when I woke up, I didn't feel great. But by the time my two-hour personal window was up, I was on fire. Literally, I couldn't wait to get to the gym and train my athletes. When you don't feel your best, it's a skill to stand up and say, "We got this."

For me, those little things over time add up to a "success" or what I yearn for, which is more significance.

Let's segue into that morning routine. What does it consist of?

The first 30 minutes is spent nurturing the soul. It's spent in the Word; I'm a man of faith. It's spent in journaling and listening and praying. I have a form when I'm praying as far as doing more listening and writing as much as asking for blessings of how I want to use my energy.

Here's the thing: This is not easy for me. It's really easy to go right into my workout or to do email. But I have rules for my life and one is that I don't turn on my phone before I'm done with my morning routine.

Part of that is making sure I don't get distracted. I want to get up and dominate the day before the day dominates me. In the first 30 minutes, I fill my spirit. When my spirit is filled up, I've got a gym at my house and three or four days a week, I'm in my home gym. I'll do 30 minutes of cardio while listening to a podcast and then I'll get into strength work. That's an hour of "me time" before the family gets up and the day beings.

Sometimes you have to pick yourself up and try to make something a habit. It makes such a difference, and it sets you up for the day.

It's everything…and the days you don't have it are the days you've got to find it. Sometimes a workout routine becomes a 20- to 30-minute routine. For me, the 18-minute mark is the magic. Sometimes in the first 10 or 15 minutes, I feel like a dog. All of a sudden, energy pops in, and I'm ready to rock and roll. Then I'll switch gears and start ramping up. Around that 30-minute mark, I'm ready to start hammering and getting after it.

By that point, the day is already rolling because I'm finally amped up and ready to go. There's nothing like starting the day like that. Over the last many years, having that morning routine one or two hours early in the morning has been absolutely essential to having a successful day.

It's an evolving process, which I learned because I beat myself up thinking I wasn't doing it perfectly. People have to remember that: It evolves.

You have to carve out one or two hours a day of personal development time. It could be that you only get 15 minutes of quiet time in the morning before you head out. Fantastic. Take that time early in the morning before everything gets rolling. Maybe later, you can listen to a podcast at lunchtime or when you have a break in the afternoon.

The key is to get personal time. Get that quiet time, prayer time, meditation, breath work—whatever you want; it's honoring your spirit, the inside, to reduce anxiety. Make sure you're grounded and you can conquer the day.

Having a brick and mortar business can be really challenging. How do you push through the worst times when you feel like you want to give up?

Number one: Don't ever wish you had someone else's life. You might look at social media or read a book and think, "I want to be him." No, you don't; just be yourself and be the best version of yourself.

The way I get through tough times—of course I have them—number one is faith. I try to pray all the time, but I really try to be in faith when I'm being challenged. I make sure I stay true to my deepest and best self and tap into that.

Here's the conversation I have with myself, "Is this my ego talking or is this God talking?"

The ego is usually the one shouting at me, "Do this, do this, do this," and then God is the one whispering. How do you discern what you're supposed to do? As a man driven by purpose, I want to listen to the whispers. That's hard because all of us have an ego and we've fed that ego. Where I am in my life, I'm trying to tap into that spirit and that quiet self of listening to the whisper that comes different times of the night or early in the morning.

The other thing when I'm going through a tough time is remind myself that this shall soon pass. At Fitness Quest 10, if we have to fire someone or someone quits, I have to shift the energy of our culture because it's not where I want it. I pride myself on building a positive, energetic culture. Sometimes I have to make tough decisions and I often remind myself that this too soon shall pass. Great leaders step up during tough times.

On a daily basis, I'll say the word "next" to myself because I'm not going to dwell on an issue or a challenge too long. I'll literally say, "Next." Then I can compartmentalize life into different silos so I can move on and not get pulled into an area that might be holding me back. I want to continue to move forward.

That trigger keeps reminding you to bring yourself back and keeps you grounded.

Todd, talk about goal setting—do you do formal goal setting?

I've always been someone who sets goals. Since the time I was a young kid who aspired to be a starting varsity athlete, to someone who wanted a college scholarship, to getting a degree, to my career plans—I was always the guy who had the pros and cons on a piece of paper.

Now I have a much more sophisticated system. I build an annual roadmap. I spend probably 20 hours on this at the end of every year when I set out the plan for the coming year. It's for the year, but it's for my life.

I work backward; I reverse engineer where I want my life to go. I update it every 90 days, "the 90-day wonder," where I review and adjust my annual roadmap. Then, every week on Sunday night, I do my W-LAGs. My Wins, Losses, Aha moments from the past week and Goals for this upcoming week: W-LAGs.

That's everything broken down to the biggest things I want to achieve to make it a great year. It's broken down into micro goals by W-LAGs. This allows me to focus on little things each and every week and, of course, every day.

Then I have micro goals. Every day I have five goals I must achieve to make it a winning day. If I have a winning day, a winning week, a winning month, or a winning quarter, I can guarantee I'll have a winning year.

I reverse engineer success from the annual roadmap into the 90-day wonder into the W-LAGs. While I make it sound simple, I take time for review each and every day and week and every 90 days. And I work every year to set goals, adjust goals, tweak them and take action on them as well.

The review piece is a something many people miss. We need to do it to stay connected to the goals.

Most type-A high performers are always thinking, "What's next, what's next, what's next?" I'm no different. But stopping, slowing down and reflecting allows me to go further and more in-depth. Stopping every Sunday night to reflect on the aha moments from the past week allows me to stay present and aware.

That's a skill, not a gift. It's a skill to learn. Slow down and be present in conversation, be present in everything you do so you can enjoy the process.

If we're always focusing on the product, it feels empty, just chasing product after product versus actually enjoying the process. It's something I've ingrained over the last 10 years.

You talked about being a type-A personality, a high achiever. A lot of type-A people don't celebrate the wins. That's why the Sunday night reflection is important as you move forward. Dan Sullivan talks about "the gap and the gain." There's that line, that gap between where we are and where we want to go. Even though we might've gotten 80 percent done, we always focus on that gap, the part we didn't achieve. With your system, you're focusing on a lot of wins. Most of us don't do enough of that.

I was working with an NFL athlete who said, "If there are 52 plays on the offensive side of the ball, in a game you might make one or two bad plays. You focus on the one or two bad plays versus the 50 great plays."

That's the human brain—that's where it goes. Mindset is important because it allows us to accentuate our strengths. Our minds often go to the things we're not doing well. How do we accentuate the things we're doing well, strengthen those and correct things that aren't going well? We do that by reflecting and stopping and thinking about the aha moments.

I share my W-LAGs with my leadership team; this allows them to see where I am in life and business. I ask them to do the same with me, so I understand them, not just in their roles at Fitness Quest 10. They might have a struggle they're facing. This way I can connect with them better as a leader versus always just addressing what might be going on at work. It's been one of our more effective ways to communicate at Fitness Quest 10.

That's a great piece of advice for any leader. Todd, you're traveling so much for business and speaking and you've got a lot going on personally. In your lectures, you often talk about the different color zones. Can you explain that?

That's my color-coded calendar system. I have four colors: green as Green Machine; blue is Blue Sky time; red is Red Tape Organization; and yellow is Mellow Yellow time.

When I'm working at Fitness Quest 10, that's Green Machine—that's making money.

Blue Sky is when you're working *on* your business and not *in* your business.

Red, the organizational side, is when you're organizing and doing the things you need to do to be organized.

Then yellow is Mellow Yellow time—vacation time, time away from everything so you can think clearly.

The most important two colors are yellow and blue—Mellow Yellow and Blue Sky time. During your Mellow Yellow time when you're away from work is when you get your big ideas. For me, when I step into the mountains, typically I can think big and get great ideas. I get clarity. I get out my journal and start writing ideas; I set goals and action steps. I come back to work and I'm on fire.

Blue Sky time is when you're strategically working on your business. Try to do these two to three days every three months. You're almost auditing your business, reviewing what's going well, what's not going well, and creating specific action steps.

When you get more Mellow Yellow time and more time working on your business, it drives the Green Machine. One thing in the fitness profession, as in most others, if you work just on Green Machine time, thinking about money the whole time, you burn out. Mellow Yellow and Blue Sky times drive the Green Machine. The Green Machine in turn helps drive deeper business, a deeper strategy so you can have a greater impact.

What do you do to get in the Mellow Yellow zone?

I build Mellow Yellow into my calendar—it's scheduled time off. During Mellow Yellow time, if it's just my wife and me or with the family, we get away. It could also be a week where I have more off days.

If I build that into my calendar, I still have to be disciplined enough to take it. It's easy to say, "These athletes want to work with me. I'll get that day off later." The next thing I know, I'm spent. If I'm coming off a live event, I build in Mellow Yellow time on the back end so I'm not completely wiped out. The energy expenditure during a live event is tough.

When I have a summer field with athletes or another busy time, managing my own energy is important. I'm constantly tweaking the calendar because Mellow Yellow and Blue Sky time is important.

I learned from Tony Robbins that the more successful you get, the more time away from the grind you need to work on your business—to get more vertical versus horizontal.

How do you go deeper and create more impact? That's a challenge. It's that constant, "Wait, you're telling me I should take more time off to be more successful?" As you get deeper and impact more people, your bandwidth becomes smaller.

You have to work more on your business and be strategic about what you're doing. Otherwise, you're just busy and at the end of the day you'll find yourself asking, "What the heck am I doing? I'm really busy right now, but when I look at the numbers, it doesn't make sense. I don't feel like I'm aligned with my purpose."

Time off to work on you and on your business is essential. When I say working on you, I literally mean working on you through workshops, events and retreats—working on your best self. The deeper you go, the more you grow…or the more you grow, the deeper you can go.

You have to grow deep and you've got to go deep inside yourself. The deeper you go inside your spirit, your soul and yourself, and really try to reveal it, the world sees that and you can create more impact.

We've seen this trend with books like *Deep Work, Rest* or *The One Thing* reminding us to get away from being busy just to be busy.

Todd, success leaves clues. Give us three people we could follow and learn from. It could be in any domain.

I'll start with The Rock. I love The Rock. You know why? Because he talks about where he is; he shares his life.

On a business side, Dave Ramsey and his Entre Leadership program—I like his podcast; I think he's a genuine, authentic man and I like his philosophies.

The other one I suggest is Pastor T.D. Jakes—he's got the Potter's Touchdown in Dallas. Whenever I'm in a mood that I want to hear something spiritual to get uplifted and empowered, T.D. Jakes is someone I listen to.

People who listen to T.D. Jakes, Dave Ramsey or The Rock get well-rounded messages.

The Rock's work ethic is inspiring.

That's why when he says, "I'm the hardest worker in the room," I think, "I've got to outwork The Rock!" People want success—they say they want it, but are they working at it?

Success does leave clues and it's never as easy as people want; it's hard work. It takes sacrifice. It takes discipline. It takes consistent effort over a long time. It takes grit. When an opportunity comes up, if it fits within your wheelhouse, you have to go. The Rock is an example of someone who's capitalizing on his opportunities and gifts.

Now give us three non-fitness books that can help in our development.

A book I recently read and I enjoyed was by a guy named Gino Wickman called *Traction*. It's an awesome book about a vivid vision. It's a great business book.

The first book I ever read was Napoleon Hill's *Think and Grow Rich*, which changed my life. It's one of my favorite books of all time, along with Og Mandino's *The Greatest Salesman in the World*.

If someone wants a great book on business, Jon Gordon is probably my favorite business author. Look at *The Energy Bus, The Hard Hat, Training Camp*. He speaks my language in his writing.

Let me give you one more because it's important. When I'm speaking to fitness pros, overcoming adversity is a theme that often comes up. Stuart Scott's book left a tremendous impact on me: *Every Day I Fight*. Stuart passed from cancer. *Every Day I Fight* is about that mindset of how he was going to beat cancer even though he knew he was going to die from it. It was a mindset of fighting every single day.

It reminds me a bit of my man Drew Brees's book *Coming Back Stronger*. If you're facing challenges in your life and you need grit, Drew's book is inspiring.

You're one of the leaders in our profession who's been making such a great impact and still takes time to help others. Thank you for sharing your journey of success.

BE LIKE TODD

"I've always been someone who sets goals. Since the time I was a young kid who aspired to be a starting varsity athlete, to someone who wanted a college scholarship, to getting a degree, to my career plans. I work backward; I reverse engineer where I want my life to go and then I update it every 90 days.

"These are all the things that must be done—it's broken down into micro goals. It allows me to focus on little things each and every week and, of course, every day."

GOAL SETTING

There are so many great goal-setting programs. *Your Best Year Ever* (Hyatt), *The Perfect Day Formula* (Ballantyne) and *The 12-Week Year* (Moran/Lennington) are all amazing resources for deeper study.

After working with all three of these programs, I've come up with what I call the "3x3 Goal Matrix." I go over this in more detail in my online course at *CONTINUEfit.com/Propel,* but here's a simple version.

You're going to pick **Three Goals** with a completion date of **Three Months.**

You can pick up to **Three Domains** (physical, career, financial, non-vocational, relationship, intellectual or social).

Be specific in your goals. For example:

"I will increase my monthly training revenue by $1,000 by March 1."

"I will lose five pounds and get to 13 percent bodyfat by March 1."

"I will get 1,000 new Instagram followers by March 1."

For each goal, write **Three Reasons Why** you want to achieve that goal.

For example:

Goal: "I will increase my monthly training revenue by $1,000 by March 1."

Why I want to achieve this:

"I can start a 401k and feel better about my future."

"I can attend more continuing education."

"I can do more fun things I want to do."

Think of **Three People** who can help you with each goal. It's always easier when you get help! You only have to personally know two of the people you choose. The third person could be an author with a book on the subject. But you want to use the other two people for support and accountability.

Having a daily planner for this section will help tremendously. I recommend Michael Hyatt's Full Focus Planner.

Three Weekly Tasks—Every Sunday night or Monday morning, write three tasks, one for each goal, that will get you closer to your three-month goal to complete by the end of the week.

Three Daily Tasks—Every day, write three tasks that will help you achieve your three weekly tasks above, one for each goal. Ideally you will do this in the evening (see Alwyn Cosgrove's Be Like).

Every evening, write **Three Wins** for the day. Keep them related to your goal so you can start feeling good about your progress.

Under your wins, write **Three Things You're Grateful** for. It doesn't have to be related to goals. (see Dana Santas' Be Like)

Charlie has been a physical therapist, certified athletic trainer and strength and conditioning coach for nearly 20 years. His workplaces have included the NBA, the United States Marine Corps Special Operations and has been consultant for dozens of high-profile sports and business organizations, professional athletes and Hollywood celebrities. In 2009, Charlie began publication of his Training=Rehab DVD and Seminar Series, which has been credited as profoundly impacting the profession with his approach of integrating fitness and rehabilitation within a systematic and cohesive thought process. Find more about Charlie at charlieweingroff.com.

Our shared history goes back over 10 years. Because of your knowledge, even back in those early years, we put you on a pedestal. You were also powerlifting on the international level and were a leader in our strength community. Let's start out with your exponential rise to success. How do you define success?

I'm stumbling at the thought of being on a pedestal. I'm only 5′4″. I'm not very tall.

Success is being able to do what you want, when you want, how you want, how much you want. It's not just about dollars, but if the options you want require dollars, that's success. If the options you want require other things, that's also success. Success means having the life you want, waking up when you want…being able to be home in the afternoon to engage with your kids if that's what you want.

Sometimes success might be challenging because you can't verbalize exactly what you want or you're apologetic for it. I'm not sure if I'm successful and maybe claiming success for yourself isn't flattering or necessary.

I've watched your progression and knew you were successful early on. In the last few years, you seem to be on a path of designing your life and being able to have options. Do you feel that way?

I do. I eliminated certain things from my life a few years ago. That might also be around the same time people started to see different things in me, when I chose to reveal some of the things I do in my life on social media. What appears to be an open book is only as open as a person allows it to be. I have some components of feeling successful.

Number one: It's not always the case—there are things that aren't shared publicly.

Number two: I don't ever want to feel like I have it all. Most people who know me know I'll never retire. I might work less, but I don't know that I'll ever say I have those options 365 days a year. I'm aspiring to it, and I know what those options are, but at the same time, they may change.

What is it that motivates you? What gets you out of bed in the morning?

There's an easy way to answer that, and there's probably a more spiritual or existential way to answer it. But the endgame is, "Can I do the things I love, which in my case sometimes costs money?"

There's a certain amount of money I require to live the type of lifestyle that makes me happy. I'm aspiring to that and I try to direct all the arrows at that target. It's not always easy to think about the long term when you have short-term responsibilities as well as other interests.

It's all targeted. Continuing to be good at what I do allows me to do that. That arrow is like a curved arrow. Not every hour is directed at the bulls-eye. Some will be curved; some will be like JFK's magic bullet. They'll go all sorts of different directions, but they always get to the target.

The other answer is almost a spiritual chase: What motivates a man?

I want to be the best ever to live. I don't even know how that gets judged and I don't care if it ever gets judged. But that's what motivates me.

It feels great to have someone say good things about me. It's very cool to have other people think we're successful. But I want to be the best ever at what I do, and that'll never be judged. I'm going to try and fail a lot. In the end, I'll know I tried—not to be good at what I do, not to be the best around, but to be the best ever. That's an athletic mindset.

You mentioned powerlifting. It's very easy to be the best in powerlifting; that's winning to me. To be the undisputed champion motivates me every day. That's why I act the way I act and I do what I do.

There's a confidence about you. As a patient of yours, your open-mindedness to different approaches shocked me. You were admitting, "I'm wrong on this, so I'm going to try this, and do that." This search and level of care impressed me. The ego is taken out.

You use the hashtag "best in the world." It's always top of mind with you. Sometimes people might think, "Charlie…he's the man. He's confident. Everybody goes to him for help." But, you're still working on that.

My drive is about problem-solving and creating a solution. I can't keep running into a brick wall; no one wins. In your situation, we were looking for a certain pathway that seemed to make sense, but it wasn't there. We'll pick another one and find the right way.

To me, that's the motivation. You have to go into every situation assuming you're going to be wrong because if you are, you can change.

It's easy for me to accept criticism. That doesn't mean I'm going to change what I do. That will depend on how I evaluate the criticism. Over the last several years, the criticism at worst is like a bee sting that goes away in seconds and it's not a big deal. I may choose to go into that hornet's nest again or I might learn from the sting and do something different.

There's never a right or wrong way to integrate criticism. I'm okay with being wrong because when I admit I'm wrong, I won't do it again. It's a pragmatic, Socratic approach, highly driven by ego because I want to be right. I want to be correct in the end.

If you show me I'm wrong, I won't do it again…and then I'll be right. Just do the opposite and good things will happen. That's a pragmatic approach to being wrong, but still using ego to drive you.

To do what you do, you have to spend a lot of time at work. You have to travel. You're speaking on an international level and working with Team Canada and the NFL.

What do you feel are some sacrifices you've had to make?

I eliminated some things when I got divorced; the choices I made motivating my career had to have been a part of that in some way. My close friends might say, "She didn't support you or the process and it was the right thing to happen." Maybe that was it.

Several years ago we moved into a house in New Jersey after I left North Carolina under negative circumstances. We thought we'd never be able to afford a house like we were leaving because things are much less expensive in North Carolina than in the tri-state area.

But we were able to get a house because things started to click. The first summer of living there, I think I was in the pool twice. Around that time, I spoke with Alwyn Cosgrove, who's like a big brother to me. We were at a Nike conference and he said, "Anytime you say 'yes' to one thing, you say 'no' to another." Not going in my pool that summer was the complete embodiment of what he was saying. There were a lot of things I was saying yes to. I didn't use the pool, and I wanted to. I made changes in my schedule the next summer so I could use the pool more.

I give up a lot of sleep, which is not a healthy thing to do. I rationalize that I'll sleep later. But then health issues come along and we have to match up procedures to fix them. It's a puzzle.

You're lucky when you have more puzzle pieces to make the picture because sometimes you have to scrap it and start over again. There are many things I'm missing, but you have to have faith in whatever you're doing so you feel good at night when you go to bed.

I left the bar business because it's a single young man's business. I had to be out late if I was going to be successful. I'd probably be waking up at 10 or 11 and I wouldn't see my wife much. It's hard to be successfully married in that business.

We have plenty of successful people who are married in our profession, but I wonder if we'd be more successful if we were single.

I don't know if people have to be single to be in professional sports. The coach will live in the city where the team is playing and the family might live 3,000 miles away. The coach just comes to town to see the family. Some people could never live like that. But many people do and it works for them.

How we analyze different relationships is a delicate thing. What's right for one is not always right for someone else. When it comes to success where marriage would be another illustration of the options, it would depend on the relationship.

It's not just person-to-person in a marriage. It's business partnerships; it's working with people. Those are all levels of relationships and the more depth you have, the more democratic the relationship can be. If there's only one link between the two, it has to be autocratic because once you lose that link, you now have nothing in common. If you thought you had something and then realize you didn't, it can turn into a damaging situation that usually leads to discord. Depth in the relationship allows options and one of those might be a working lifestyle where you can gain.

But you're going to have to give up others; you say yes to one thing, you say no to another.

What helped you get through the tough times a couple of years ago? How do you push through those worst of it?

I said to myself, "I don't lose. There are many versions of winning, but I'm not going to lose." You respect that it's a process, and you're getting your ass kicked in the first quarter. But you still have the second quarter, third quarter, fourth quarter. You have many opportunities to make decisions to get yourself out of that.

Going through the divorce wasn't the first awful thing, either. When I was 22, I was driving over the Outerbridge Crossing—one of the many bridges connecting New York and New Jersey—when I got a phone call; it was somebody from the New Jersey Nets saying they fired the head athletic trainer. The person said, "John Nash, the general manager, wants you to show up tomorrow. You're going to temporarily be the head athletic trainer for the New Jersey Nets."

I was driving to one of my minor league games—in the minor leagues, you drive the van. For the next week, if you called the training room for the New Jersey Nets, I would answer the phone as the head athletic trainer. Then, after being told I would get an opportunity to interview for the job, a couple of weeks went by and I didn't get the time of day and had to move on.

It's very hard at that age to be told something that doesn't happen. At 22, you haven't been through enough in life—you haven't been through enough disappointment.

A few years later, I got back to the NBA and…then I didn't get a new contract and everything happened all over again. I thought I was going into my end-of-the-season meeting to talk about the following year's plans and get a new contract. Instead, I was told, "We're going in a different direction." I wasn't given any criticism or reasons why they were going in a different direction. We'd been number one in the standings; we had the fewest games missed of any team. I probably was a part of the staff who did something well.

That happened twice…and you go on.

I don't talk about it often, but I was fired from my job at Marine Corps Special Operations, where I'd been thinking, "This is it. This is my career. What better opportunity to be a part of serving your country and doing your job, and for the greatest men in the world." I got fired, and I thought, "Everything will be okay; everything happens for a reason, blah, blah, blah."

And then I got divorced. That's at least four life-changing disappointments.

Right now, I feel so good about where I am because those clichés were right: Everything did turn out okay. I wound up in a much better place every time. Every situation not only got better, but I significantly upgraded the quality of those environments. That doesn't mean it doesn't suck while you're going through it, but if it happened before, it's a lot easier to believe the good part's will happen again.

Going through that sucked, but you keep fighting with whatever tools you have. Sometimes, it's challenging because you are beholden to other people. You don't just control yourself. It's not like you can just change rehab techniques and try something else.

Things are much easier if you look at the big picture and have other good things in your life you can hold onto. When you're 22, you don't have that many things. I don't mean possessions; you don't have many things to hold onto, and that's why people find religion or seek pack relationships. You find whatever gives you a reason to believe.

What I believe is, it's happened four times; it'll happen again. All four times, I got more tangible things when I was done, so I have no reason to believe that won't happen again.

Do you have a formal process for your goal setting?

The business and financial goals are so pointed that I don't need to write them down. I know exactly what I need to do or at least what's been recommended so that in 10 years I'll have a certain amount of money and will have the options I want. If I follow the plan, the worst thing that can happen is that I have more money than I need.

I don't have those written down because I think about them every single day. Every arrow I have is pointed at those processes to get to that 10-year point, and then if something changes, we change it.

How do you recharge on a daily, weekly and yearly basis?

I try to train as much as possible. I embody what I know. I'm not a powerlifter anymore and I don't think I will be again. I love feeling good. I love being my age and looking the way I look, which is a lot different than other people my age. I can't imagine not training, and I can't imagine not lifting heavy things. I'm not as comfortable with myself when I go a week without training.

I'm getting ready to take a vacation—meaning, there's no work whatsoever. I never really did that before because I love what I do. When I go places, it's usually the back- or front-end of a trip where I'm making money.

When I was younger, I never understood why the world would race to happy hour at 5:01 on a Friday evening. My whole day was a happy hour. I never felt the urge to recharge.

Now I'm doing things I like. I like going to the movies. I like going to Disney; that's the most expensive luxury I have. I like those, but I never really feel I'm being recharged by them. In fact, sometimes when I've gone off the grid, I've found that doesn't really work.

I worked in Costa Rica for really good people and afterward, I took a couple of days on the other side of the country. I stayed at a nice resort by myself and designed a schedule where in the morning, I'd train and have breakfast. I'd go back to my room, get my gear and go to the pool. I'd get something to eat, go to my room, train again…go to my room. I asked myself what I wanted to do for three days and that's exactly what I wanted to do. I enjoyed myself. But then when I got back, it wasn't a cathartic event people talk about.

When I find a recharge that works for me, I'll probably stick with it, but I haven't found it yet. Still, I haven't needed that; it would be cool to experience it, but maybe I don't need it.

Name three non fitness–related books we should read to help in your development.

Let's see: *Keep it Simple, Stupid* and all the different versions of Dale Carnegie's *How to Make Friends*, because they're so easy to try. Some of the things are amazingly powerful, like smiling and touching people. It really moved me because it's so simple. It's one of the few things you can do on Monday.

Say Anything is another book that's been valuable for me. I'm in many situations where I have to manage people and have to keep all those arrows targeted the right direction. Doug Crandall, the author, was a colonel at West Point; his message is that when you're working with people, everyone should be allowed to say whatever they want. They should always feel respected.

It also coaches the other side, to the people saying whatever they want, which has to be presented respectfully. You also have to be able to hear "no," and in the military, you don't always get to say things to people who have seniority. But when run this model where everyone is valuable, it works.

If there's someone above me and someone below me, the person below is allowed to talk to the person above. The conversation doesn't have to go through me. A part of that is because it's the right person. In the military, it's probably the right person because people don't move up in promotions if they don't meet certain standards.

Say Anything had a big part in crafting how I deal with people. But it's also predicated on having the right people. Great leaders who do amazing things and love talking about how their strategies have the right people. Sometimes that begins with an autocratic or dictatorship approach to getting them to be who you want them to be. But you hire the right person who has those values.

Those are books I can reference easily.

What about a couple of people you feel people should follow?

In our profession, it's very easy for me to say Mike Boyle for a number of reasons, one being that most people wouldn't know who I am without him. I'm very open about that and it's easy to say that—that leads me to say thank you. Remember who got you to the dance.

I crafted my speaking style after Mike's, where it's a "Say anything" or "This is where it's at and it's cool if you don't agree. We can talk about something else." Many people struggle with that, but there's a level of simplicity that makes sense. There's an organic level of respect in what Mike does. I aspire to conduct myself like that and more importantly, I want somebody to look at me the way I look at him.

There are other people such as Greg Rose and Lee Burton and Chris Poirier. They're all people no one ever says anything bad about. These are like big brothers; they're the people with whom I would attach myself.

From my perspective, "Best in the world" is not just a hashtag. You're achieving that status, Charlie. We appreciate you sharing your journey on your road to success.

BE LIKE CHARLIE

"I want to be the best ever at what I do."

THINK BIGGER #BESTINTHEWORLD

We are often our own biggest obstacle. Whether it's through negative self-talk or not believing in ourselves, our own self-limiting beliefs can keep us on a career plateau.

Charlie is on a quest to be the best in the world. Not just the best where he works or in his area, but in the world.

The only way he can get there is by setting his sights on it and believing he can do it.

"Whether you think you can or you think you can't, you're right." ~ Henry Ford

To be the best in the world at whatever you want to do, you have to reverse engineer the goal.

Start by focusing on being the best trainer you can be. Go to as many workshops as you can, network with people (see Patrick Ward's Be Like), visit other trainers and strength coaches (see Derek Hansen's Be Like), read or listen to as many books that you can (see Geralyn Coopersmith's Be Like), engage with people on a deeper level (see Bill Parisi's Be Like) and focus on one goal (see Ron McKeefery's Be Like).

Focus on being the best in your city. Branch out to volunteer your services in different programs throughout your area. Help as many people as you can.

Create an online course that will teach your methodologies and philosophies.

Focus on being the best in your state. Join any organizations where you can speak (see Mike Boyle's Be Like) and start to travel to different places to educate other trainers and clients.

Look for national conferences like the Perform Better Functional Training Summit to speak at in other cities.

Try to get on different podcasts to spread your message and increase your brand awareness.

Stay humble and continue to immerse yourself in topics that are out of your comfort zone (see Gray Cook's Be Like).

Take it one step at a time. It has to start with you being the best trainer you can be.

Molly is a certified strength and conditioning specialist, former figure competitor, powerlifter, and gym owner, and woman-in-charge at Girls Gone Strong, the world's largest platform for empowering women through evidence-based, body-positive, sustainable health and fitness information. Molly is also the creator of the Coaching and Training Women Academy, the world's first online Academy offering comprehensive, interdisciplinary, evidence-based women-specific coaching and training certifications for current and aspiring health and fitness professionals. Learn more about Molly's work at girlsgonestrong.com.

You've had success in a few different areas and you're always pushing the envelope—you're always growing. Tell us how you define success.

I recently started doing a values clarification exercise as we're working on the organizational development structure of Girls Gone Strong. Because Girls Gone Strong is a movement and started out of a deep desire to help people, we already have inherent values established in the organization. But determining my personal values and the values for the organization has been very helpful and provided a lot of clarity.

My top three personal values are: making a difference, having integrity and being resilient. I'd define success as embodying and practicing those values on a regular basis.

Making a difference is by far above everything else…the most important thing. How I define being successful is ultimately making a difference—with Girls Gone Strong, with the organization and the movement—and to be able to do that in a way that maintains my integrity. And both personally and professionally, it's practicing resilience.

Entrepreneurship is not for the faint of heart. But for me, knowing Girls Gone Strong has to exist in the world, it would be more painful not to have the struggle.

Success as making a difference, doing it with integrity and being personally and professionally resilient.

When we scroll through social media, it can feel like others are more successful. That's one reason you used the idea of being body-positive. It's such an important piece of what you're doing.

That's part of what we're doing, making a difference being rooted in our integrity. For example, when we're looking at something related to marketing for Girls Gone Strong, we could market in a spammy way and might reach more people and that would help us make a bigger difference. But would that be rooted in integrity? The answer's no.

It's interesting to have gotten super clear on those values and realize where I'm willing to make concessions and where I'm not.

I first did that after reading Tony Hsieh's book, *Delivering Happiness*. I was working with the Cosgroves at Results Fitness University, where they had us write down our values. After that, decisions become much easier. You can ask yourself, "Is this in line with my values?" Sometimes it is, but sometimes that's a no.

When did you start feeling you were becoming a success?

I have such high hopes for what Girls Gone Strong is going to do in the world. It's hard for me to see myself and the organization clearly because I'm "in it" all the time. We have over 600,000 women from 70 countries around the world in our community. And we have thousands of health and fitness professionals taking our certifications. Making a difference is my ultimate value. I'm grateful for that and consider that a success.

But I don't know if I consider myself a success. In my life and in my work, I believe what I do is never enough and good enough—and both can be true at the same time. The "never enough" keeps me hungry, and the "good enough" gives me peace. It's hard to describe how I came to that place or how I believe both of those can be true at the same time. But they are.

Things I've done so far are never enough. Feeling that way makes it a little weird to say I consider myself a success. I know I've done great work and that Girls Gone Strong has touched millions of people. When I step back and look at what we've done, I feel proud of it and it feels successful. That's a tricky question.

That's probably the number one trait of successful people: They don't feel like they're a success. That's part of what helps them get out of bed in the morning. It's what drives them.

The concept of "never enough" and "good enough" is helpful in terms of taking feedback—learning and being open to growth. I'm a huge fan of feedback and constructive criticism, and pride myself on taking it well. When I've worked hard on something and someone has suggestions to make it better, having that simultaneous feeling of never enough and good enough is helpful because I can appreciate the ideas.

My work will never end and I love that because I love what I do. But I also like the idea of being able to simultaneously feel good about what I've done versus always feeling like I'm not enough.

When times are tough, how do you push through?

People struggle with wanting to give up. I've never had that feeling; giving up on the work I've done with Girls Gone Strong has never crossed my mind, not even a little. I feel so fueled by the work and I believe so deeply in my bones that it's going to work, giving up has never been an option.

I was talking to a woman who asked what I do with my time and what would I do if I didn't need to get paid for it. For years, I didn't get paid for years for my work with Girls Gone Strong, so my answer was easy: exactly what I'm doing right now.

There's a lot of pressure to find balance in your business and personal life. For what I want to do with Girls Gone Strong—if I want to grow it into what I want—I can't be balanced. My life has to have imbalance.

In October of 2014, my hair was falling out from stress. There were originally several other members involved with Girls Gone Strong—2014 was the year I took over, sold my gym and launched our first program and went all in.

I have an autoimmune disease called Hashimoto's, which is autoimmune hypothyroidism, and I have polycystic ovarian syndrome. Hair loss is a symptom of both. I hadn't experienced it before, but it was starting to happen. These are stress responses.

I've sacrificed my health, some personal relationships and time with family. I've had to sacrifice a lot to make Girls Gone Strong the thing it can be in the world. But I'm okay with that; I'm super aware of the tradeoffs I'm making.

That might be a different answer than we normally hear about pushing through the worst times. For me, it doesn't feel hard at all. It's not hard to work for a week or two weeks straight, 12 hours a day on a big project to get it out into the world because it's what I want to do with my life.

This level of unbalance isn't something I want to last forever. But the drive to make Girls Gone Strong what it's going to be surpasses any other desire I have or challenge I've faced.

There's a nice push back against the concept of balance. Craig Ballantyne uses the word "mastery." It's life-work mastery because you're never going to be in balance. If you want to be good at something, you're going to have to focus on that one thing. If you're going to push through the thing that makes you the happiest or something that makes the biggest impact, there's going to be an imbalance. You said you made sacrifices. What are you doing to make sure you have better mastery over that?

There are some big rocks in place in my life, things I put into my schedule, commitments I make to myself and my family to ensure things stay in place while I'm working hard.

One simple example is working out on a regular basis. For the last 14 years, I've been in the gym working out three to five days a week. I've never taken more than a few weeks off at a time. That's important for my personal health. I also have some big nutrition rocks I hit every day—staying hydrated and eating enough protein and vegetables.

When my grandmother was alive, I made a commitment to spend two hours twice a week with her unless we had something major going on. I have similar things in place for spending time with my family and friends. I make sure to schedule that time, but I'm not spending as much time with the people in my life as I would if I weren't working so hard.

We have to figure out the essentials that need to be in place and make sure those bases are covered. We have to do the same for ourselves physically.

Our readers want to help as many people as they can. It's not easy, though. What are some habits or personality traits you attribute to your success?

I'm pretty good at knowing what I'm good at and what I'm not good at—and outsourcing the areas where I'm lacking. I'm in charge of mission, vision, content and voice. I have other people who do the business, strategy, marketing, finance and accounting.

I love to focus on the mission and the vision, interacting with my community and making sure the content we produce is high quality. I'm terrible at prioritizing my time. If it were up to me, I'd be on my computer or on calls all day with women around the world, crying and telling them how amazing they are. I'd just be connecting with our community.

But there are actual things that have to be done. So…I have someone in charge of my schedule. We brought a project manager on board about a year ago, Sarah Thibadeau—she's absolutely incredible. She was a high-level project manager at Microsoft for 15 years; she's a Ninja.

When she stepped in, she asked, "Molly, how do you want to spend your days? Every time you're doing something you don't want to be doing, write it on a card in our project management system and we'll take it off your plate."

For the last year, I've been working with her to determine what activities are outside of my unique abilities. Unique abilities are things we enjoy, that we're good at, that an organization needs and that brings value.

Anytime something's outside my unique abilities, we put it on a card in our project management system and she assigns someone else to take care of it. It's wonderful, but it took me time to get used to it, gaining humility knowing I'm not allowed to be in charge of my own time. It's been tough, but has also been super helpful because I'm significantly more productive. Realizing my weaknesses and not spending time bringing up my weaknesses has been helpful.

Krista Scott Dixon was one of the first people I heard talk about this. She asked, "Why would you want to work on your weaknesses? If you're a two at something, you could devote a ton of time to it and you might bring it to a four. Why don't you focus on your strengths, where you're an eight that you could bring to a ten—where you could be one of the best in the world at what you do?"

I don't spend a lot of time focusing on getting better at my weaknesses. I outsource those; let someone else handle them. I spend my time focusing on what I love doing and am good at.

In his productivity book *Free to Focus*, Michael Hyatt calls that getting in the "desire zone." Things we like doing and things we're good at—that's where we should spend our time. Molly, talk about your goal setting—what that process is for you. Do you write out goals and review them?

This is another area where I'm not strong. I have big long-term goals for Girls Gone Strong on a whiteboard in my office/living room/dining room, which is all the same room. But having a big vision and breaking it down into macro or micro steps is not one of my skills.

My boyfriend, Casey Sasek, runs the business side of Girls Gone Strong. Strategy, marketing, finance, accounting, legal—he oversees all of that. He and I and our project manager map out what we want to do. We've got long-term five- or 10-year goals. What are we going to do this year? What programs are we going to release; what's our focus going to be? What do we want to complete by the end of the year? The two of them get to work breaking things down into the steps we need to take to get things done.

They handle all of that because that's just not how my brain works. I can't look at a giant project and break it down into the smaller steps we need to do to finish. I figure out where we want to go and let other people on the team determine the actual tactical steps.

Molly, could you give us three non-fitness books everyone should read?

The E-Myth by Michael Gerber was a game changer for me. If you're a coach or a trainer and you want to own a gym or another business in the fitness profession—are you actually going to be doing fitness-related work or are you going to be doing something different? Are you going to be the manager of the business? Or are you going to be the entrepreneur? It's important to recognize there are distinct roles needed if a business is to be successful.

People get into this field because they love what they do; they think they're just going to do fitness stuff all day. That's not what you're going to be spending most of your time doing. And if it is, you need other people in those other roles.

I loved a book I read recently called *Give Work*, by a woman named Leila Janah. She's a Harvard graduate, a first-generation Indian American; her parents emigrated from India before she was born. She developed a business model that's an evidence-based way to eradicate global poverty in our lifetime. I'm extremely interested in learning more about social justice and liberation. Her book is incredible as she talks about how business owners can have a huge impact on eradicating global poverty, not through charity, but through giving work. She talks about impact sourcing and how we can positively impact people all over the world through the choices we make as business owners.

The Brené Brown book called *Braving The Wilderness, The Quest for True Belonging and The Courage to Stand Alone* is another book I read that's been valuable in my personal development and for some choices we've made in Girls Gone Strong. It's been huge in getting clear on my values and discovering, "This is what I want to do; this is what's right for me, and what's right for the organization."

Even if no one else in the fitness profession agrees, I'm going to have the courage to stand alone and do what I believe and be okay with the fact that people might criticize it or might not be on board. That book was impactful in helping me understand I can go against the grain and do something different—not only is it okay, it's important.

Those books are different and impactful.

They say success leaves clues; give us three people we can follow. They don't have to be on social media or even have to be alive.

John Berardi of Precision Nutrition—a person everyone who's reading this book will be familiar with—has been hugely impactful on both me and Girls Gone Strong. I adore him and the way he and Phil Caravaggio run their organization. It's the apex of making a difference, of helping people, of being financially successful and of running an organization where the people who work for you absolutely love what they do.

He doesn't get caught up in fighting and trolling and the petty stuff that happens in the fitness profession. He's not feuding with people. He does a fantastic job and is a great example of both a business person and a fitness professional with integrity.

I mentioned the book *Give Work*. The author, Leila Janah, is an incredible person to follow. She has a nonprofit called Samasource that educates and gives work to people, mostly in developing countries. They also have centers here in the United States to train people to do jobs plentiful in the tech space. Her organization is a nonprofit, but they also have contracts for work the people are performing to the point where they no longer need donations. They're now a self-sustaining nonprofit.

She also developed a for-profit business. It's a skincare line that uses a nut harvested in Africa by the Nile River. It pays women a fair wage for the work they're doing and because they're making so much money, they're doing stuff that's better for the planet. They're seeing it makes more sense to take care of their land instead of slashing and burning and selling it to cattle farmers.

The third person is kind of in the Brené Brown crew—Glennon Doyle, the author of *Carry on Warrior* and *Love Warrior*. She started off as a Christian mommy blogger and has parlayed her success into doing incredible work in the areas of social justice and liberation. Her number one value is love—showing love to people, being good to people.

She's doing an incredible job of bringing people along with her who might not normally be open to her type of work and elevating the voices of black women and women of color. She's showing up and saying, "If you're interested in doing social justice or liberation work, congratulations. Specifically white women, we're all late to the party. We're not here to lead; we're here to follow behind all of these incredible women of color who've been doing this work for long time."

I love her for her bravery, for using her platform to do work that matters, for being totally unapologetic and unafraid of doing things a lot of people would consider controversial.

Molly, I think of you as one of those people doing such incredible work, having such an amazing impact, making a difference through your values with integrity. Thank you for talking about your continuing journey to success.

BE LIKE MOLLY

"My top three personal values are making a difference, having integrity and being resilient. I define success as embodying and practicing those values."

WHAT ARE YOUR VALUES?

Defining your values can help give you purpose and provide you with direction. It can help you make decisions and keep you on track with what's important to you.

Get a pen and paper and find a quiet spot to write.

Start writing some words or phrases you think are important to how you want to live your life. Molly used Making a Difference, Integrity and Resilience.

When I did the exercise along with the Results Fitness University program, I used Focus, Pride, Education, Lifestyle, Fun, Evolve, Committed and Run Your Own Race.

Other examples include Family, Faith, Friends, Balance, Honesty, Humor, Service and Growth. The possibilities are endless.

Just keep writing favorite words and phrases; you can sort them later.

Don't hold back—no one is going to see this.

Once you're done, start to prioritize the words. What are your top five?

To go deeper, turn the words into phrases that will guide you. For example, for pride, I wrote "Have pride in everything you do."

Think about your values when you have to make a decision. Is that decision in line with the values you determined?

Think about some of the things you do daily.

Are those actions in line with your values?

If you want to go deeper in this, research the book *Delivering Happiness* by Tony Hsieh.

Ron McKeefery, MA, MSCC, RSCC*E, has worked as a strength and conditioning coach at both the professional and collegiate levels for over 20 years. He has twice been named Collegiate Strength and Conditioning Coach of the Year. Ron has also authored the international bestseller CEO Strength Coach, and hosts the popular podcast Iron Game Chalk Talk. He currently works as the Vice President of Performance and Education for PLAE Perform. To keep in touch with Ron, visit ronmckeefery.com.

Ron, you not only have achieved success in your own life, but you have also mentored coaches to successful careers. How do you define success?

Early in my career, I was chasing success with every ounce of me, trying to be a leader in the field. But, ultimately, for me success is being a fantastic father, husband, citizen and living a biblical lifestyle. And…someone who's successful embraces the journey and takes as many people as possible along for the ride.

When I went to my first NCAA conference, I talked to exactly one person during the entire conference. I remember looking at all the coaches and thinking, "I hope one day I can walk through here and someone actually knows my name."

You're certainly doing that with the education you're providing, bringing some of the best strength coaches on your podcast and with the books you've written. When did you start to feel like you were a success?

When you have as many mentors I've interacted with, to call myself a success is extremely hard. But I've had successes throughout my life. I started to feel like I'd begun to see some success when I was able to pay something forward and when coaches who coached for me went on to good jobs—being a part of NBA championship rings, Major League Baseball rings, Super Bowls and Heisman Trophies. Seeing them achieve success is probably when I first felt like I was living the life I want to live.

What are some habits you can attribute your successes to and that you try to teach to young strength coaches?

I'm definitely not the smartest, the best looking or the most fit guy, but I work really hard. I'm relentless and that has led to some wins. When I get fixated on something, that's all I think about. It's all I do; it's all I research; it's all I talk about.

I'm an action taker. When something worked, it's because I took action. During every success, there was a moment of vulnerability where I thought, "Who am I to write a book? Who am I to stand in front of these people and speak? Will people make fun of me for starting a podcast?"

I didn't care—I took action. There's a difference between people who have ideas and people who have ideas and take action.

Everybody has ideas. It's the people who take action and then keep pushing who make the most impact. What is it that motivates you? What gets you out of bed in the morning?

I grew up in a single-parent home with five kids. My dad was a Navy SEAL with post-traumatic stress disorder. He was in and out of our lives with drug and alcohol problems.

There were a lot of things we were lacking in our family dynamic and resources. Fast forward some, I had a brother who was changing a tire on the side of the road when a guy driving by was reaching for a cell phone, swerved, hit and killed him.

Those events motivate me to make them the most out of every minute of my life, my faith and my family. That's what motivates me. I want to be the best dad and husband I can possibly be and to make sure I provide a comfortable life for my family.

Providing them the things I missed growing up gets me up in the morning. We adopted our four kids—three from the Ukraine, one from Honduras. I coached all over Europe and traveled quite a bit and I realized how small the world is.

I have a deep desire to use the gifts God gave me to make a global impact with the strength and conditioning vehicle I've been given.

Let's move into things you do to be successful. Do you do any type of journaling?

I'm pretty active on social media, which has become an online journal of sorts. I talked online recently about my wife going through having a seizure. It's one of the first things I did once she was okay. I went online and shared the story and encouraged people to go home and make a file and add every medical detail they could think of. We hadn't done that and I felt like the worst husband in the world when the medical team asked questions and I didn't have the answers.

Social media is the modern-day journaling, but it's important to share the wins and losses.

You were away when your wife had medical issues. That's obviously tough. What are some other sacrifices you've had to make to be successful?

The thing that seems to resonate the most with coaches is me being vulnerable and transparent—at one point, we had five dollars in our bank account that we had to live off of for two weeks.

Right before I started coaching for the Cincinnati Bengals, I was a strength coach for the University of Tennessee. I got the Bengals job and had to move away from my family. They stayed in Tennessee while I rented a one-bedroom studio apartment in Cincinnati that literally had a box spring and a mattress and a folding table. I looked like a serial killer living there.

I had to be away from my family for two-and-a-half years when I was coaching at Eastern. The sacrifices have been time away from family, missing youth football games, wrestling matches, swim meets…all those kind of things. Those are things we never get back. Time is the most precious commodity.

Do you have any rules of balancing your work and home life?

The whole work–life balance dynamic doesn't exist. There's no way to have things 50/50, especially if you want to be a success in a career. It takes too much of an investment.

The rule I've adopted, even back as an intern, was that when I'm at work, I'm 100 percent at work and when I'm home, I'm 100 percent at home. When I'm home, I'm with my kids—outside doing something; we're together—it's the same with my time with my wife.

If you have to stay at work for an extra hour to get the email done, do it. But when you go home, make sure you're present.

Was there a time when you thought, "I need to settle in one place, work in town and take a job with benefits"? Was there a time when you felt like you wanted to give up?

Never. There have been tough times—no doubt about it. I've questioned, "Which door am I supposed to go through?" God gave me an entrepreneurial spirit. Should I own my own business? I'm really good in a team environment—should I stay here?

I have had those questions, but I've always kept the long-term vision in mind. Anytime that's changed through prayer and focusing on what's important to me, I've taken action and relentlessly chased the new goal. Business, life or a profession can get hard. If you have one foot out of it, you're not going to make it.

Can you give us three non fitness–related books we should all read to help in our professional development?

In my top five are the Chip and Dan Heath books: *Switch, Made to Stick* and *Decisive*. Those are three critical books that anybody who manages people should read.

The book *Promise of a Pencil* by Adam Braum is fantastic. He did a semester at sea and came across different cultures and wrote about the cultures. That blossomed into an initiative where he creates schools all over the world. It's powerful to look at your experiences, your life and what's around you and find inspiration to do something great.

Uncommon is a great book by Coach Tony Dungy, a guy I worked for in the Tampa Bay Buccaneers organization. His mission is important—being uncommon, doing things differently and doing them for the right reasons, having principles and sticking to them.

Raising a Modern-Day Knight by Robert Lewis is a valuable read for those who are raising kids. In medieval times, there were ceremonies and tasks that had to be completed before the community considered the kids to be taking the next step. You relate it to when your kids become adults. Are they adults when they have sex for the first time? When they smoke cigarettes? When they turn 18? When they can drive a car? The world defines when our kids become adults now, whereas it used to be ceremonies and rituals the family and community participated in. These are interesting ideas.

Success leaves clues; give us three people we can learn from.

I don't want to pull from just a coaching or the entrepreneurial stage, although I still have to go with Tony Dungy. He's so much more than a coach—he does so many unbelievable things for his community with his faith. He's an incredible human being; having worked with him, I know that to be 100-percent true.

Elon Musk is doing incredible things. When people say he's crazy, he just keeps going. I like his perspective on the future.

Gordon Ramsay, the *Kitchen Nightmares* and *Master Chef* guy is a guy who was a chef and is a household name now. He figured out branding and marketing and he's also someone who doesn't mince words. He tells you like it is, but he has a heart. What he's telling people is for their own good, to make them better.

As coaches, that's something we need to practice. Having difficult conversations is a lost art. People don't want to do that and they let people get away with negative things. That's not helpful.

That's why we have five-star recruits and professionals who act like children because somewhere up the line, a coach didn't have a difficult conversation. Ramsay does it extremely well and we can all learn from him.

Ron, thanks so much for all that you do for the trainers and coaches in our field all over the world. Your work has been truly inspiring and I really appreciate you sharing your journey with us.

BE LIKE RON

"When I get fixated on something, that's all I think about
It's all I do; it's all I research; it's all I talk about.

"I go after anything I deem as a goal with a tenacity that's unique for a lot of people."

30 DAY, ONE GOAL CHALLENGE

Pick one of your goals to work on (see Todd Durkin's Be Like). Just one! Make it your priority to really work on that and only that most of the time.

For accountability, tell three people close to you what the goal is for the month (see Frank Nash's Be Like).

When you wake up, write out the goal—make that the first thing you do.

Get something done related to that goal every morning, even if it's something small (see Craig Ballantyne's Be Like).

Make a sign to put near your computer stating five reasons you want to accomplish that goal. Put it in other places you will see often.

Get two books to read or listen to that pertain to your goal's topic and read or listen at least 30 minutes a day (see Geralyn Coopersmith's Be Like).

Every night, list two or three wins that relate to that goal (for example, set up a meeting, read 20 pages, wrote 500 words for the book).

Get fixated on the goal.

Go after it with a tenacity like Ron's.

Brett is a strength and conditioning coach, bestselling author, keynote speaker and founder of the performance coaching and consulting company, Art of Coaching.™ His experience includes working with professional, collegiate and high school athletes from over 20 sports, both in the team environment and private sector, along with members of the United States Special Forces and with Fortune 500 companies. His book, Conscious Coaching: The Art and Science of Building Buy-In, achieved bestseller status in the categories of sport coaching, business/money, and was ranked in the "Amazon Top 100 Books Overall" in 2017, selling more than 50,000 copies worldwide in just two years. Brett's coaching thoughts can be found at artofcoaching.com.

Brett, you have drive and passion evident in everything you do. You've been successful on many different levels and have overcome so much. How do you define success?

I define success through two primary lenses. One is the legacy we leave, which for me is about helping people think about and experience things in a different manner. Seeing things in more of a big-picture perspective and living life through a sense of urgency were both heavily inoculated in me.

I lost a lot of people early in my family. And after being hospitalized myself, I live a bit more like a 90-year-old from the standpoint that if you ask older people what they regret, it's always not taking more risks.

I regret focusing too much on small things. Now I try to live without that stuff. I don't want to get caught up in the minutia. People do and they forget to live in a way that leaves a legacy and helps people think differently.

The other piece is self-acceptance. John Wooden always said that to a degree, success is peace of mind, which is a direct result of a sense of self-satisfaction in knowing you did your best. But it was Maya Angelou who said, "Success is liking yourself, liking what you do and liking how you do it."

I define success through a combination of legacy and then self-acceptance.

Sometimes we don't consider ourselves successful because we're our toughest critics. When did you start to feel, "I'm starting to get this right; I'm starting to become a success."

You hit it spot on: There's a lot of impostor phenomena in life. I don't think many people in our field really feel like they're a success; I don't, but I'm working on it and becoming more comfortable at admitting when I do something well.

Humility used to be imprinted in our psyche. Humility is great. But people can be brutally honest in our field. Sometimes people can be prideful in their sense of humility, where if you accept a compliment, it shows a sense of class and growth, not a conceited nature.

Look at Stephen Covey's funeral experience from his book *The 7 Habits of Highly Effective People:* Eventually, how many people show up to your funeral will be how you define success. I'm from the Midwest and hope it's not bad weather that day.

The idea of the funeral experience is always the biggest piece for me.

You've helped many people on many levels and you're certainly on a mission. What is it that gets you out of bed in the morning? And how do you plan your days?

I like taking on new challenges and I like continual growth and evolution and that's the only way I'm going to do it. That's my biggest motivator to get out of bed.

We have an illusion of this sense of predictive mastery and planning, that if everything is planned meticulously and if we structure the day, everything is going to work out the way we wanted. It's okay to have a plan, but resilience comes through adaptability.

I just get into the day because anytime I've tried planning, something throws a wrench in my day. I'd rather get started on solving those problems than pontificate about what's going to be the best strategy.

You're a driven and disciplined guy. What are some of the habits that contributed to help you get to where you are?

My biggest habit is when I meet an obstacle, I just dive in, although that was something that wasn't always the case. I'm a perfectionist and that used to get the best of me. I'd sit and, especially when it came to anything creative, would review all the different aspects.

I looked at it like a musician writing a song. I've always been inspired by music and artists, people who were uniquely focused on the smallest details of their work. And sometimes I would take that overboard, being a little OCD.

Now I just dive in and get to work. My book was a reflection of that. *Conscious Coaching* was originally going to be about 60,000 more words. Eventually, I had to hire a non-biased editor, who told me, "Dude, stop. You don't have to address everything in one book."

Sometimes when you look at things through the spectrum of a big picture, it helps you obsess a little less and you just have to *do* it. Steven Pressfield states, "Overcome the resistance and get to work." Diving in has been a big piece of the puzzle for me.

And then there's reflection. You have to be brutally honest with yourself. That was a big part of the three stages of internal identification in my book. Be your toughest critic and just dive in and continue to evolve.

Talk about the idea of not having the specific path. Do you set goals and is there any kind of a formal process?

The three stages of internal identification was a process that came to me sitting in a Denver airport. I was looking at areas I needed to improve as a professional and as a person.

Through an aspect of motivational interviewing, I don't allow myself to sneak by with surface-level answers. I'm looking for a really clear picture, as in a research article. You have to go into the methods section and have to describe every aspect of how you measured this. What did you do you can recreate it?

That's the kind of depth I went to. I remember in grad school, Nate Green wrote an article about three whiteboards. One whiteboard was the big-picture view of where you want to be several years in the future. Another was how you could chunk that into months. And then the smallest whiteboard were weekly things you could do to move ahead.

I liked that because I'm visual; I love having visual representations of where I want to go and the small nudges I can use along the way.

Obviously, you're a prolific writer. Do you journal?

You might be the first person to call me that. But no, I'm not actively journaling now. The closest thing I do to journaling is my Instagram feed. I gravitated to that more than Twitter or Facebook because it's minimalist almost in the way that Seth Godin writes. Nobody expects to open up an Instagram feed and be wowed with an Iliad-type insight. You don't have to commit too much, but you can post something visual that inspires people or makes them think, add a short caption that shares an honest thought…and then just move on. You don't have to worry about design. You don't have to worry about sharing something; it just does it.

I tried journaling at several points in school, but I was always embarrassed by my entries. I'd look back at them a couple of years later and think, "I thought like that? What was going on?" There are chunks of it here and there, but I'd say Instagram and *Conscious Coaching* are the closest to representations of a journal.

As coaches and trainers, we're always talking to our clients about recovery regeneration, sleep and fuel. How do you recharge?

I've found there are three things that work for me. One is music, down-tempo music. At the end of the day, I'll turn on Spotify and play some kind of reggae or a calm, spa-like ambient instrumental playlist. I try to down-regulate through music.

Massage is huge for me. I don't care what research says with the yo-yo, back and forth of, "Is massage beneficial?" If somebody hands are on you and you're able to get enough pressure to stimulate the lymphatic system and knead the muscle tissue with human touch, it's enough to put you into more of a parasympathetic state.

I find I can recharge through music, massage and then for me, it's to be near water. Anytime my wife and I can go to a lake or the ocean or go hiking by a river, those are my biggest switches.

It's huge when I can periodically isolate myself. When I present or coach, I'm extroverted. But other than that, I like to be left in my bat cave.

People forget that recovery is not always about taking a nap or sitting on the couch and relaxing. There's a lot of research about deep play, trying to do challenging things. It's really interesting and goes back to the idea of finding what works for you.

When I lived in Phoenix, I'd sometimes go get lost, walking a trail to lose myself.

I'll take a nap if I can. I don't always get that option, but I bought a heavy-duty sleep mask through Kickstarter, the Manta Sleep Mask. This thing is unbelievable. It transports you into another world. I use earplugs because I'm sympathetically driven. If I hear anything in the middle of the night, I'll jump. Those have both been critical for me, especially when trying to sneak in a nap during international travel.

Let's talk about when you ended up in the hospital. Some of your childhood friends started experimenting with hard-core drugs, and your parents got divorced. You turned to training and exercise to help deal with tough circumstances. Training hard turned into an exercise addiction that brought you to the point of near cardiac arrest as well as kidney and liver failure.

You're such a high-energy person. You're a high achiever. Maybe you took things a little too far, but that's your personality. For every yes, there's a no. What are some of the sacrifices you've made to be successful?

Many of the sacrifices are the same as anyone's, so I'm not going to glorify them or act like I'm special. I'm 31 years old. Already I've lived in 10 states, moved 15 times and have had relationships fall apart.

When I was a graduate assistant, there was a girl I was really close to who wanted to live in a small town for the rest of her life. I knew strength and conditioning wasn't going to allow that to happen for me. Sometimes, there are people who are important to you that you have move away from or valued friendships that grow apart.

And there's the not-fun side of things: I've fought legal battles; I've taken out loans to complete projects. At one point, I even had to turn my back on a dream job in the NFL working with a close family friend because I'd already made a commitment to take another job.

This is challenging for a number of reasons. There's still a sub-faction of strength and conditioning coaches who don't think we should scale our message or be more visible. When I put out the book last year, thankfully I had 90–95 percent supporters and then maybe five or ten percent of people asked, "Have you sold out?"

Anybody saying that usually only sees the book or the product. They don't know that I left a situation where it would have truly been selling out. In that situation, people didn't want to follow great strength and conditioning ethics, but there would've been a lot of money for me to stay. Instead, my wife and I decided to go out on our own.

Not only is it the sacrifices we make, but there are also the perceptions we face and judgments when people see what they want to see.

Maria Popova from *Brain Pickings* said: "If you haven't read or seen something, if you don't have the patience to read something or view it all the way through, don't have the hubris to comment on it."

People constantly do that about lives they observe from afar. We struggle with stuff like that because innately, we're people-pleasers. We want to make people happy. We want them to see the greater good we're fighting for.

Life is chess, not checkers. And people are going to judge the moves, not really for the strategy that hopefully evolves from each one.

You've had some serious struggles. What are some of the strategies you've used when you wanted to give up?

One: I've learned to double down. You have to isolate yourself so you can get some clarity when you go through tough times. But I also try to surround myself with relics from my past that remind me of previous struggles I overcame.

One thing I always do when I'm going through moments of self-doubt is play a playlist I listened to when I was hospitalized. There's music that stuck with me that takes me back to those moments and makes me reconnect with feelings that were so impactful in terms of pushing me through something.

I used to do it when I was an undergrad at Kansas State as well. Whenever I felt anxious or like there was something more I should be doing or when I was confused, I'd throw on a hoodie, go out in the middle of the night and dial up a specific playlist. I'd come back reconnected with who I am and what I'm about.

I keep elements of discomfort nearby so I never really feel comfortable. The physical side is huge for me. When I'm training, I'm literally exorcising my demons and that cheesy double entendre is intentional.

Here's the other one that's not going to be very popular everyone: I talk about how I feel. I have a small group of close friends with whom I feel like I can openly share things.

In our culture, it's not cool to talk about struggles because everybody's supposed to have this impermeable Superman membrane that surrounds them. But the healthiest way to deal with problems is by talking about them.

That's it. The physical activity; the music comes into it, the settings and then talking about things and not trying to hide those feelings.

Many people don't realize how cathartic talking can be. Moving along, what are three non fitness–related books you feel can help people in their development?

Mastery by Robert Greene is always one I recommend. Robert Greene is my favorite author, and *Mastery* is tremendous. You really have to read and think about it all the way through. If you have a short attention span or are trying to do it on Audible at triple speed, you're going to miss it. Read the book and digest it.

Then there's *The Vital Spark*, which is an older book by Lowell B. Tomas. He talks about 101 of the greatest lives of the most unique people who ever lived. Literally, people from Cleopatra to now, he writes about how they shaped history through their journeys.

And then I'd suggest *The Obstacle is the Way* by Ryan Holiday.

What about some people? Success leaves clues. Give us three people you think we can all learn from.

Let's start with Jeff Wiener, who is the LinkedIn CEO. I love the way that guy communicates and throws out his ideas on scaling and doing quality work.

Then, I have to again point out Maria Popova from *Brain Pickings*. She's uniquely insightful, although I don't always understand everything she writes.

And then this last one may make people laugh, but again, I love studying people from history: Henry David Thoreau. I even follow some of his quotes on Twitter and there's a timeless nature to that.

The take-home is, don't just study people who are currently living. We're all reliving the same stories throughout history. I'd urge people to find one or two historical figures and dive deep into their lives and really learn from them.

We've followed you through your whole journey and have been there with you. It's great to see the impact you're having, not only on trainers and athletes, but on both the fitness and the coaching professions.

BE LIKE BRETT

"I'm really visual— I love having visual representations of where do I want to go and what are small nudges I can use along the way to get there.

"I remember Nate Green wrote an article about three whiteboards. One whiteboard was the big-picture view where you want to be several years from now. Another one was how you could chunk that up into months. And then the smallest whiteboard held weekly things that you could do to lead to that."

THREE WHITEBOARDS—ORIGINAL, SLIGHTLY DIFFERENT CONCEPT

Not everything works for everyone and this is one approach that can work for visual people.

Once you have your goals and mission set (see the Be Likes of Todd Durkin, Christa Doran, Mark Fisher, Dan John and Ron McKeefery), get three whiteboards or poster boards, whatever works for you.

On the first board, put the big picture 1–3–10 year goals on it. On the top of it, write your mission statement.

On the second board, for each goal write where you want to be in relation to those goals in three months.

On the third board, after reverse engineering what it will take to achieve your three-month goals, write what you want to accomplish for that week to get you closer to that goal.

Put it in a place where you will see it often and you can check in. The whiteboard is great because you can erase and modify.

Another good idea is to put your Vision Board next to it as well (see Nikki Metzger's Be Like).

Mike is the founding owner of Ranfone Training Systems in Hamden, Connecticut. RTS is home to over 400 athletes and adult fitness members. He is an LMT, CSCS who has also worked with numerous small businesses and professional teams from the NHL, NFL, MLB, NBA and MLS. Catch up with Mike and RTS at rtsct.com.

You've had success as an athlete and as a business owner. You've gotten into the education space and you're helping lead the way in educating trainers. But let's turn that around. How do you define success for yourself?

This may sound corny, but when I looked at some of the people included in your book project, I was honestly thinking, why did Anthony invite me into this? You've interviewed some monumental people. I'm so honored and humbled to be mentioned in the list.

My definition of success is feeling good about what I do every day and in retrospect, I can be proud of what I did. As simple as that may sound, that's really the only litmus test I care about.

Your son is four; five years ago, your definition might have been different, too. There's a lot underlying that answer.

I've gone through so many iterations of success. I don't think you can have the definition of success without owning your failures. And five years from now, I'll have a somewhat different definition. But if I look back and can honestly say I was happy with the process and afterward was proud of the work, that's a pretty good starting point.

When did you start feeling you were getting control of this and were feeling good about what you do?

I would never say I'm successful, but I've had success. And that might be a common thread for everyone. There's a perpetual feeling that we have to improve, do or become more.

I don't know if there's a finish line—I don't think I'll ever be satisfied with what I've done. It's not that I am not grateful or don't value what I have, but it's a constant push in the back of my mind that says I've got to keep going. Most of the successes that define me are with other people and with making sure people are moving with me on this journey. I can't discount the many people, mentors, clients and athletes I've worked with who validate any definition of success in my life.

Let's discuss that drive, that constant push. What is it that motivates you?

A lot of it stems from being an athlete. Maybe another common theme people will see is we're always trying to push ourselves to physical, mental and emotional limits because no one else could do it for us. There's an intrinsic drive that makes us want to put everything on the line to compete, prove or justify a means to an end.

Having been injured and told I would never play again, there was a lot of thinking, "I'll prove you wrong." I couldn't wait to show people they were incorrect about my trajectory in life. And that works for a while; it really does. But if you keep needing to prove people wrong or disprove an impression, you're going to run out of steam. It just doesn't provide fuel for the long haul.

Maybe that's a matter of maturity, but most of the solid fuel comes from being positive. I want to have that feeling of being there when it matters, of having clients reach their goals. I need to have the freedom to go somewhere with my family or to help develop a coach.

I have coaches who have been with me for 10 years—some of my coaches are kids I used to train. To see them follow in the coaching profession is rewarding. There's a little bit of not ever wanting that feeling to end because that's where the impact is felt.

I had a young guy I trained, a tennis player. He got so into training that for his college graduation, I paid for his ACE certification. It was a great feeling to have had such an impact on him. And now he wants to pay it forward with what I gave him.

One of the most humbling things is without the spoken word having people emulate or try to improve upon what you've laid down. This is quite intriguing, especially now as a business owner where I have coaches working for me—I must have something that attracts them. Then to see how they take that, to see what they're going to develop, how they're going to create and what they're going to project as evolving professionals.

Mike, when you get to bad times, what is it that gets you through?

The last couple of years have been personally hard for my family. Then the business took a toll on me. Following every time I've had a dark period in my life—however long that might have been—there was always a huge upswing. I think of the old phrase: Without struggle, there is no progress.

One of the motivating factors in tough times is if I just stick through this, things have to get better. I'll adapt and it won't kill me. Maybe that's just a matter of perspective. You never know when those lessons are going to pop up—that's the crazy thing about life. You never know who's going to be the teacher or what the message will be, but if you're not willing to learn and adapt, you will stagnate at best.

You had low parts of the rollercoaster and got back up, and it happened again and you got back up. Do you think that's a product of that experience?

This is, again, the athlete in me: I hate to lose. Think about how much of the American culture is based on the idea of the underdog. It could be the story of *Rocky* or maybe a war story—we root for the underdog to come out on top. We see great stories of people overcoming huge adversity.

Ask yourself: What is the depth of me, of my personality, character and ultimately, willingness to figure things out? Often, it's not a matter of resources, but how resourceful you are to get a job done.

That's a big part of who I am. And it's always been; I had to learn that lesson at an early age. That's not to say things get easier every time we're exposed to them, but because we grow in our resiliency to stress and adversity. We have a bigger reservoir to pull from.

Mike, let's go a little deeper into the idea of struggle. What are some of the sacrifices you've had to make to get where you are?

I've put personal things on hold when it would benefit the business. The biggest upside of that is if I do right by my clients and staff, things will come back to me.

That's the difference between an investment and an expense; an investment should come back to you. I never feel like something was a bad move. It's just that sometimes you don't know when things are going to come back to you, especially in terms of time, money and energy. Owning a business is like having a kid; it's a full-time job that doesn't really end.

Most businesses don't get out of the infancy stage. If you're away from your business long enough, much like an infant child, the child suffers and so will the business.

I'm always in that period in business development because we push growth. I'm never in a state of comfort. I've made that concession, knowing the price I'm going to pay to get to where we can become successful as a business. There are plenty of things I would have liked to have done or still want to do, but this is not the right time.

I want to touch on the idea that having a business is like having a kid. Sometimes you're in a relationship and the other person doesn't understand that about business. In the beginning, my wife would say, "It's Sunday." But there is no Sunday. A business owner's life partner needs to understand that having a business is a lot like having a kid.

Mike, let's talk about some of the habits that helped you become a success. Do you have a morning routine?

We have a young child and my wife has quite the commute, so most of my time in the morning is dedicated to getting up, feeding and changing our kid, getting him ready and dropping him off at school, and then coming to work.

I'm productive because I have no choice. When I get up in the morning, my kid doesn't care if I've had a rough night's sleep, if I'm stressed or tired. It's an honest alarm clock. I'm doing it for him, and I'm doing it for the family. I'm trying to make sure I have a good platform to propel myself for the day. It's an easy, quick motivator to get up and answer that bell.

You talked about your drive not to lose; it seems like there's a lot of tenacity. What are some other attributes that have contributed to your success?

Tenacity, yes, but also resiliency. You can't have resiliency without capacity, and capacity only comes through repetition and experience. There's nothing I've really shied away from in my life. If I was bad at something, I had to get better at it. Or if I was afraid of something, I had to confront it.

Also, there's a willingness to understand that no one's perfect, but to never hedge on who you can become by introducing a little struggle. I've always been open-minded toward change and that's allowed me to be fluid and dynamic.

I'm the consummate white belt; I'm always trying to pick up something that can benefit me. If I don't know something, I find the person who knows the most about it and pay to learn. I've never been one to say, "I know everything…I'm good, thank you."

I would never call myself an expert in anything; I'm more of a generalist. And that's where I pursue people who have information and the ability to communicate things I need to know or think about to get better.

What about goal setting? Do you have a formal process with goals?

Anytime I have to be concrete about a goal, I hire a coach. If there's a business goal I need to set, I talk to a business coach, not only to help me think through the goal, but in deciding if it's really what I want.

When you're younger, you can "just do this one thing, do it as hard as you can," and you'll get it. It's harder when everything is variable, where I wear a lot of hats. I want to be a mentor, coach, business owner, good dad and husband. You can't go after one thing without making concessions on others. If I wanted to compete in a powerlifting competition, it would be a huge amount of time and energy. I'd have to forego other plans. Everything has an opportunity cost. I have to figure out the opportunity costs to pursue new ideas.

If I'm going to hire a business, training or life coach, the idea would be to help me not only to make a concise, clear goal, but also to figure out what it's going to take. That's the nature of coaching: understanding the risk, reward, costs and benefits. Can you do it? That's the ultimate question to ask anytime you write a program for anything: Can you execute?

That's my formal goal-setting routine. It's more about figuring out the other facets rather than defining the finish line.

Grant Cardone tells us how our goals aren't big enough. But at the same time, whatever you think it's going to take, multiply it by 10. We always underestimate what something is going to take—how much time is it going to take, what's the effort and can we do it? Are we willing to do it?

For every yes, there's a no. When you have a workshop on a weekend, you're saying no to something else you could have done with the family. Unless we have clarity on that, we're not going to make the right decisions.

It's hard to do that. That's partly why we have this job. People want to run a 40 faster; they want to bench 500 pounds and so on. They can do that, but they don't know the costs. They don't know what it actually takes to get there.

That's why I'm willing to ask a financial, health or business coach to help me discover if a goal is not only attainable, but is it something I want to pay for, whether that's a short- or long-run payment process. Do I want to forego time I won't get back?

You could be saying no to your own health as well. We talk to our clients about rest and recovery. How do you recharge?

If you had asked me this a couple of years ago, I would have said something like, I'll stop when the wheels fall off. I was always like that. It was like a war of attrition. I wanted to be the last man standing. Thank God, I have some perspective now, where I know that's not the only way to some success. I try to take a more moderate approach.

For me, it's all about time management of my responsibilities and actions. You can never go wrong figuring out personal time, whether that's better nutrition, sleep, recovery methods—all the things we preach about on a daily basis.

If my life is stressing me out and I walk into my business wound tight, I'm not doing right by my business. If I go home and walk in the door feeling like shit because I had a rough day at the office, I just doubled my stress because now I'm making my home life stressful. I try to get in front of that by being able to not necessarily predict, but have a prophylactic approach to where I need to say no, and how I'm going to make amends if needed.

Being in control of things and having a wider lens is key. I've been myopic and short-sighted in my life, and that's not bad when the goal is right in front of you. It's really hard when there are multiple goals and things that aren't right in the forefront.

Mike, give us three non fitness–related books people should read.

A couple of years ago, I read book called *Resilience,* written by Eric Greitens, a former Navy SEAL. It's an insightful book on many different aspects of life. I love war history. I love the armed forces—I've learned so much from the military and from military philosophy. I gravitate to that type of book.

Greitens had a great interaction with one of his former teammates about life—each section was about friends, family, humor, death and more. It was a voyeuristic approach to two guys having a real conversation over the course of a few months. It resonated with me. Anytime you can have a step-back moment, have it. Use that to capture things in your life; it's invaluable.

Daniel Pink's book *Drive* is a must for anyone, but especially for people who have an entrepreneurial spirit. *Drive* is all about what motivates people. If you work with or for people or you want people to work for you, it's an important book. There's a great 20-minute YouTube video about it. I watch it a couple of times a year and show it to my staff. It's all about the things that get you out of bed and why. It has tremendous depth.

And for the third one, I would suggest a book called *Generation IY* by Tim Elmore. It's about the cultural difference and generation gaps, specifically the millennial crowd. When I first started reading the book, I hated it because it looked like it was just pointing out flaws of a new generation—I never want to be that curmudgeon, "When I was a kid…" Even though I do that sometimes, I didn't need to spend time reading about it.

Before I quit reading it, I gave it one more chapter and realized it wasn't him complaining, but pointing out patterns. He also went through other generations, like describing the hallmarks of Generation X, Gen Y and so on, and explaining the reasons for the trends. It gave context; it's mostly about millennials and generation Y and describing how those age groups tick.

It's incredibly important because I've been dealing with 15- and 18-year-olds for 20 years. Guess what? I'm going to change and they're going to change. How can I anticipate what they're facing and understand why they think the way they do?

It's important to have an understanding of the cultural or generational divide when you're hiring people. I'm hiring people who are in their early 20s. I need a better understanding of how they work, think, listen and respond. There's no right or wrong. We can always say our music and movies were better when we were their age, but that was then and this is now.

That book made me think about how I can change, because I'm the one who's ultimately going to lose if I don't. I'm the one who's going to lose clients. I'm going to lose business; I'm going to lose staff.

It's in my best interest—my sheer self-perseverance—to make this work. They can find a job elsewhere if I'm an asshole. If I want them to stay, I have to figure out how to keep them here.

Mike, let's finish up with three people we can follow to learn from—they could be from fitness or another profession.

This is a provocative question because it also lends to the cultural or generational idea of voyeuristically and superficially following people on social media. I don't look outside of people I know for inspiration. Some of the people who have been most inspiring and continue to be motivators for me are people no one knows about.

If Gary V does it for you, great. But if you're always watching from a distance, but can never have a personal relationship, I don't know how much that person can give you. I've been lucky to have phenomenal people in my life who have traits and characteristics I want to emulate.

Maybe one guy you should look into is a kid I played college football with named Kevin Flake, who you can find at *woundedbywar.com.* He's a former Green Beret who was wounded in Afghanistan in 2011. His odds for survival were very low, but he came back. He's walking; he's got a family; he went to MIT. He's doing motivational speaking—he's a tremendous guy. He's on all social media. He's real; what you see is what you're going to get. I like that authenticity; I know what I'm getting when I get in a conversation with him or see him on social media.

We look to you to see what you're doing—you've helped a lot of us get better. Thank you for your sharing your journey to becoming more successful.

BE LIKE MIKE

"If I'm going to hire a business, training or life coach, the idea would be to help me to not only to make a concise, clear goal, but also to figure out what it's going to take."

HIRE A COACH

I loved the way Alwyn Cosgrove started off a lecture he used to do. He asked, "How many of you are coaches or personal trainers?"

The whole room raises their hands.

"How many of you believe that hiring a coach or personal trainer is the best way to achieve your fitness goals?"

The whole room raises their hands.

"How many of you hire a coach to help you achieve your fitness goals?"

Three people raise their hands.

It's interesting that in a profession selling a service they believe is the best way to achieve a goal, only a small percentage practice what they preach.

A few of the "Be Likes" have addressed going after specific goals (See Gray Cook "Full Immersion" or Ron McKeefery "30-Day Goal Challenge") and having an accountability partner on your journey (see Frank Nash's Be Like).

For this "Be Like" challenge, you're going to choose one of your goals (see Todd Durkin's Be Like) and get some outside help.

Hire a coach to help you not only achieve the goal, but also to help you clarify the goal and figure out what it will really take to help answer the question, "Can I execute this?"

The best part is that once you hire the coach, you will have a new level of commitment to it.

"The more you pay, the more you pay attention."

Justin is the bestselling author of the book Man Up and is the CEO of The Sport and Speed Institute. He started his first sports performance company in South Florida while still in high school and grew that to 39 facilities before selling and starting in business consulting. Justin has trained over 50,000 athletes and helped prepare hundreds of college and future NFL players for their Combine and Pro days. He is regarded as one of the top speed experts in the country. Coach Kav has worked with Olympic gold medalists and UFC heavyweight champions, a third pick in the MLB draft and the NCAA All-Time TD and Rushing Record holder. He also speaks to high performers giving strategies and techniques to become a world-class coach and business professional. Learn more about the SSI programs at sportandspeedteam.com.

Justin, you have had success at a young age as an athlete and entrepreneur. You've established yourself as a leader and educator in the fitness field. But how do you personally define success?

Success is an individual idea that comes down to doing what you love and are passionate about. Then, make sure you're on a path of progress. Success isn't necessarily about being happy with the end goal, but being happy in the process.

You should never be content with where you are, but be content with the path you're on. If you're doing something you're passionate about and are making progress along the way, you're going to enjoy the good and the bad that comes with it. With anything you do, if you want to be good at it, there are going to be some bumps and bruises.

A lot of people get into the fitness profession to help people, but they forget the "why." It's a cliché now—everyone talks about knowing the "why," but it's important to remind yourself. Just because you're passionate doesn't mean it's always enjoyable.

The "why" is going to change over time. When you started your career, the "why" might have been that you wanted to help people. Then it might have changed into wanting to help more people have an increased level of significance. And then the "why" might change to wanting to provide for the family. And it might go back to wanting to create more significance because it's self-fulfilling.

It's very hard to work with people if they don't enjoy what they're doing. There are going to be times when the valley—the low of the job, the day to day—is going to suck. If people don't embrace that, if they're not passionate about the outcome, they only enjoy the peaks of the day. They're only going to enjoy the successes. Success means enjoying both the top and the bottom of the process.

Not only does the "why" change, but it's okay to have multiple "whys." You should have five or six. People get caught up in not wanting to say work is for the money, but that could certainly be a piece of it.

For example, in outlining this book, I wrote out a few "whys." I want to help people achieve success. It will make me an authority on the subject. It will raise brand awareness. It will help create additional revenue opportunities. It will be cool to have a book. It doesn't have to be formal.

Wanting to give back and make money doesn't make you a bad person. If you're trying to make money in this process and you're successful, you can give more.

But if you have very little because you haven't obtained success, you don't have the notoriety in your field; you haven't worked your way up and no one's going to follow you.

One of the things I had to learn had to do with doing a lot of things for free. It was good to do things without pay, and I still do that. What I like to think about is: If I make a bigger impact—if I make more money, if I have more success—I could have more of that "pie of my life" for philanthropy because I have more to give.

You have your priorities out of order when you're giving to other people and the people closest to you are getting hurt because you haven't provided for them first. You're no longer able to fulfill the most important thing, being happy with the job you're doing because you're going to resent the people you help.

This might be a tough question: When did you begin thinking you were starting to be successful?

I went from having an athletic career, but after getting hurt, my identity changed. Overnight, I went from being a star football player to not being able to walk. I had a long-term identity crisis for the better part of two years when I was half-baked. I was dipping my toe in the water on coaching because that made money. I was forced into that role because people respected me there, but I still wanted to play. I was trying to serve two masters of interest—I was trying to catch two rabbits at the same time. I ended up empty-handed and wasn't fulfilled.

I started to realize success was about enjoying the process. I had to go all in because I wasn't happy at 75 percent or being in the top 10 percent…or being just okay. I wanted to be the best.

I wanted to have some level of mastery where I could do something that takes a long time, but I could do it quickly and be so proficient that the results spoke for themselves. When I did that, I felt with my crew, with athletes, the fact I got kids stronger and quicker or kids got faster in a shorter period of time, I was able to capitalize there.

That initially made me feel good. I started to understand that success was my ability to coach other coaches to do that—they'd start making an impact. There was a compounding effect. I felt good about being more efficient in my work because that makes the lifetime value of my coaching longer and wider.

I started to feel I was somewhat successful when I started coaching other people to coach or coaching other people to make better decisions so they wouldn't have to go down a hard road.

What motivates you to get out of bed in the morning? What's your "why?"

I'm not one of those people who bounces out of bed, puts my feet on the ground and attacks the day. I'm a slow riser and, honestly, I think, "This sucks." I went through a lot of physical pain in my life and if I wake up and am not in pain, I'm thinking, "Am I dead right now?"

I'm not being cliché; I'm being transparent. I wake up in pain, I'm almost thankful for that pain. I'm thankful I have another day in some level of physical pain, so I can be in emotional pleasure and spiritual gratitude.

I truly believe that. I'm very lucky to have some of the pains I have because the alternative isn't what I want.

What motivates me on a daily basis is the idea I'm going to be gone one day and someone else is going to be telling my story. I want to do right by people, to do right by my athletes and coaches.

At the same time, I work my tail off and I have no problem saying I like to work. I enjoy the hustle, but it's not a grind because I enjoy the process. My "why" is to represent myself, my family, and my faith in the best way I can. I don't want anyone to feel like they're walking on eggshells around me. They'll know if it's a good or a bad day, and they'll know if they did something right or wrong in my mind.

That also puts me in a tough area because I'm shining the light on myself to be judged directly. I have to be okay with some of those comments—good or bad.

What are some of the habits you attribute to your success?

It's persistence. A lot of people give up too easily—they give up right before they turn the corner. It's like entrepreneurship—being an owner of a business or having an interest in pursuing a job—don't think of it like digging gold, like the story of the guy who left his patch and the next guy who came dug two feet and hit gold.

When you're digging for gold, you have the choice to stop, but you should think about it as if you're under water and have no other option. You don't know if you're swimming up or down, but if you stop now, it's certain you're going to run out of oxygen. My thought is, just keep going. You'll crack the surface at some point if you're persistent.

That being said, you need to make good decisions. This holds true for everyone, for athletes, entrepreneurs and owners of facilities. You can't make too many bad decisions. I've made some good bets over time, and that's because I haven't put my back up against the wall very often. There are only so many bet-the-business moments you can have and still come out on top.

People who surround themselves with better people are automatically going to make better decisions. People in their circles who are leveling up their leadership or coaching or their business acumen are not going to allow them to consistently make bad decisions.

When you're out in the water by yourself, it's a little scary. You allow yourself to make bad decisions because you're the only person who's going to get mad, and you accept mediocrity. But if you want to level up in the other areas of your life, surround yourself by people you want to be like. You'll start making better decisions.

You probably set goals, but what does that process look like?

First of all, a strategy for goal setting needs to work for each person. I've been to a bunch of events and have spoken with people—and they all have different ways they do it. You have to figure out what works for you.

I used to have goals of "I want to do this," but they were too distant. You don't know where you're going to be five or ten years from now. I'm big on having a two- or three-year plan. I try not to go further than that because you never know what will happen.

I break everything into 90-day chunks and do little sprints. I look forward to my big rocks and I work backward and I wonder, "Once the stuff starts to overlap, does it make sense? Is there synergy with this goal and what I'm doing today? Is there synergy from one goal to the other? Does it layer?"

If I didn't accomplish a segment, I automatically don't accomplish the next because now I've set myself up for more risk. That doesn't mean you can't do that, but understand that if you don't accomplish one goal and you have seven other goals that are partly on top of it, you're going to have a disappointing year. If there's something in that one goal you can't control and it goes south, you're unfortunately in a situation where the rest of your year's goals are a wash.

Many people take the Christmas break right before New Year's to set their goals. But I use the Thanksgiving period as the time for me to step away from the busyness of work because we have a natural holiday break. I'm with my family and we're giving thanks.

The best time to write goals is when you're giving thanks for something and you have a level of gratitude. If you're writing goals when you're aggressive and motivated, you'll write goals without a strategy behind them. Or you'll write goals with aspiration, clueless on what it takes to get there. But when you're saying thanks is a good time for setting new goals. You're putting things in a better perspective.

How do you recharge, whether it's on a daily, weekly or yearly basis?

About three years ago, I did a bunch of sleep studies and was thinking, "The doctor says I have to try to nap," and I tried to. But if I take a nap, I crash, which is not good. I've unfortunately never been able to nap.

I even have to wind down to go to bed. It takes me a few hours to go to sleep. I tried one of those sleep pods, but I was just staring at the ceiling. I've tried everything from eye shades to music to scent. I haven't had success. I wish I knew a solution.

I'm around people all the time and I'm good in an environment with a lot of people. But when it's "me time," I like to be alone. Normally that's on the water somewhere. I grew up in Miami, so this can just be just putting my feet in the water. It doesn't need to be on the water, but it does need to be by myself or with my wife and the family. I need to give myself time to process. I almost need to give myself time to get bored because that's when I get a creative energy where I want to do things.

Talk about a sacrifice you've made to be successful.

On one hand, I want to say I've made a ton of sacrifices. But I would be a complete hypocrite because those were choices. Sacrifices are a requirement to achieve what you want.

If you want balance at any level, you need to prioritize things. You can never be 50/50 for something to be successful. If you get a 50-percent mark on a test, it's not even passing. If you do things half-assed or if you divide your efforts between multiple things, you're not going to be successful. Sacrifice almost always came to strategic priorities, down to, "If I want this right now, does that sacrifice give what I want long term?"

Eventually, it's maturity.

Now that I have the facility, I don't have the freedom of being able to travel and do whatever I want. I had to give up job opportunities overseas. Sometimes there's glory in being the owner, but there's also a lot of responsibility. You probably don't have the freedom you thought you'd have.

Obviously, we learn from mistakes. Thinking back, what were some of the mistakes you made?

I could probably write a book on mistakes; I actually believe you have to fail and fail fast. That's the only way. People learn more from doing something wrong than doing something right when things go in one ear and out the other. Just because you see it, you think that's the way it's supposed to be done and you forget 30 percent of it. But when someone does something wrong, it stands out.

As an athlete, I couldn't care less about warming up and I never prepared for a training cycle. I hit every session hard. I had no level of intensity variability; it was always 100-percent effort. My body is paying the price for that now, even though I've never had a non-contact injury.

I wanted everything to be perfect, but perfect is just an excuse for insecurity. I've learned to value someone calling me out when I delay releasing something because I want everything to be perfect.

The other mistake I've made as an owner of a business is in restricting projects by my having to be involved in the process. By doing that, I could make a mess so I'd be the one to fix it; I'd get adrenaline from fixing things.

I wouldn't write workouts; I'd write a 12-week program and lay it all out, but I wouldn't give out the next phase because I wanted the team to come back and learn from me. I wanted to make myself significant so they had to come back and ask the next step. As owners, we do that often. We create structures where we're the only person who can solve a problem; we don't empower other people to help solve things for us. The more I relinquish control, frankly, the more control I have in my life.

As you get older, you start to realize it's almost like therapy. You start to understand different things about yourself and that's why it's important to have a coach. You have one; I have one. It's important. There's no filter—they tell you the real deal.

Let's talk about a time when you almost gave up but didn't.

Not to sound egotistical, but I rarely give up or feel like I could quit. That was never an option. My parents made it very clear there was no quitting—it didn't matter what "it" was. I've had some times in business when it's been tough, but I've never made that an opportunity to give up.

You have to be careful with limiting beliefs. Quitting is just an excuse you give yourself. It's a choice. I haven't quit; I've had to step away; I've had to step sideways; I've had to pivot. I've had to make adjustments, but I haven't quit. I say that because the word "quit" is a big deal to me.

The rules I have in my life are number one: Don't panic. Number two: There's always a way. If you know you can't panic and that there's a way, quitting is the worst thing you could do. It's not an ego thing. This is not like, "Look at me. I haven't quit." I've made plenty of mistakes and I've failed. But I haven't stopped. And because of that level of persistence, something good will come out of something negative.

That persistence theme keeps coming up in this book. It's such an important trait.

Give me three non fitness–related books everyone should read.

The Greatest Salesman in the World by Og Mandino is a book I highly recommend. It's a short read that gives people the confidence they could sell—and sell for the right reasons. A lot of people are scared to sell, but if they're pursuing something they want that's not a nine-to-five, they're going to have to sell themselves.

I'm going to go way out in left field on my second suggestion and tell you that my favorite book is *Crime and Punishment.* People need to have a creative side and see how stories are told—and this one's a page turner. It's intriguing and there's a lot of depth to that book.

My last suggestion is *The 48 Laws of Power* by Robert Greene. I did an interview at the United States Naval Academy and the Blue and Gold officer saw me reading it and was offended that I'd read a book like that. I was taken aback because reading it doesn't mean you have to be conniving or manipulative. You could use the laws and know what happens when people are using them against you. You can choose to do them with the intention of good.

Success leaves clues. Give us three people we can all learn from.

Your parents are first. You're going to mirror a lot of their behaviors. It's wise to study them and to realize what you like and don't like because those are some of the traits you're given.

Number two, I would say from a marketing standpoint, review every presidential election. Every president you like or don't like—it doesn't matter your political beliefs—look at the person from a marketing standpoint.

The third is the most important: If you want to look at success, look at the life of Jesus. Even outside of a religious standpoint, you can't argue with the fact he was able to command attention. He lived by his word.

Justin, thanks for imparting some of your wisdom on your path to success.

BE LIKE JUSTIN

"I put my 'review' in my binder. I have it on one sheet on my desktop on the computer, which I set as a reminder to review. I put my goals in my calendar based on when they're set so I have the reminders. Sometimes after we write things down, there's nothing else to remind us. And we'll only look at that sheet much later. I have reminders in the digital side of things on the calendar. One of the best strategies I used as an athlete was a screen-shot of my goals."

KEEPING YOUR GOALS TOP OF MIND

Once you set your goals (see the Be Likes of Todd Durkin, Ron McKeefery, John Berardi and Brett Bartholomew), use a few different strategies to keep your goals top of mind.

1—Make a Word document of your goals and take a screen shot to use as the wallpaper on your phone. It's best to put it on the lock screen so you see it more often.

2—Put the screenshot on your computer as a screensaver.

3—Print out the document and put it in a place you will see it often.

4—Write the goals down each morning in your journal or in a notebook like Justin uses.

5—Set recurring reminders in your calendar that pop up to remind you of your goals and when they're due. You can use Justin's idea of having the reminder say, "Did you do anything to accomplish your goals today?"

6—Make writing out your goals part of your workday shutdown (see Alwyn Cosgrove's Be Like).

7—Put your goals on a whiteboard (see Brett Bartholomew's Be Like) where you'll see them first thing in the morning, such as in your bathroom (see Dana Santas' Be Like).

8—Add a "goal progress report" to-do to your calendar for the end of the week on Fridays or the beginning of the week on Monday mornings. Review the things you did the previous week that brought you closer to your goals, and what has to be done for the next week for greater progress.

9—Make sure your accountability partner (see Frank Nash's Be Like) knows what your goals are and pushes you to achieve them.

10—Have an accountability partner text you every weekday morning to ask what you're doing today to move forward on your goals. Do the same for that person.

Keeping your goals top of mind is the best way to achieve them. You need laser beam focus and with all the distractions of the modern world, you need all the help you can get!

Frank is the co-founder of the Secret Trainer Society. He's a consultant for numerous top fitness brands (Spartan Race, Freemotion, Retro Fitness, MYZONE and more) and lectures internationally on numerous fitness topics (coaching, marketing, business, balloon sculpting). Frank is a partner at dotFIT and the owner of STRONGER Clubs, AKA the Shaolin Temple of Fitness. Follow Frank on Instagram at @byfranknash.

You've had success in both the training and gym spaces, as well as in the consulting arena. How do you define success?

Success is doing what you love, whatever that is. There's no price tag on that. If you're a garbage man and you love being a garbage man, you're successful. If you're fulfilling whatever needs you have on a daily basis and you're a happy dude or dudette, you're successful.

If you're unemployed and you're happy, on some level you're successful. It doesn't equate to dollar bills or status. I'm just lucky enough to have found what I love and be able to make a living from it at the same time.

When I first started my business years ago, I met with a gentleman who owns a ton of real estate. He's a real jerk; he's unhappy and miserable. Every time his name comes up in conversations, someone always says, "That dude's loaded, but he's really a jerk." If you're that unhappy with the way your life is going, I don't care how much money you have, how much property you own or what car you are driving, if that's success, I don't want to be successful.

There's no specific measure of success—it's more of a feeling. When did you start to feel you were becoming successful with what you were doing in your life?

When I first graduated and was training people, I was a typical trainer working 90 hours a week. I loved what I did and I knew this is what I'd do the rest of my life. At that age, I didn't care how much money I made. I wanted to make a living, but if I could do this the rest of my life, I'd be fulfilled.

The trickledown effect of being a coach and trainer is the coolest part of the job. When you help one person and she comes back a couple months later and tells you how her husband lost 30 pounds, her kids are eating healthier and she got her aunt to work out with a trainer. It's so freaking cool and we're fortunate to be in this profession doing what we do.

If you're a trainer who loves it, I don't care if you make 10 bucks an hour or you're making a million dollars a year. You're successful.

You own a gym and have gym members, but you're also helping gym owners by consulting. What's driving you?

I call it "the coolness factor." I just love the fact that when I get up in the morning, I head to the gym. I walk in my club and it's cool! It's rocking; the energy is awesome—people are happy.

My staff is happy. Everyone's wants to be there. The coolness factor is through the roof and I will never, ever not be a part of that. People ask if I'll ever sell the club and the answer is no, because I could never get that coolness factor back.

If I'm speaking at a conference, there's a coolness factor of being there and inspiring potential gym owners. To have an impact, whether it's one on one or in your community or doing a podcast, you could transform the world.

You would think in a club like mine with a few hundred members and seeing them all the time, I would hear a lot positive feedback. I really don't. I see them on a daily basis; I get a high five—everything's good. But two or three times a year, I get handwritten letters from clients telling of being down 50 pounds and off all medication. They tell me they're the happiest they've ever been.

Those heartfelt stories don't come around too often, probably because people are so familiar with us. Humans get in a routine and we forget to notice things. Those four or five letters I get every year keep me going.

In order to be successful, there are certain habits that arise. What are those habits you know attributed to your success?

There are opportunities that come up in this field and you've got to jump on them, then you've got to execute. It's easy to say no, but I'm always saying yes. I'll always help. If someone wants to come to my club to visit for a day, if I'm in the area, just come and hang out. Hopefully, you can pay it forward. The more giving you are, the more you get back.

If I got a call tomorrow from Chris Poirier at Perform Better about needing someone to fill in at a conference, I'm doing it. It would be a lot easier to say no. It's a pain to travel to do an hour-and-a-half speech. But you have to jump on those opportunities because they don't come around all the time. People want to work with people who are willing to go the extra mile.

And I've always been the person who would go anywhere and do anything to help a partner. People are often too scared to take a leap. They're not sure of themselves, but these opportunities come up. It's not going to be the most convenient thing for you. Just do it.

Recognizing those opportunities and taking action is key. We all have dreams, but if you don't execute, you're not doing anything.

In my early days when I had to leave the club to take advantage of opportunities, it meant missing work and losing money to take the risk of a potential partnership. It's all risk, but you've got to be fearless. You've got to be scared to death and take those risks with your career. When things come up, you can't play it safe.

Training one client on the hour, every single hour and hoping that one day you'll hit the lottery, you're never going to advance. It just doesn't work that way. You've got to attack and execute on your opportunities.

Talk about your goal-setting process: Is there a formal process?

I'm part of a really awesome group called "the Secret Trainer Society." It's a group of successful club owners who share best practices. The heart and soul of this is that every six months we meet and come up with two goals—a personal goal and a professional goal.

The whole group then holds each other accountable to meeting those goals by the next time we meet. Just like we hold clients accountable to their goals, we need someone to hold us accountable. I'll be held accountable to about 45 other club owners and I'm not going to let them down.

The best way to achieve your goals is to have someone to hold you accountable…or in my experience, it's not going to happen. But, things change; goals evolve and opportunities come up. Some goals are no longer necessary. Goal setting is a constant evolution.

Frank, you travel a lot; you're speaking and you have obligations at Stronger Personal Training. You have a lot of energy and that's what people know you for—it's part of your brand. If you're off, it's obvious. That's got to be hard. How do you recharge?

I'm very lucky that I get to be in this field and I do mean this: I love it. It really is everything. So this isn't work for me in terms of keeping up my energy.

A lot of successful people say they don't watch TV; they don't go to the movies and they don't play video games. Me? I'm all about the movies. I'm all about Netflix. I'm all about videogames because for me, that's my quiet time. I could be playing *Destiny 2* or *Call of Duty* with my brother, but problem-solving is going on in the background.

It's like the old "control/alt/delete" shortcut. You see all those processes in the background, but things are still getting resolved while I'm playing.

There's a lot of research into "deep play" and how one part of the brain is working and allows the other part to rest. In that rest, it's still able to work out problems. It's why when people put a problem on paper, then go do something else, the solution comes to them. From the outside, successful people often make things look simple, but it can be a roller coaster of ups and downs. How do you push through?

We have such awesome community of rock stars of this field. I can reach out to people who have gone through what I'm going through. Sometimes we think these people are untouchable, but they're usually super accessible. To be able to share that experience with someone helps me get through those times.

It can be lonely when you think no one understands. You're responsible for all the members and employees and if things go down, there's a black hole in your community that will never be filled. That's a lot of responsibility.

But there are a lot of people who share your experience. We've got the technology; you can use it to reach out to someone who's gone through what you're going through and can talk you through it. This business can be frustrating.

I still, to this day, get upset if a member cancels a membership. I'll fight for every member because I look at it as I failed that person. If people trained here and leave, they're not going to Planet Fitness—chances are, they're not going to work out at all. I feel I've failed them and I'm frustrated.

My employees don't get it. I'm not going to talk to other members about it…and my girlfriend doesn't get it, but my friends in the profession get it.

That's a good segue into my next question. It doesn't have to be people in this field— give us three people we can all learn from.

Thomas Plummer might have the best social media going right now. He's a brilliant writer.

I love John Berardi. He is such a super smart dude and I love the behavioral modification information he teaches. He's always been way ahead of his time.

If you're living under a rock and you don't know who Mike Boyle is, you really need to follow him. You will not meet a nicer person. I love that he's still "doing it" in the trenches to this day. I was up at Mike Boyle Strength and Conditioning a couple weeks ago. We were talking in the office and he had to cut the meeting short because he had to train someone. I love that.

Frank, what are some books we can learn from?

I'm really not into books as much as I'm into podcasts right now, so I'll give you podcasts: You have to subscribe to Bill Burr and Joe Rogan. They're awesome. If you're driving or maybe you're on a train and get some downtime, put on your headphones and you'll be entertained by not just some funny dudes, but really smart guys.

Frank, you have such a unique perspective and have inspired so many to get out of their shell and find their voice in the world. Thanks so much for sharing your journey to success.

BE LIKE FRANK

"The best way to achieve your goals is to have someone to hold you accountable or in my experience, it's not going to happen. Just like we hold clients accountable to their goals, we need someone to hold us accountable."

ACCOUNTABILITY PARTNER

There are different levels of accountability.

You can do it though social media, by making what you're doing public.

You can do it with peers, by getting on the phone once a week, or you can get into an accountability coaching group.

Usually, the types that work best are those you pay for *("The more you pay, the more you pay attention.")* or one with someone you respect and don't want to let down. Both elements together is the best situation. Go to *CONTINUEfit.com/Propel* for more info on my coaching and accountability program.

Find an accountability program or mastermind you can pay for or ask someone you respect and whom you don't want to let down to get on the phone every two weeks to review your goals and your progress toward them.

On each call, start by describing your "wins" since the previous call. Did you accomplish the tasks you said you would?

Make sure they're tasks that are getting you closer to your goals. Finish by stating the tasks you'll do by the next call.

Don't get overwhelmed by creating a big to-do list for the next call. Keep it simple: three to five tasks that will get you closer to your goal.

Michol is the creator of the ViPR and the new ViPR PRO, a functional training product designed to train tissue resiliency and athletic performance. He is also the founder of IoM, instituteofmotion.com, a health-based company dedicated to providing solutions and strategies for fitness and preventative health.

You've had success as an entrepreneur, inventor, professor and as a high-level trainer. But how do you define success?

When that question is typically posed, many of us naturally assume it's success in business. But what success boils down to is the idea of peace of mind. That means living consistent with who we are and achieving what we set out to achieve. That could be in the workplace, in a relationship or as a parent. True success is having peace of mind. From that peace of mind come the abilities, comfort, joy, mindfulness and presence. All those are typically products of being comfortable with where we are. That's true success.

Let's expand on that a bit. You're going nuts right now because things are happening at a huge level with your businesses. You have chaos, but within that, you still have peace of mind.

I see it as a constant wavelength. I've never met anybody who has had the experience where there's only success. I've crossed the finish line of success and am forever more successful, but I see it as a wavelength. We move to and fro over that wavelength and get to degrees of separation from that wave, then we come back to it.

In my workplace, we're having success; there are challenges and we navigate that water. It's the same with parenting. As parents, we face daily challenges, successes and learning opportunities. We're anchoring into that wavelength, trying to get close to that wave, understanding that to achieve success every moment of every day is impossible.

Not achieving success teaches us about resiliency, grit and learning so we can give that learning to the next generation. We go through the experience of life, which teaches us and makes us grow.

This idea also evolves as we get older—we have a different outlook. When did you start to feel you were becoming successful?

For me, understanding who I am and knowing how to live consistent with that is a picture of success. I don't see success as a binary choice. Every entrepreneur has a story of challenge. I've gone through challenges in various businesses, which allows us an opportunity to come out the other side. By going through problems, we can understand truly who we are if we have that presence of mind.

When we learn to that degree, not only does it help us achieve that wavelength—that "I want to live consistent with who I am" idea—but we also have the gift of understanding and being able to teach that to others, to serve others based on what we've learned.

Success is married with failure, the opportunities and the challenges we have to go through in order to grow and to get to know who we are. Those are gifts. We often look at it as a binary choice—I'm either successful or I'm failing as if there's nothing in between. Those two are synonymous. The challenges of not reaching a goal are absolutely a part of success. They're not different.

"You have to fail" as an idea is becoming cliché. I like the word "challenge" better because we're all going to face challenges. You talked about serving and helping others. Is that what gets you out of bed in the morning?

If I live for myself, there's only so much motivation I can foster. But when I serve others, I have a greater capacity to endure, withstand, anchor toward and to be mindful. All of that is amplified when people are not living only for themselves.

I heard a great analogy about the needs of the personality and the needs of the spirit. Everybody fulfills the needs of the personality, which are certainty, uncertainty, significance and connection. Only a few people who have an enriched life go to the needs of the spirit, which are growth and living beyond yourself.

Everybody I admire has the capacity to look and serve beyond themselves. I have a greater capacity to get up in the morning, to motivate myself or to charge my enthusiasm with purpose when I'm serving those around me. That's why parenting is so magical; it teaches us to live with servitude.

In order to be where you are and to have this much going on, you need to build habits. Let's start from the beginning: the morning. What's your routine in the morning…if you have one?

I get up in the wee hours of the morning. I like to sit and think. I have a waking strategy and a sleep strategy—anybody who's a high performer needs both. My wakeup strategy is a sound that starts to permeate the environment to wake me up.

There's a stillness in the morning. Nobody's up yet and I can just sit and think, and I engage in whatever thoughts come to me. I'm not distracted by light, movement or anything in front of me. It's me in the dark, just thinking. Every day starts with waking up early and thinking.

As thoughts come to me and I want to flush them out, I may put pen to paper and start to write. I allow my mind free access to journeying. By journeying, I go in different directions and let my mind wander because a wandering mind is a critically important thing.

I cannot tell you how many times I've been on flights; I'm a big observer and I see that everybody's engaged in something. These are distractions if there's too much dose response. If I'm trying to fill my space with things I'm consuming, I don't spend enough time in my head.

There's a dose response; too much time in the head is unproductive as well.

There needs to be a balance between a wandering mind and a focused mind. People need to focus, especially in the kind of success dialogue we're having these days. You need to have ambition. All these are aspects of a convergence. In the balance aspect, you need divergence, which is a free-flowing, wandering mind.

Having a balance of both is a great part of success. Everybody's pounding the mantra of focus, focus, focus to be successful, and while that's true, it's not entirely true.

Michol, let's stay on "sit and think." I love this idea. This isn't meditation. This is sitting and thinking.

If I let some of the peripheral light in from the outside, it's enough for me to see pen on paper; I don't turn on lights. I like to keep it dark because just as noise can be a pollutant, we're discovering that light is a pollutant too.

There was a great study of how too much light in big cities around the world is disrupting natural animal circadian cycles. We're animals too—light regulation is important for us. Light is the number one thing to regulate serotonin. The light goes down and comes back up. Those are huge influencers for us to manage circadian rhythms, to be healthy… to recover.

Talk to us more about the sleep strategy.

We go back to the notion of "environment dictates behaviors." Think about a physical training environment—a trainer or coach creates an environment. We're going to put you on a bike today and expose you to aerobic exercise. We're going to put you under a bar today and expose you to heavy loads. Those are all environments.

Based upon those environments—the chemistry of the body, the hormonal expression, the cytokine activity, the neurotransmitter activity—all these start to increase, change or alter in response to the environment.

We fall asleep based on chemistry. We can't will ourselves to sleep. If we do that, the opposite happens: We stay awake. We need to get serotonin and dopamine and all the neurotransmitter activities to a certain level to respond to circadian rhythms so we can fall asleep.

A part of that comes from what we do during the day. Sunlight provides UVB rays on the skin and in the eyes, which will increase vitamin D production and enzymatic activity increases. Tryptophanhydroxylase goes up; we get more serotonin and will sleep better. It's what I do during the day to prepare for the night.

At night, an hour-and-a-half before bedtime, I start shutting off lights. I light candles—I diminish the amplification of light—and slowly lower the temperature. I use white noise to allow brainwave activity that puts me in a restful state. A body takes 90 minutes to naturally wind down because of the environment.

Control light. Control temperature. Control sound—all those are environmental manipulators we can use in order to get to sleep. Those are some of the things we can do to develop a sleep strategy.

What are some of the habits that have contributed to helping you get where you are?

We're learning to teach young people how to have more grit and resiliency. Part of that is something I've learned recently, the idea of 20x.

There's a group called SEALFIT—Mark Divine and his group do a great job of instructing and part of their message is about resiliency. They're all military, ex-military with great mental capacity to endure, deal and cope with things. About 12 of my Canadian friends were on a retreat and came to visit me in San Diego. One of them was a big fan of SEALFIT and saw that the head office was here. Through a number of conversations, they convinced SEALFIT to have them down for a five-day "Hell Week." This was authentic Navy SEAL training.

The initial response from Mark and his team was, "No, there's too much liability, and you're not what we look at in terms of physiological readiness." They're all fit, but there's a different capacity when you're thinking about Navy SEAL-type training. They took a year to train and prepare.

The first thing Mark and his team taught was that the people who are the most physically fit would not do the best in the those five days because when the chips are down and you need help, you're going to rely on yourself because your identity is rooted in being physically fit. It's those who lean on others who can do more; they call it 20x. When you lean on your tribe, platoon or network, you're 20 times stronger than you are by yourself. Twenty is an arbitrary number, but the theory behind that is relevant to everybody, including kids—especially kids.

When we go through hardship, there's a difference between distress and eustress. Distress is the negative consequence of stress. Eustress is the idea of stress making us stronger. One of the major differences between distress and eustress is our abilities or our perceived abilities to cope.

Imagine you and I are here in San Diego. It's evening and you walk to the ocean. The sun's setting and you're sitting there looking at a tsunami wave. It's a 50-foot wall of water coming at you and you're on the shore by yourself. Let's say that wave was a metaphor for stress in your life. If you were by yourself, would you have a greater or a blunted capacity to deal with that stress or that wave versus if you were arm-in-arm with 20 of your best buddies saying, no matter what happens, we're going to lean into this wave together?

It's clear you're going to have a much greater capacity to deal with more when you lean on others. That 20x could be friends, faith, prayer…mindfulness. It could be anything in your life you can lean on in times of strife. That's a great contributor and attribute of the people who are successful because grit and resiliency are fundamental to our lives, success and sustainability.

How do you get through the worst times in your life? How did you push through times when you almost gave up?

Here's the irony of it all: When you achieve greatness, whatever it is, you always have to go through adversity. Always.

There are many people who want to numb adversity and they do it through substance abuse, shopping and other diversions. Those who are truly successful aren't diverted away from challenge and strife; they go through it. The only way to get to the other side is through, and if we don't have a team around us, we cannot make it through.

I've been through some challenges in the workplace, and the only way I was able to make it was leaning on the backs of others during that time. When we get to the other side, we're stronger. We're more anchored and grounded; we get more perspective and a greater degree of understanding.

We also have more empathy because adversity humbles us—and we need that, particularly as we get older and wiser. That humility is not the youthful kind of exuberance and arrogance we typically hold when we're young. The wisdom of humility is as a product of previous challenges.

To segue this into a goal conversation, we're trying to get to the other side and that other side is the goal. Talk to me about your goal-setting process.

I'll delineate this into different spheres. Any business objective we have, we "cause map" it. Via the cause map, we look at an end goal and go through reverse engineering, "What is it going to take to get to that one step before the goal is completed?" We write down all the steps and determine what we need to do to get those accomplished.

Working backward step by step from the goal, that's called a cause map. Writing a goal is not good enough. We need to strategize how that goal will be met and the reasonable expectations to achieve it. Writing down a goal is a great start; it's just not direct and tangible enough because it doesn't provide a roadmap.

A goal as a New Year's resolution to lose weight is an outcome. We need much more planning and mapping to realize the steps.

Think about family goals as rituals. Every Friday night, our family does a certain thing. Every Sunday afternoon, our family does a different thing. These are rituals and family goals that can lead to a specific outcome, or they can anchor into safety, camaraderie, unity and love. All these are important, not only for kids as they grow up but for the adults as well. Rituals anchor us.

The book *The One Thing* does a great job breaking down the goal process like a cause map. We definitely need a plan, but at the same time, people need to think bigger and not worry about the "how" until they've expressed the big goal. It can hold us back sometimes.

Being so busy, how do you stay organized?

I surround myself with really good people.

I'm a dreamer, but I know where my limitations lie. If you're going to be successful, know where your limitations are and accept them. You can work at them and you can also surround yourself with people who have the missing ability.

I'm not a details person; I'm more of a broad-picture thinker. I surround myself with good details people who can leverage what we're doing. Know who you are and understand that you don't have to be excellent at everything—we call that a multiplier. Take a look what every successful corporation, message or movement all have in common: They use multipliers: They use other entities, people and communities to multiply the message.

Michol, let's finish up with some recommendations. Give us three non-fitness books people should read for their development.

Reading is so important for many reasons. On an overarching level, read poetry, biographies or educational material that allows you to reach a different level of understanding. Those are three things successful people do.

By poetry, can you actually enjoy the art form—the cadence of word and the beauty of language? Biographies allow us to see what successful people are doing. You can glean certain truths that still exist through successful habits and the creative and intellectual processes you can learn about in biographies.

Include some sort of educational material to allow yourself the opportunity to grow and to learn more. Those three elements are really important—poetry, biographies and educational material.

What about some people we should follow from whom we can learn?

Look at your parents and see how they navigated their world…and see how they navigated their challenges, wins and losses. It teaches us a lot.

Generationally, we need to learn from our past generations. We marginalize older people, but they have so much wisdom to share with us. We often think because it's not youthful exuberance, it's an inconvenience—that we have to take care of them. The reality is they can take care of us because they have so much experience. Let's take a look at the generation before us. We don't do that enough.

The other people to look to are your happiest friends. Study them and see what they do. If success leaves clues…it's going to leave clues. Look at your happiest friends and see what they do.

The last idea is to look toward your faith leaders. Whether you follow a certain religion or are anchored in faith, follow and understand what the leaders do. That keeps us grounded, and that's important.

If you look at those people, they will yield many clues as to what makes a person successful when success is defined by peace of mind.

We don't do that enough. We look for something specific because we want a shortcut.

You're going to be even more impactful, not only in the fitness field, but in the world on health and wellness systems. We appreciate you sharing your journey.

BE LIKE MICHOL

My wakeup strategy is a sound that starts to permeate the environment to wake me up. Then I sit and I think. There's a stillness in the morning. Nobody's up yet. I can just sit and think, and I engage in whatever thoughts come to me. I'm not distracted by light; I'm not distracted by movement or anything in front of me. It's me in the dark, just thinking. That's part of my morning routine.

"Many times, as you would expect, as thoughts come to me and I want to flush them out, I may put pen to paper and start to write down some of these aspects."

WAKEUP STRATEGY, A 21-DAY CHALLENGE

There are so many ways you can set up your morning routine. It's important to try different approaches to see what works for you. Some people like to get right to work; others like to exercise. You have to figure out what works for you through trial and error.

This will be a tough challenge. You need to give it the full 21 days.

Set an alarm that allows you to wake up gently before the sun rises and before anyone else in the house gets up. Don't use a traditional alarm! Instead, wake up to light music, preferably what you would hear in a spa. You can use your phone or get an alarm clock that gradually increases the volume. The Bedtime app on the iPhone is great for this.

Find a comfortable, dark spot in your house where it will be as quiet as possible.

Just sit and think. This is not a traditional meditation; you want to engage in whatever thoughts come to you. Allow your mind to wander—that's the point of this exercise.

Have a pen and paper close by in case you want to write.

Gradually increase the time you sit. In week one, do 10 minutes; in week two, do 20 minutes and in week three, try for 30 minutes.

Craig is the creator of Turbulence Training and contributed to Men's Health magazine for 17 years. Today, he's a coach of coaches, and has written two books, The Perfect Day Formula, and the Wall Street Journal bestseller, Unstoppable. Craig now helps high performers overcome entrepreneurial anxiety, make more money and work less. Learn more about Craig at his site, CraigBallantyne.com.

You're considered one of the most successful fitness professionals with Turbulence Training, your mentorships and coaching. How do you define success?

Success is living according to your values and moving toward your legacy every day. Success is not about money in the bank. It's not about Instagram photos. It's not about cars in the garage. It truly is about knowing your values. As Shakespeare said, "To thine own self, be true."

There are pastors and social workers who are very successful, but have no money because they're working on their gifts and taking that to the world. If you're a trainer or a gym owner, don't worry about the people next door or the other trainers in the gym. Focus on delivering the best service you can.

You also have to make sure you're playing up to your potential. Just this week I had a couple of mediocre mental days; I was in a funk. It wasn't that I didn't make as much money as I wanted to on those days. I didn't close a couple of sales, but as I reflected on why I was feeling depressed, it was because I didn't perform at the level I know I could. I didn't do the best on my sales calls. I didn't write the best articles for our newsletter list. They were about 85 percent of the way, but they could have been better. That's what bothered me; I wasn't as successful as I could have been.

Is it a barrier when people lack clarity defining and recognizing their successes?

The biggest problem is that people compare themselves to others, even when they know their own definition of success. It's a stupid human trick; we always compare ourselves to others. Very few people have the strength—or the disinterest in what other people are doing—to avoid comparing themselves to others. It's a natural tendency, so we do it, but it gets us off track and misaligned.

Even if we know what success looks like for us, we begin to emulate others. We chase shiny objects. We end up putting energy into something that doesn't matter to us, which can take us down a slippery slope. Then, three months later, we begin to wonder, "How did I end up here? Why am I spending all this time on this?"

People will put thousands of dollars into Facebook ads to promote something that's not even what they want. It can get us off track and that will happen at every level.

One of my core values is "Run your own race."

I used to have to teach that to young managers when I was in the bar business. We were working in New York City, where female bartenders were making $500 a night, three nights a week, six hours a night. The managers I was training were making $40,000 salaries and seeing these young women making all this money in a quarter of the time.

I'd remind the managers they had a steady paycheck and health insurance. They were learning new skills and building their resumes. Run your own race. You can't compare yourself to what others are doing.

It's difficult. And people don't understand how much you have to invest in yourself at the start when it comes to working and studying. It's like that hockey stick exponential curve. You're going along the flat line, and then suddenly things are going to take off. You have to invest the time.

Everybody you think has an amazing life—just put yourself in their shoes. Those female bartenders get hit on by creeps all night. They're probably scared and even if they're working in a classy place, somebody will say something weird to them. Then they have to get their butts home at 4:00AM; being a single woman in New York City can be a scary thing.

Those opportunities they might get from partying may lead them down the wrong path. You have to think about what's really going on in other people's lives despite all the amazing things you see from the outside. We only see the tip of the iceberg. Some of my clients have over 500 million-dollar manufacturing companies, but I see what's underneath the surface, what's driving them, what's troubling them. Everybody has problems.

Neil Strauss recently wrote an article about Elon Musk for *Rolling Stone*—most of the article isn't about Tesla or Solar City. It's about how he wakes up depressed every morning because he's lonely; he'd broken up with his girlfriend. We're all human. Everybody goes through pain, even if they look like they're on top of the world.

Your *Perfect Day Formula* changed my life. I worked in the bar business for 18 years and I always had the limiting belief that I'm a night owl and would never be able to do anything in the morning. Your book inspired me to make small changes to get up a little earlier. I've gotten so much more done and have taken things to another level since then.

Neil Strauss used to do books on rock stars, so as you can imagine, he was a night owl. He eventually went from being a total night owl to getting up early—and found he was more productive that way.

Joel Marion, who's big in the fitness world, has built BioTrust into a $100 million supplement company. He used to work from 9:00PM to 4:00AM. Until recently, after going through my book and workshop, he had only gone to bed at the same time as his wife seven times in the seven years they were married. That puts so much stress on a relationship, but they've overcome that. He now goes to bed with her every night and works first thing in the morning. He's so fired up and is having a huge impact.

Ultimately, it isn't about the hour you get up, but what you do with the hours when you're awake. The world is set up to reward the person who gets up earlier than everybody else. It's like that old joke: When you're in Africa on a safari and a lion starts chasing you, you only have to run faster than one other person. It's the same with life; we just have to get up a little earlier than most people—not hours earlier, just a little earlier—and get something big done. We feel that momentum and progress, and we keep moving ahead.

You can have good habits take you on the right path. One good habit leads to another. On the other hand, you can have bad habits take you down a slippery slope, where one glass of wine leads to two and eating a pizza, and away you go. We have to be cognizant of the habits we choose because habits define who we become.

When did you start to feel like you were getting this right, when you considered yourself a success?

I considered it pretty early. Writing for *Men's Health* gave me the credibility to connect with people. Speaking at events in the hockey training world in 1999 when I was 24 years old, being on stage gave me a level of success. It gave me an ego boost. I was doing the work, using that ego boost properly.

I've always believed I'm successful, but I'm also hungry for more. It's both sides of the coin; you should always feel successful when you're helping people every day, but always be hungry for more. If you have a healthy understanding of those two sides, you'll continue to run your own race.

That's a good segue to my next question: What gets you out of bed in the morning?

I can't describe why I'm driven to do this, but I'm driven to help people I've never met, never will meet and who live halfway around the world. I love hearing their success stories.

I'm driven by the frustration I feel when I hear people say, "I can't do this" or "I'm failing at this." In high school, I was frustrated when sitting around the lunch table at the nursery where I worked and people were struggling to lose weight. I wanted to yell at them, "It's so simple, just do this, this, this and this." I just wanted to help people. I don't want to yell anymore, but I still want to help them because most success is simple.

It's not easy, but it's simple. It's like climbing Mount Kilimanjaro: it's simple. You follow the path; you put one painful step after another and you get there. It's simple, but it's not easy. Those are different.

For our weight-loss clients, success is simple. You have to do the work; you must show up and do the workouts. You must follow the nutrition program. You have to get better sleep. You have to drink water.

It's simple, but it's not easy. I want to show people the simple path to success and be the person giving them the support, encouragement and direction they need. That has always driven me, even though I don't know these people.

What's your morning routine these days?

I follow the Brian Tracy rule of "Eat that frog!" from the book he wrote about doing the hardest things first. I do the hardest things first in my business, which is to write 1,500 words because it propels me ahead; it helps me write books, newsletters, sales letters and video scripts. If I didn't do it first thing in the morning, I'd procrastinate and at 5:00 at night I wouldn't have finished. So…I eat the frog first thing in the morning.

I encourage all my coaching clients to spend at least 15 minutes as soon as they wake up focusing on their number one priority in life. Do whatever that is to you, whether it's taking advantage of an opportunity in sales or marketing or getting out of debt. If you spend at least 15 minutes a day, six days a week—totaling 72 hours a year—of clear, uninterrupted thinking on your number one priority in life, it will get you ahead.

We get crazy with the pendulum swinging one way or the other. It's like one of your videos where you were saying you've had enough of the two-hour meditation morning routines where people are essentially spending two hours doing nothing.

I made those videos because I had coaching clients saying they were already stressed by 7:30 in the morning. They'd been up since 5:00AM and had done so much, but accomplished nothing. All the work for the rest of the day still had to be done! I want people to stop that because that's going to get you as stressed out as if you just slept in. There's something valuable in all of that, but do five minutes of gratitude or 15 minutes of meditation or 10 minutes of Bible study. Then get to work on something so you have a victory before the rest of the world gets up.

When you have that, it doesn't matter how crazy the rest of your day goes. The toilet in your gym can plug up and you need to deal with that all day, but you still had a victory in the morning that the world can't take away no matter how crazy it gets.

As a trainer, at first I couldn't understand why the CEOs were fighting over my 6:00AM time slot. I wondered why they didn't just train at lunchtime or after work. Turns out, that would never happen. All heck breaks loose as soon as they get to the office. Their lives are no longer theirs because they have to serve their team members. They have to train first thing in the morning or it won't get done. We have to do the important work early.

That also takes a lot of discipline. What other habits have helped you succeed?

It's actually easier to get the work done early. It takes more discipline to be a night owl. It takes less discipline to get up a little earlier and focus on the work in the mornings. The habit that makes that easy is making sure you do the preparation the night before. You've got to get up and hit the ground running; make your to-do list at the end of the workday the day before.

Start with a brain dump: Write all the things you need to do the next day. Organize those into three major projects you have to finish and cut out everything else. If you get to those other tasks, fine, but first, focus on the major projects.

The third thing after the organization of priorities is to do a little work on them, just set them up. If I'm going to write 1,500 words, for example, I do a bit of an outline so I don't sit down at a big blank screen. If I've prepped a couple of prompts, it's going be easy for me to write. That's what we need to do.

There's clear research I read about in the book *Rest: Why You Get More Done by Doing Less* to the efficacy of starting something, stopping to allow the brain to have a break from it and then coming back to it the next morning.

Hemingway always said that when writing, you need to stop in the middle of a sentence. When you're really into your writing, that's when you stop and come back the next day. It seems counterintuitive. He doesn't mean you should write one sentence, stop, and then come back to it the next day. He means, get your work done and then stop in the middle of your last sentence.

Think of some of the greatest figures in history from Beethoven and all the composers, to Charles Darwin, Charles Dickens and so on. They only worked for a couple of hours in the morning. They did their deep work in the morning and then they went for long walks.

Charles Dickens walked two or three hours around London every afternoon; maybe he'd make a few notes, then he came back to work the next morning. Chopin did the same. He took notes while taking his afternoon walks and the next day, he took those notes and built them into symphonies. It was not something they did because they were bored and didn't have Netflix. They knew even back then that it was the secret to productivity and success.

One of my favorite books is called *Daily Rituals* by Mason Currey. It's a fascinating read describing the daily routines of about 150 profiles of successful people such as Victor Hugo and Beethoven. You learn some quirky facts about them, but you also see the patterns. Stephen King, for example, writes from 9:00AM–1:00PM every day. While we're eating our Wheaties, he's writing *Pet Sematary* and other crazy stuff. He does it every single day, and if he's in the middle of a book, he does it on holidays. Stephen King doesn't have Christmas Day when he's in the flow; he sticks to it and then he goes for a walk.

I know you set goals because I read your book *How to Set Goals: Ultimate Goal-Setting Guide to Having Your Best Year Ever*. It's a great book on goals. Can you explain your process for setting and reviewing your goals?

I used to set so many goals that it was overwhelming. I would set 20 or 30 goals for a year, basically taking a shotgun approach to life. At the end of the year, I had only accomplished three of the minor goals and would look back in frustration. My mentor, Mark Ford, said, "You can only set four goals, one for each of your major values in life," which are family, health, wealth and personal development.

It's taking the bulls-eye approach. You set one major goal for your health, which is in the middle of the bulls-eye, and if you hit that with a laser-focused rifle shot, everything else around the bulls-eye will improve. But if you take a shotgun approach, you have these little pellets all over the place. Nothing hits your major goal and you end up disappointed.

We set four major goals, but we need to be careful when they're outcome goals because, as Alwyn Cosgrove once told me, we don't control outcome goals.

Let's say Mrs. Jones comes to the gym and wants to lose 25 pounds. We say, "You might lose 21 pounds. Would you be disappointed if you lost 21 pounds and looked amazing?" Let's not get too focused on the outcome goal. Let's focus on the process goals, which are the action steps we control to get there. You want to lose 25 pounds. Here's your workout program. That's within your control; that's a process goal.

That's how we do it: four major goals, three process goals—and that's how you achieve the big things you want in life.

It's important to stay organized. I know you have the *Perfect Day* planner. What's different about your planners versus others?

We have the *Perfect Day Formula* kit, which is a planner. We have a new 90-day planner for the team training sessions we do—we have all types of planners. There are lots of other great ones, but frankly, I just use a Word document.

We have a daily scripting pad. You script it the night before; block out your time, then write down the people you need to connect with the next day and write out your major to-dos. It's not a big planner where you're planning out months in advance; it's a day-by-day scripting path.

We have a gratitude journal that goes with that, and I have tools to help you create your vision. You have to have a vision before you can create your perfect day. We get more information and more clutter out of people's heads and give them more clarity through that system.

As somebody who is driven and focused, are there sacrifices you've made to be successful?

I sacrificed the partying, which was fine because that got me in trouble. I had to cut out bad relationships. Sometimes I wish I could still go out like I did when I was younger, but you give that up; you draw the line somewhere and end up doing other things. I haven't sacrificed travel—I have been to 40 countries because the more success I have, the more opportunities arise.

You have spoken about anxiety you've had in the past. Sometimes, we all feel anxious or depressed. When those times occur, how have you picked yourself up? How have you kept going instead of giving up?

It comes down to having values that drive you and knowing why you do what you do. When you struggle, put yourself in a client's shoes. What would you tell clients to do if they were struggling? You need to take your own advice, and that's what I did when I had anxiety. I turned over every rock. I tried everything from meditation to qigong to yoga. I didn't enjoy any of them very much, but I had to do it to overcome the anxiety.

It was a painful time in my life, and those were the things I did and what I'd tell other people to do in that situation. Nothing lasts forever, neither the bad times nor the good times. We have to enjoy the good times more, and realize we're going to get out of the bad times soon enough.

Sometimes we look at successful people and think they have things easy, no health issues or other problems. But everyone has something they've had to overcome.

Absolutely, and those are the best success stories. The people who have had the most adversity often turn that into the biggest advantages in life. You can look at everyone from Oprah to your favorite transformation story at your gym and think of what they've had to overcome. There's always more to the iceberg underneath the water than the tip you see around you or on social media.

Give us three non fitness–related books everybody should read.

First, read *The Art of Living* by Sharon Lebell. It's a translation of the stoic philosopher Epictetus and his big lessons—it's my bible. A couple of times a year, I'll go through it and read a page a day. It's almost like a horoscope, the one page you read that makes you say, "I needed this today."

Then, Viktor Frankl's *Man's Search for Meaning*. I wish every kid had to read this. If I was president, that's the rule I'd make, that everyone had to read that book in high school. It's such a powerful book on so many levels.

The third book I'd suggest is Elon Musk's biography by Ashlee Vance because it makes you realize "You ain't doing anything." It's a good kick in the butt to go out and do more.

Let's make it four books and add *Daily Rituals* to that list.

Yes, it's a great book, and, of course, *Perfect Day Formula*.

Name three people we can all learn from.

The first person is Bedros Keuilian. He's one of my best friends and is awesome on social media. He helped me with selling—he teaches fitness entrepreneurs how to make more money. He's great and I highly recommend him.

Grant Cardone is another guy to follow. I really like how he uses social media; he has great sales training information and, like Bedros, he's a great mix of how to use social media for business, but also puts a nice personal touch with it. He's fun and everybody gets a lot from following him. He wrote *10X,* as well as *Be Obsessed or Be Average.* He's going to rub you the wrong way on certain days, but just overlook that; read between the lines and focus on the positive.

The third person is Jason Ferruggia. He's done an amazing mental and personality transformation over the years, and I highly recommend people follow him too. He's one of my best friends and has one of the top podcasts in the fitness space. If you want to learn how to do podcasting and be connected, he's a great guy to follow.

Craig, your work has changed the way I look at priorities, productivity and focus. You have inspired so many people by leading by example, and not only in the fitness world. Thanks so much for sharing your journey to success.

BE LIKE CRAIG

"I work as soon as I wake up. I get out of bed as quickly as I can and don't hit the snooze button. I go downstairs and turn on my computer and start working on the project I set out for myself the night before."

15 MINUTES EARLIER CHALLENGE

In his book *Perfect Day Formula*, Craig instructs people to start by just getting up 15 minutes earlier than normal and then gradually build upon that to wake up earlier and earlier.

Get up 15 minutes earlier starting tomorrow and get at least one thing done that will get you closer to your goals. It doesn't have to be a big thing—just get something done.

After two weeks, get up 15 minutes earlier and then two weeks later, another 15 minutes earlier. Too often people try to make too big of a leap and try to start getting up two hours earlier! It's like training; you have to take baby steps.

Do something in that time that will move the needle toward getting closer to achieving your goals.

Use this undistracted time to get work on your most important task you've at least started on.

Let it give you momentum for the day, knowing you are making progress toward your goals.

If you did this five days a week for 48 weeks (I'm giving you a month off!), you would accomplish 240 tasks toward your most important goals.

Don't you think you'd be a little closer to achieving the things in life you want to achieve?

Emily is a Functional Podiatrist, Human Movement Specialist, Global Educator in Barefoot Science, Founder of EBFA Global and inventor of Naboso Technology. With a spirit to challenge conformity, Emily has taken her conventional podiatric medical degree and combined it with years of experience and expertise in human movement and sensory science. It is her mission to change the way we look at foot function and human movement as it relates to sensory stimulation, integrated stabilization and fascial sequencing. Find more about Dr. Splichal at dremilysplichal.com.

You've had success in a lot of areas: as a doctor, as a founder of EBFA Global, lecturer, business owner and consultant. How you define success?

The definition is changing depending on where I am in my life. When I was younger—and I think a lot of readers will agree with this—success was equated with a monetary level. You reach "this much" and in your mind, you're successful. The older I get and the longer I'm in this profession, my perspective of success is shifting more toward happiness and the passion I have and how satisfied I feel. It comes down to impact; that's my success.

That can be a hard thing to quantify. When did you start feeling you were starting to achieve this happiness?

I had always wanted to use fitness in my profession. When I went through medical school, I knew I wanted fitness and movement involved in my practice. That's usually where someone would move toward sports medicine, physical therapy or physiatry—the medicine of movement. However, that still wasn't right for me. It wasn't just treating athletes; my vision was more about education.

I didn't know how I was going to combine the fitness with movement and medicine into something that inspired me every day. It wasn't until I started my education company and gained the satisfaction I got from teaching others and saw the impact they were having on their patients, athletes or clients that I found what drives me. I started to see myself as a success when I started EBFA; that was a huge pivotal point.

And each year over the past five years, how I started shaping the way I treat my patients has led me to feel more successful.

I recently left my former medical group to start my own practice, purely built around functional and regenerative medicine. Pulling out of all insurance was a risky step. But now, I'm able to treat patients the way I want to treat them. I mark that as another feeling of "this is where I need to be in my life." That feeds success. That feeling of success started five years ago, and each year it grows stronger.

It's a domino effect, especially when you start to reach more people. What is it that motivates you?

The Mark Twain quote, "The two most important days in your life are the day you're born and the day you find out why," speaks to me.

Some people might think my calling is to be a healer—a lot of doctors are healers; that's their passion. I have a way of looking at movement and the human body and compensations. My gift is to share that with the world. I see myself as an educator.

Sharing the gift of empowerment—that's what gets me up in the morning—inspiring others, giving them hope, helping them give others hope based on the unique way I look at movement; that's my gift.

Your approach is different from other doctors. You're not just saying, "Let's use an orthotic." You're talking about corrective exercise and preventative measures. Because you're marching to your own drum, has that been hard to get buy-in from peers?

You should see some of the hate mail I got from the podiatry community when I started challenging some of the traditional Westernized concepts. I have thick skin, partly because I have to—but I definitely had days of crying over email. Now it's like, screw you to the people who wrote those letters.

I know I'm not doing harm. I'm empowering people and giving them hope. I'm teaching them another way. There's no single way. There's no orthotic, isolated way of looking at foot injuries. Once you see that, you have to challenge the norm.

Anyone who's challenging the norm is going to have haters because you're shaking up conforming. That's part of what you're signing up for when you question things. I am a black sheep in podiatry. But I believe so passionately in what I'm doing and I know I'm helping people—I'm not going to stop.

I'm grateful that my education company has taken me to countries that don't have podiatry, that don't have doctors who know how to help with foot pain. People in these countries think it's normal to have foot pain, but it's *not* normal. I'm able to empower other professionals about foot pathology and foot pain and show them how they can help people. They shouldn't have to accept that as a normal aspect of life.

Was understanding your impact what got you through all this?

When I started looking at movement and teaching, I didn't have that confidence. I read more and more—just reading and educating myself and being diverse in the way I was speaking and educating.

Since that time, I've seen more patients and I take ongoing additional education. Right now I'm in my fellowship for functional medicine, because I constantly challenge my knowledge base.

As I gain that confidence, I see feedback of the lives I'm impacting. That's inspiring. Think of when the patient is someone who had a stroke and you can help the person walk again or get down on the floor and play with the grandchildren. I've started integrating Naboso Technology with multiple sclerosis patients, and am now getting email from people with MS—the insoles are helping them walk better.

That's why I do what I do.

With this kind of a resume—you're a doctor, entrepreneur, educator, student—let's get into some of the habits of being such a high achiever. Do you have a morning routine you do to set up your day?

Every single day for the past three years, whether I'm traveling or wherever I am, I listen to 30 minutes of a motivational talk or lecture. I listen first thing in the morning when I wake up, when I'm getting ready for the day. I'm listening to something to shape my state of mind. This is powerful in the morning because your brain waves are a little different when you first wake up.

Do you have a specific, formal plan for setting goals?

I do meditation on a regular basis. It's not like formal "sitting in a lotus pose" meditating. But I take time out of my day to do some mental vision. I don't write goals in the sense of a vision board, but I'm very focused from a mental perspective on where I want my company to go, things I want to do…my bucket list of career goals, one of which is writing a textbook on barefoot science.

You meditate on that specific vision for where you're trying to go. Taking action steps is the key. If you don't execute, you're not going anywhere.

One thing that's helped is listening to Tony Robbins. I do the best meditating not in the formal way, but while I have certain music. I do a power flow with my eyes shut. It's just bodyweight movements. The entire time I'm doing that, I'm seeing myself and feeling the emotion I would feel when I achieve a goal. It's completely vibrating through my body that I believe I will achieve it.

Naboso is my newest venture. I know that Naboso is going to make a massive impact in the field and is going to be a multimillion-dollar company. I'm not focused on the money; I'm focused on making an impact. But I feel what it would feel like when I'm at that level with the company.

We're always talking with our clients about recharging and resting. You're so busy with multiple parts to your business. What do you do to recharge?

I am big on a reset. That's definitely something that has allowed me to achieve what I did academically. You have to shut everything down and have a night out or connect with friends, but know the next day, I'm back focused. That's something I believed throughout medical school. Otherwise, I wouldn't have been able to burn the candle at both ends.

Now I'm big on infrared saunas, halo therapy and massages. Resetting my physical wellbeing is extremely important to me. And I do aerials; I make sure I take time to do a workout or a movement that's only for me, something I don't teach. It's my disconnect—it forces me into the now. This kind of thing forces an entrepreneur out of the future.

Doing aerials forces me into the now because they're challenging. I'm learning something new—and they're dangerous. I have to be in the now when I'm in that hour, and nothing else in the world matters. I don't want to hurt myself and, certainly the most important thing, I don't want to die. That's why I like the effect aerials have because it has a risk element that forces me into the now.

It's very easy when I'm sitting in the infrared sauna or getting a massage and trying to meditate to think of all the other tasks I need to do. I get the most empowered from something that's still my time, but is forcing me into the now. This is super important. I encourage professionals to do that.

I just read the book *Rest*; there's a chapter on deep play and even finding life-threatening activities. There are a lot of scientists who go mountain climbing. They do it

because when they're climbing a mountain, they have to think of only that—that's what gets them away from thinking of work. There's a lot to be said for that, and there's some science behind it.

While we are talking about books, are there three non fitness–related everyone should read to help in their development?

One that completely changed my life is *The Power of Now*—hence why I was talking about being in the now. Any of Eckhart Tolle's books are great; they change your approach to the ego. Part of being successful as a public speaker and an educator is knowing that my style might not please everyone. When I first started educating and people had negative comments, I'd take those to heart. Then I realized I had to put the ego to the side—let me take that as constructive criticism. Understanding the ego is huge for personal growth.

A second suggestions is *Emotional Intelligence* by Daniel Coleman—I wish I'd read earlier. It's about understanding EQ instead of IQ. Emotion is so important when you're dealing with people, whether they're patients or clients or when you're educating other professionals. Interpersonal relationships are partly emotion, partly your ability to read others' emotions, and responding back and forth. That's really powerful.

The third book I'd suggest is the Stanley and Danko book, *The Millionaire Next Door*. That's a good, inspiring, financial get-your-stuff-together book.

What about some people? Give us three people we should follow.

I love Gary V. He calls us out and does a little ass whooping every once in a while.

From a personal growth perspective, especially on the functional medicine side of things, I'm a big Dave Asprey fan. Even if you're not into him as an individual, his Bulletproof Radio podcast and the people he interviews can introduce you to forward-thinking innovators, doctors and entrepreneurs. It's a great access point.

Another person to look into is my NLP life coach, Judy King. She's an Australian currently living in Bangkok. Her website is *The Judy King*. Doing NLP coaching has completely changed my life. I encourage everyone to check that out. Even coaches need coaches.

It helped me when I made some of my biggest changes, when I was scared to leave my practice, pull out of insurance, stop doing surgery and tiptoeing the line of doing what I really wanted to do. She asked, "Why are you not?" Just get over there and do it. Stop being in your head, and just believe in the process.

Instead of looking at things as a what-if and a fear, look at the excitement of what might open up. That will really change your perspective.

Good point: Even coaches need a coach. It's one of the things we should encourage younger coaches to do sooner. Emily, I wish we had more doctors like you, not only talking the talk but walking the walk. We're excited to see where this takes you.

BE LIKE EMILY

"Every single day for the past three years, whether I'm traveling or wherever I am, I listen to 30 minutes of a motivational talk or lecture. I'm listening to something to shape my state of mind. This is powerful in the morning because your brain waves are a little different when you first wake up."

MORNING MOTIVATION

This is a great way to start your day.

Start with a goal of listening for five minutes as part of a morning routine. It doesn't have to be as soon as you wake up, but try to place it strategically into your morning.

Make it easy for yourself and get it ready the night before.

There are great people to listen to: Tony Robbins, David Goggins, Gary V, Grant Cardone, Mel Robbins, Brené Brown, Will Smith, Dwayne Johnson… whoever you respond to.

Google "morning motivation" to get a variety of people—mix it up. There are many on YouTube.

Once you feel like you are in a groove and you can do more than five minutes, download some books from Audible, your favorite podcast app and the TED Talk app to go a little deeper.

Allistair is a world-renowned sports performance consultant, author and speaker. He has worked with numerous Olympians, Paralympian's, world champion athletes and Grand Slam winners. Allistair consults for coaches, athletes, teams and college programs, where he teaches and implements the Champion Minded culture and approach. He also hosts the Champion Minded Podcast, available on iTunes. He's based in Florida, USA, and you can learn more at allistairmccaw.com.

You've done a great job of unpacking the idea of being "champion minded." Give us an idea of how you define success.

This is something I often ask attendees at events. Today's society has somehow taught us to believe that success is money and material goods. Success to me is as simple as waking up in the morning and getting to do what I feel like doing. Spending time with clients, with people I love to spend time with, doing projects I love to do. Right now, I believe I'm living success and I couldn't be in a happier place.

Any great coach—lifestyle coach, mindset coach or business coach—always starts out by asking what you want. What's your perfect day? A lot do some sort of "perfect day" exercise, and it's important. When you start to think about what it is you really want, you begin to figure out your progress.

We're programmed from an early age to get out and make money. One of the mistakes I find younger people make is just looking for jobs that make money…and eventually find out they're not happy.

In my journeys, I've been on the roller coasters of making and losing a lot of money. Ultimately, the search for happiness was in discovering what success is to me, which is doing what I love with whom I love to do it. It's as simple as that.

We'll get to that roller coaster story, but when did you start to feel like you were a success? You played tennis as a kid and then got into the duathlon and reached high levels at both. High-level athletes are known for always pushing themselves. They're never satisfied, and you're of a similar mindset. When did you begin to feel, "I'm making an impact. I'm starting to be a success?"

Here's the funny thing: I've never felt I'm a success. I have always had the mentality that there's no finish line regarding how much better, smarter or more knowledgeable I can get.

I've had this drive from a young age to be champion in a sport. It started with tennis, but that was financially difficult for my parents with four other boys in the house. I took up running, which was cheaper because it involved only a pair of running shoes. Then I went on to triathlon.

I had the mentality from an early age that good is not good enough. That's how I can relate to other high performers—there's always something better. It's an endless journey. My career has evolved to helping athletes or high performers understand that it's fine that excellence is out there. There's no finish line, but you have to be happy where you are—you have to find happiness in your life.

Happiness is not a destination; it's an action—it's a decision. That's so important to realize.

You always talk about drive. What drives you? What is it that gets you up and moving in the morning?

I'm going to flip this. My drive is at the end of the day knowing I gave it my all and could not have done any more that day. That's what drives me and it's also what scares me. If you were to ask what my greatest fear was, it would be that I didn't get enough out of myself.

Is there a routine you have in the morning, specifically, that you do to set you up for the day?

Yes, I call it my "4x20s." The first 20 minutes are spent reading or researching. My second 20 minutes involve exercise; sometimes it's a little longer. Usually, in the morning I have more of a regeneration routine.

My third 20 minutes are for thoughtfulness. I purposely spend 20 minutes thinking about others and putting others before myself. I spend my final 20 minutes in the morning on breakfast. We're always in a rush to get out of the house, but breakfast is the most important meal of the day. I purposefully dedicate that 20 minutes for breakfast. Those are my four 20s of the morning.

What are some of the habits you attribute your success to and that you try to instill in your athletes?

I have a habit of waking up in the morning automatically thinking of two things I'm grateful for, but I had to practice that at first. I had a sticky note next to my bed to remind me to think "gratitude" as soon as I woke up.

When developing a new habit, I cover my whole house with sticky notes. It can be on the bedside table, stuck on the mirror, in the kitchen, where I'm brushing my teeth and by the phone. That's how I develop habits.

As coaches, we know our athletes are watching and we must lead by example. For me, one of the biggest resources of performance is energy, how I'm taking care of energy. You can't take care of and lead others if you're not taking care of your energy. My habits are surrounded by energy and a better mindset. Those are the two important things I try to bring in each day.

I know from reading *Champion Minded* that you're very big on goals. Do you have a formal process for goals?

Here's the thing: Goals are good, but the most important thing to have is a vision. It's important to have a vision of where you see yourself because goals can be fleeting. You wake up and sometimes you're unmotivated, but your vision can drive you.

I like to set Olympic-type goals every four years. Those are big goals; they're Olympic goals. Then I also set interim goals each year. Last year, for example, it was to complete the book *Champion Minded*. Next year I'm going to look at doing another book, possibly run a few marathons. That's how I set goals. I make them big so they scare me into action.

And here's another thing about my goals: I like to make them public, not for ego or bragging rights, but because that catapults me into action. It puts me out there, and I must live up to what I said. There's no way out; that has always driven me to achieve goals.

There's nothing like public accountability. This book has 50 interviews and I've been taking time out of people's day to help me with it. That accountability was why I went into action; I knew accountability to others would help push me.

What about recharging? How do you recharge?

I'm probably one of the worst at this because I am fueled by working. Let me rephrase that—I don't have "a job" because I'm doing what I love. I'm one of the luckiest people in the world to have found what I love to do early in life.

I go crazy if I don't have a book in my hand or if I'm not learning something, or if I'm not interacting with somebody I can help. I'm not the best around holidays when things are quieter.

During the day, I take a nap after lunch so I can shut off my brain. I don't necessarily sleep; I turn the phone off and shut down my brain so I can recharge for the afternoon. I want to be the same person, coach and mentor at 5:00 in the afternoon as I was in the morning. This work is all about consistency and conserving energy, and that's how I get mine.

I have little cliché sayings that some people probably find corny, but I believe the most important time is the first two hours of the day. I call it *the two for you.* Before your day starts, before you're dictated by others, before you're dictated by your work commitments, you're spending two hours for you: the two for you.

Then at the end of the day is a shutdown routine before I sleep because I value my sleep as a great energy source. It's called "the one before I'm done" and involves switching off all electronics, dimming the lights and doing a little reading.

It's not all rosy though. You travel a lot and you're often at the demand of athletes. What are some sacrifices you've made?

I've never seen anything as a sacrifice. I wrote about this in *Champion Minded*; the champion minded don't see things as a sacrifice. We see things as a choice. I've chosen to spend days away from family, to spend many a Christmas away working with an athlete.

Those have been my choices, not sacrifices. No one has pushed me and I've never been forced to do anything.

I believe success comes down to making hard choices. You must be willing to go to the places others aren't willing to go, especially during the more sentimental times like holidays. Those are days I've used to my advantage.

Be grateful for your health; be grateful for your family and all you have. I don't want to sound corny, but for me, every day is Thanksgiving. I'm grateful.

You can't be sad when you're grateful. It's really important to be consistent with your gratitude. Even if those weren't sacrifices, your life isn't all good times. How do you push through your worst times?

Going back to past adversity, I have been ill multiple times in my life. I had a serious virus called "coxsackievirus" that put me out for a long time in sports, and it depleted my immune system.

And I suffered from depression in the early 2000s, when I was always incredibly ill. I lost 45 pounds and I had no ambition to work…no ambition to do anything. I lost my identity, and it was just by the grace of God and through some simple steps that I made it through.

My mom said, "You have to add structure to your day, even if it's only two things you do today." Those two simple things were to get up, put some nice clothes on. I went out and did one thing for somebody else, and that's how I got out of that.

When we're in that state of mind, we're only thinking about ourselves—woe is me, look at me, pity me. Life hasn't been a bed of roses, and I'm thankful for all the difficulties I've had because they have made me the person I am today.

If I could make it through that time in my life, I can survive anything.

Sometimes, I wake up and think, "I don't feel like reading through this gratitude thing right now," but I do it anyway. The day keeps going up, and the more you do and the more you get into those habits, the better off you're going to be.

I couldn't agree more. Here's the thing, people might think we're super motivated and positive all the time. But no. We have to use self-talk; we have to get ourselves going every day.

Besides *Seven Keys to Being a Great Coach* and *Champion Minded,* give us three non fitness–related books everybody should read.

The first suggestion is the *Slight Edge* by Jeff Olson, talking about the power of simple, small habits to practice every day. It's easy to do, but also not easy to do; it's the choices we make.

The second one would be *Unstoppable*, by Dave Anderson. That's a fantastic book. It has a lot to do with the mindset and the choices we make, what some might call sacrifices.

The third book is by Ryan Holiday. He has a few great books, but *Ego is the Enemy* is the one that resonated most with me. It's about getting past your ego—we all have an ego. I see ego as the borderline of confidence; confidence is important, not just in our careers, but in our lives as well.

Ego is important in how we feel about ourselves because if you don't love yourself, how can you expect others to love and accept you? It's a fine line; *Ego is the Enemy* resonated with me.

I've read *The Obstacle is the Way,* and I read *The Daily Stoic* every day. I have to get that one. What about three people we should follow we can all learn from?

John C. Maxwell is a motivational speaker who gives great lessons in leadership-building culture. He's a smart guy with a great sense of humor. He brings his message across in a very simple way, and I enjoy him.

Richard Branson—his story is fascinating; he's a maverick, a guy who has taken so many risks, so many chances. He has owned record labels and airline companies; he's planning on sending passengers to the moon. He's a fascinating guy. He's on Twitter and other social media quite a lot; he's good fun and interesting to follow.

The third person, and this will probably surprise you, is Rafael Nadal—the tennis player my guy recently lost to in the final of the U.S. Open. Nadal is a class guy, in victory, defeat and adversity. He's a solid guy with a great character.

Keep fighting the good fight and keep helping not only athletes, but also coaches. Thank you for sharing your journey on the road to success.

BE LIKE ALLISTAIR

"The first 20 minutes are spent reading or researching; it could be something motivational or spiritual. My second 20 minutes involve exercise; sometimes it's a little longer. Usually in the morning I have more of a regeneration routine. My third 20 minutes are for what I call thoughtfulness. I purposely spend 20 minutes thinking about others and putting others before myself. I spend my final 20 minutes in the morning on breakfast."

THE MORNING ROUTINE—4X20S

Morning routines are tricky. There is no right or wrong way to do it. You just need to be consistent. You have to play around to find out what works best. Give Allistair's idea a try.

You don't have to do what he does, and it doesn't have to be for 20 minutes or in the same order, but try to structure a routine you can consistently follow. That's the key.

It could be "4x10s" or "3x15s." That part doesn't matter; do whatever works for you.

ALLISTAIR'S ROUTINE	
TIME	ACTIVITY
20 Minutes	Reading or Research
20 Minutes	Exercise
20 Minutes	Thoughtfulness
20 Minutes	Breakfast

YOUR ROUTINE	
TIME	ACTIVITY

NICK WINKELMAN

Nick is Head of Athletic Performance and Science of the Irish Rugby Football Union. He's the former Director of Education and NFL Combine Lead at EXOS® with a doctorate in coaching science, skill learning and speed development. Nick has published peer-reviewed publications through the NSCA, UKSCA and IDEA. Nick is most active on Twitter at twitter.com/NickWinkelman.

We met 10 years ago when you were doing the education for the Athletes' Performance mentorship and at the time, I considered you successful. Since then, you've accomplished so many incredible things. Let's talk about how you define success.

Obviously, I'm in the wrong field; I should have gone into acting because that's all that was working back then.

The success question is an important one and I've thought about it quite a bit. How we define success changes over time. Like many people, when I first started in the profession, I defined success by external things. The job, the accolades that came with the job, achieving degrees, training more athletes, bigger name athletes—those are all part of our early definitions of success. It's how you benchmark yourself; you benchmark yourself by what you do and what you achieve. And that's part of defining the success journey.

However, I now define success by the personal satisfaction I get from what I do. If I wake up every day excited to go to work and leave work fulfilled and excited to start again in the next day, I've created a world where I'm successful. It relates back to intrinsic pieces.

John Wooden said, "Success is peace of mind, which is a direct result of self-satisfaction in knowing you made the effort to become the best of which you are capable."

It's the intrinsic satisfaction that comes from what you do. And in that moment, you're being successful.

We looked up to you even in the early stages of your career, "He's head of education at Athletes' Performance." It's not easy to get that gig; you better know what you're doing. When did you start feeling you were becoming a success?

I still feel I have so much more to give and so much more to do. The idea of, "I've achieved it; I've reached it; I'm successful" doesn't permeate my thinking a whole lot.

I noticed at certain points when people found value in what I was doing. In those moments, you could say I was marking that as one notch on the success belt. It's the small things in life that build up to what we might call macro success. But micro success is just getting incrementally better every day, reflecting and doing things a bit differently, exploiting your strengths and building on your weaknesses.

I was quite attentive to what I was doing as a coach. Anytime I did something that had a successful response from a client or from an audience, I marked that as successful. I logged that as a behavior I wanted to repeat. I've simply tried to build on that, incrementally, every day of my career.

A lot of people probably do that and don't realize it. You might use a cue on another person and that doesn't work and you take a little hit, but then you use something else. You start to build that up and it creates confidence.

We understand with clients and athletes that many of their long-term goals are just that—long-term. You're not going to see the fruits of your labor for weeks, if not months. And intuitively, what that leads you to do as a coach is try to come up with authentic daily wins for your clients, where you highlight things they've incrementally and honestly improved.

You're not giving them false feedback. As coaches and personal trainers and physios—whatever your occupation—that's reflective practice, reviewing your sessions.

I call it the "Two plus Two" review. What are the two things I did in that session that I want to continue to do, and what are two areas where I can recalibrate and get better. From that, every day you get face-to-face with areas where you're successful and with where you can be successful in the future. That's process-oriented thinking. That's the micro success definition that inevitably leads to macro success.

I had a turning point during a lecture when you filled in for Mark Verstegen at a Perform Better Summit in Providence. You talked about figuring out what our "it" is. What gets us out of bed in the morning? What's our "it"?

That really changed my mindset in terms of "What do I really love?" I love it when I'm helping people—when people say, "I love the podcast" or "I love *Strength Coach TV.* I watched them all before I opened my facility."

I started to look at my past life in the bar business and asked myself, "What did I really like to do?" I liked to teach young managers when they were new hires and had to trail me. I loved helping them become better. That lecture changed the course of what I do. I'll turn it around on you now. What's your "it?" What gets you motivated to get out of bed in the morning?

It goes back to looking at core values in life. You need to understand your core values—what you define as important, your personal "why," what we're calling your "it."

Obviously, there's nature and nurture. So, nature aside—the nurture, what was it about my upbringing that shaped who I am as a person? What are my core values?

Now that I have two children, I'm thinking hard about how I want to shape their experience, especially in their formative years, knowing that will inevitably influence things like their personal "it" and their motivations.

When I look back at being a kid, the number one thing my parents hammered was honesty. For them, honesty as a core value superseded any other value. They felt that if we're honest, it forces us to reflect on all of our choices and helps to calibrate our other values in life. That was how they raised me; inevitably, honesty has manifested into this search for truth.

When I say truth, I mean that in the broadest sense: the view you have of the world, whether it be through personal interactions with others, evaluating science, evaluating a decision, evaluating a circumstance in front of you…or evaluating how you should do program design for that matter.

It drives me to seek truth. I want to make sure I have clarity and honesty and truth in my thoughts and in my understanding of the world around me. That's how I'd answer that question today.

For me, that's why evidence-based practice is as important as practice-based evidence. I love research for the simple fact that it helps me calibrate my personal biases. It helps me calibrate my personal views of the world to help me get closer to seeing truthfully what is around me versus something manufactured in my mind.

I wrote a presentation recently on the idea of cognitive biases and illusions. The motivation behind that is that I like to study where we can go wrong in our thinking because I want to be as clear in my thinking and as truthful in my understanding of the world as possible, not just in my job but in all aspects of life.

My search for truth centers around understanding how people learn, understanding how people get better, specifically how people get better within the realm of human performance. The core of what I do in strength and conditioning lies in the bed of an inner desire to understand the world around me better: My "it" is truth.

Those are important questions we all should ask ourselves. "Am I doing this right? Am I being honest with people? I promised these people I would help them get better. Am I doing whatever is in my power to do that?"

To get where you are, you have to spend a lot of time on education, whether it's doing research, preparing workshops, lecturing or traveling. You and your family moved to Ireland for your job. What are some of the sacrifices that you've made to be successful?

My wife could answer that question far better than I—and my saying that is part of my answer. What we're dealing with is a fixed resource called "time." We have to prioritize how we use that. In prioritizing my personal development, which allows me to help develop athletes and other people in our profession, I've sacrificed a lot of time with my family. We haven't gone on nearly as many holidays (as they say here in Europe) or vacations (as we would say stateside). However, it's never really felt like a sacrifice simply because my wife understands what I do has never been a "job."

Just as when we lived in Phoenix, I supported her in her endeavors to rescue animals through her animal lifeline rescue or work with kids with disabilities and late nights at the Horse Riding Center that was next door to EXOS, she supported me in my travel. Many weekends, early mornings or late nights required her to do more with the kids, especially when I was finishing up the PhD. But it all goes back to my wife, our family and me having a shared desire to do good things in the world and to help make others better.

As we get older, our values probably stay the same, but how we prioritize the deployment of those values changes. As our children get older, more time goes toward them, which requires me to be more finite and focused in how I use the time for my personal passion.

This isn't always easy. You won't say this, but I will: You can write your own ticket; anybody would take you at any job right now. You could decide what you wanted to do and where you wanted to do it. That's a fact, not an opinion.

In those times when you're traveling and your flight gets canceled and you can't see your kid's play, what helps you get through?

The key area for me is management of my attention. When life isn't going your way, it's very easy to get into a negative thought process.

To use your example of traveling, I try to be as present and open-minded as possible. If I'm waiting in an airport, it's easy to get locked into my own head and start thinking, "My flight's delayed. This is horrible. That person over there is talking on the phone too loud; that's annoying," and I've made a bad scenario worse.

This idea of mindfulness—simply being present in the moment, a Buddhist concept—teaches a nonjudgmental thought process; you don't see your circumstance as good or bad. So I'd think, "The vast majority of my flights are on time. There are no problems; this just happens to be one where that's not the circumstance." Taking that time to reflect allows you to see something for what it is rather than trying to put a label on it as positive or negative. The second you do that, it diffuses that emotional bomb, either positive or negative. In many cases, it's negative and we want to diffuse that quickly so we can be present in the moment.

That's one way I try to stay calm. The other is that every time I get on a flight, it isn't lost on me that if something were to happen, the likelihood of survival is quite low. You can have a minor existential crisis every time you get on a plane. This is a bit of a litmus test of my life: Can I get on that plane and say as of this date, "I've been as good of a father, as good of a husband, as good of a son, as good as a professional as I could have been. Did I do everything I could to this point? Have I put as much good into this world as possible at this point in my life?"

On most flights, I can answer that with a yes. And I know if something were to happen to me, I've maximized what I could do. I try to live my life to the fullest. I know it's not perfect, but when I get on those flights, I want to always answer that internal reflection with, "Yes, I've done everything I can," and know that people would say good things at the funeral.

Hopefully, my wife would be able to look back and say, "My husband did everything he possibly could." It sounds a little bit morbid, but for me, it's not. It's simply a way to reflect: Am I doing the things I want to be doing in life? Having that sense of reflection and a general sense of being present and as nonjudgmental as we can helps us deal moment to moment with the ups and downs and struggles of life.

This is more about an awareness than it's about being morbid—certainly a similar concept to mindfulness.

I want to get into habits when you wake up. What's your morning routine?

The book *Deep Work* by Cal Newport was transformational for me in many ways. It was influential as much in my thinking about time management as it was in the behaviors it helped me to change or develop.

I normally like to start the day with a key priority. Now that I'm working on a book, a lot of that time is spent outlining, writing and researching, trying to leverage any ideas I woke up with that were embedded from the mental struggle I went to bed with, thinking about them the night before. I try to get all that fresh information recorded.

There's something fulfilling about being making the kids and my wife breakfast. My son likes to use the Nespresso machine to make coffee with me and he goes through every intricacy. Watching him learn gives me great joy every morning.

I have personal time; I have family time and then I head off to work. That's how I use my time in the morning. I run to work; my wife takes the car. I get a physical outlet as I run to work every day. That's when I listen to audiobooks and podcasts. I've listened to over a dozen books this year while running to and from work. I'm getting a physical and an intellectual primer before my workday begins.

Then the final piece, before I even touch my computer, I like to read a couple passages from Ryan Holiday's *The Daily Stoic*. I've found that to be a very important book in centering my mindset, getting back to that nonjudgmental state where things are neither good, nor bad; they just are. Seeing things for what they are allows me to move on with the day more productively.

Nick, what about goals? I know you have goals, but is there a formal process?

This year I wrote out goals and tried to break them into the least number of big things I wanted to do, which for me would be representative of a year well spent. At the top of the list was starting my book and producing a number of research articles. I haven't written as many research articles as I would've liked, but the book is started and multiple publications were submitted. I was somewhat successful in the goals.

In terms of my process for setting goals, I couldn't say I have an exact scientific process by which I approach it. It goes back to that what defines your personal success, which, for me are things that are in intrinsically fulfilling. Right now, everything is around how I can help people understand learning—learning how to move, but in a broader sense, I want to help people understand the mechanisms that sit behind learning and how they can get better at that. All of my goals are calibrated to that specific arena.

I'm a big believer in a single goal—just like when I teach people how to coach, I talk about one rep, one focus; I talk about one moment, one goal. What's my goal right now? I'd rather put everything into achieving that goal than distributing my attention over multiple things and inevitably not being able to give full effort to any of them, increasing the odds that I don't achieve all of them, let alone one of them. That's my ramble and you can tell I'm thinking out loud. It's still an area of reflection for me.

That speaks to the popularity of books like *Deep Work* and *The One Thing*. The pendulum swung so far in this distracted world that we have to reel in things. The most successful people are more focused.

The pendulum has swung and now people are back to focusing on time management and goal setting. That's an interesting concept on how humans are subject to influence by all the various trends.

Don't get me wrong; the trends you mentioned are important and are moving humanity in a good direction. They're helping filter through all the clutter, all the informational noise we have to deal with day in and day out. Are we simply reactive to the world around us? The answer is absolutely yes. We're conditioned to respond to the world around us.

One thing that drives me is discovering my path. Where do I want this car to go? I want to take ownership of that and sometimes look in areas where people aren't looking—looking away from where the trends are, not just because it's in opposition to a trend, but because it's interesting.

We should want to not be distracted by where the masses or where our tribe is going, but try to own ourselves, our vision, our truth and our values. Let those core values and the things that are personally important guide the development in our process, not just the influence from the people around us…or what gets the most social media interaction.

If what I recommend deviates from the path people are on and the current path is personally important to them, I want them to bench my recommendations until the time that my recommendations are a part of their path. I'd be disappointed if I somehow derailed someone's current attention on what was important to something that has nothing to do with where that car was going.

I like your idea of "I'm recommending this, but if it takes you off your path, make sure it's in line with everything else you're doing."

Joe Gomes, who's the head strength coach for the Los Angeles Raiders, was a friend and mentor and colleague of mine during my early days at Athletes' Performance. He always focused on the development of others.

One day he asked, "What are you reading right now? What are you focusing on?"

I said, "I'm reading Mel Siff's *Super Training,* Tudor Bompa's *Periodization* and *Anatomy Trains* by Thomas Myers. I recently finished Gray Cook's book, *Movement.*"

He asked, "Why?"

I was stunned. I said, "I'm trying to get better."

"But why are you reading those books?"

I couldn't really give him an answer outside of, "I want to get better."

And he asked, "What is your current focus right now?"

I reflected on it and said, "Understanding periodization."

He said, "Why are you reading *Anatomy Trains;* why are you reading Gray Cook? If you're saying periodization is important to you, put all your focus on that. Learn as much as you can about that. Try to give yourself some outlet to apply that information, whether it's a presentation, an article or programming for someone, and really ensure you put a bow on it. Then you'll know that information—you will have integrated it into your practice before you go on to the next concept."

You could apply that to goal setting as well as to your own development. That stuck with me and helped me prioritize my focus.

There's a wonderful book on this called *Rapt,* by Winifred Gallagher. She reminds us that our lives are shaped by what focus on; anything we focus on shapes who we are and how we think. If you feel distracted, it's likely because your attention is distributed across too many things.

The second you get rid of that clutter and focus your attention on one thing, you're going to feel clarity. You're going to feel your heart rate drop and you're going to feel success because you're able to focus and execute against something long enough to see a reward, to see an outcome.

What are you doing to stay organized with all you have going on?

I'm crediting Craig Friedman, who years ago asked, "Is your calendar up to date?" Those words changed my life. I define work hours and non-work hours, using the blocks to shape my day. Every day before I leave the office, I allocate what I'll do the next day against my priority list so when I walk in, I don't have to think. I go to my first task, which is allocated for a certain period of time and boom, I adapt. I reprioritize as the day goes on, and it's a fluid process.

It seems a bit over-controlling, but it's freeing because you always know there's a place for your attention. With that, you're less likely to be distracted. If you're less likely to be distracted, you're less likely to go down a path that ends up being shallow, meaningless work.

Talk to me about recharging. How do you recharge?

I grind until two weeks before the end of the year and then I just sit silently in a chair for 14 days. Not really, but there's a bit of truth in that.

We're trying to get better at scheduling our vacations. We try to get a couple times every year where we can push for three or four months, but know we have a 10-day stint on the back end to recharge; that really helps break up the year. That's a macro strategy.

Music is a big part of my life. I enjoy deejaying and producing mixes. There are few things in life that are as relaxing or flow-inducing as when I'm working on music—looking for music, putting music together, actively deejaying in the den where I have my mixers set up. I don't do it enough and in all honesty, how to manage my personal time to get back to doing that more will probably be one of my bigger goals next year.

The top daily recharge is the amount of joy I get for the 10 minutes in the morning with my son and daughter when we're making coffee with the Nespresso machine. If I rush the process too much or I don't allow my son to put in the granulated sugar, it disrupts the flow. I just love that in watching my kids.

The biggest joys I've had in my life was this year when my daughter started karate, stuck with it, got her yellow belt, and then achieved her orange belt. In doing this, the two days before she fought in a competition, she got silver in her technique, silver in her one-on-one fights and silver in her team fight. She had to do 10 techniques in 91 minutes when she had to do all the moves karate kid style for the 32 kids. Then she had to fight all 32 kids. It's in good fun—they're fully padded; they have to show they can endure what they're sparring. She now has an orange belt.

I take her twice a week. I'm watching her the entire time—I'm not on the phone, catching up on email or working. Because of her hard work, the instructor's son gave her one of his medals. She's only six. I tell you right now, that got me recharged. There are few things in life as satisfying as watching your kids, on their own accord, work hard, persevere and achieve something.

Let's finish up with three books, non-fitness, that can help people with their development and with staying on track with what they think is important.

Because it's a current focus for me, the first is a book called *Thinking, Fast and Slow*. As the title suggests, it is simply a book about thinking, written by one of the most important thinkers in the last century, the psychologist Daniel Kahneman. This book fundamentally explains how decisions are made. When you wake up in the morning and want to eat cereal versus scrambling eggs, you decided to go left when you also could have gone right.

It's about trying to understand yourself, to give yourself a mirror to understand how your mind works and understanding how your clients' minds work…or your siblings' or your spouse's. *Thinking, Fast and Slow* is a phenomenal book everyone should read.

Along with that, there's a very nice book along a similar line called *Nudge* by Cass Sunstein and Richard Dollar, who live in the behavioral economics decision space. You want to help yourself or your clients make better decisions, but it can be equally applied to the decisions you build around your schedule. The book teaches how to nudge behavior in a way that's almost automatic and unthreatening. The idea of choice architecture was born out of that book.

And a book that's just jaw-dropping is by Lisa Feldman Barrett called *How Emotions are Made*. In understanding where emotions come from, why do we call things scary? Why do we say we're fearful…we're sad, we're happy, rejoice? Where do those emotions come from? Where do the labels come from? In understanding how emotions are made, you truly get an inside look on how you can change your emotional state for the better.

It also relates to *Nudge* and *Thinking, Fast and Slow* because so many behaviors and decisions are based on emotional impulse. This book gives you the battery pack to understand how emotions can hijack behavior and what you can do about it.

They're not the easiest of reads, but they're worth it.

What about some people, Nick? Who should we be following?

There are so many people doing great work. A couple relate to my selfish area of interest who need a shout-out. One is a guy named Rob Gray, a professor of psychology and skill acquisition at Arizona State University. He has a podcast called *The Perception Action Podcast* in which he brilliantly unpacks how people learn skills—any skill, how to golf or how to sprint faster.

He does it in such a thoughtful way where he, unbiased, takes information, presents both sides and provides recommendations, all while qualifying his opinion. I appreciate the way he treats information, and it just so happens it's in my area of interest. Rob Gray is fantastic for anyone who wants to know more about how to be a better teacher and how people learn movement and movement skills.

I have to give a shout-out to Stu McMillan, Andreas Bam, Dan Pfaff and all the great coaches at Altis. The amount of work they're doing to make our field better is astounding. When you go to one of their courses, you get to watch the people coach all day and have roundtables and open, honest and robust conversations around how to develop athletes. Altis, as a group, is absolutely phenomenal.

The final person, the biggest influencer in my life outside of my family, is a guy named Sam Harris. Sam has an amazing podcast. His line when people ask him what he does for a living is, "I think in public." This guy is tackling some of the most important and toughest topics in modern life from artificial intelligence to philosophy to politics. There's no subject matter that doesn't draw his attention.

Sam brings people on his podcast—some he agrees with, some he doesn't. He literally is a modern-day Socrates; he uses a Socratic method from the standpoint of his ability to debate, have open, honest communication and be subject to influence, to have his mind changed, but also seeks to change others' minds.

And the way he approaches claritive communication, the truth in his thought and his idea that thinking can always improve and truth is the number one asset we can have. Everything I've talked about here reinforces why I find him a breath of fresh air. Thinking in public is what he does. And I hope he continues doing it.

There are so many big things coming with your book and all you're doing. It's been a pleasure to follow your career and to be on that journey with you. Nick, thanks for sharing your journey.

BE LIKE NICK

"Is your calendar up to date?" ~ *Craig Friedman*

SCHEDULE YOUR DAY

Influenced by Craig and the work in Cal Newport's *Deep Work*, Nick has changed the way he uses his calendar and scheduling. He makes sure to block out times during the day, not only for work, but for downtime activities as well.

Start by blocking out times of the day that will get your most important work done without constant distractions.

For example, I block out 5:30–7:00AM for undistracted work.

Then from 7:00–8:00, it's coffee, breakfast, answering email and social media posts.

8:00–9:30 is blocked for more undistracted work.

9:30–10:00 is a break, usually a walk around the neighborhood for 20 minutes.

10:00–11:00 is for catching up on to-do list tasks.

11:00–12:30 is a nap, a walk or bike ride and lunch.

Start blocking out time in your schedule for things like workouts, walks, naps, leisure activities and breaks.

"What gets scheduled, gets done." ~ *Michael Hyatt*

Alwyn is co-owner of Results Fitness in Santa Clarita, California, named one of the top 10 gyms in America by Men's Health and Women's Health magazines. Alwyn is also the owner of the fitness professional consulting company, Results Fitness University. A nationally known speaker, he's co-authored nine bestselling fitness books, is a member of the Nike Performance Council and for the past 12 years has been a presenter on the Perform Better tour. Find out more at resultsfitnessuniversity.com.

You had success in martial arts before you entered the fitness arena, where you've since excelled as a personal trainer, a business owner and consultant. How do you define success and how does that affect what success means to different people?

I recently visited my taekwondo school back in Scotland; I had a good run—I won more than I lost. Sparring or competing in a combat sport is like problem-solving in real time with devastating consequences if you don't solve the problem correctly. It becomes almost meditative because you can't worry about your bills or your college finals or your girlfriend when somebody is trying to take your head clean off. It's almost relaxing when you're doing it.

It's the same with a lot of things like fitness and training or success in sports in general: What you have to do is very simple. But don't confuse simple and easy. In fitness, you put in the work, you get the results, but that work is hard. It's not complicated, though. That taught me a lot of life lessons as we moved forward in different areas.

The most important thing about success is that it has to start inside. You can't use another person's scorecard for yourself.

I can tell you the story of a man who was presenting about 18 times a year, including doing Perform Better seminars. He had two rental properties and he wasn't doing any training at all in his own gym. A year later, he has no rental properties; he's doing two talks for Perform Better, and he's training a few hours a week at his own gym. That sounds like a backward move until I tell you the man is me and the changes were by choice.

I'm enjoying training my staff for a couple of obstacle course races and strongman competitions. I have a ball working with them—it feels like how things were back in the old days. I love the Perform Better events, but I got fed up with traveling. I took a break and cut back my schedule, which sounds like a move away from success if you're using a different scorecard, but for me it was a massive move toward it.

You have to figure out what success means for you; you can't compare it with others. One of my staff members was from Japan and she taught me the phrase "ikigai." It means your life's purpose, your reason for being—similar to the French phrase "raison d'etre." The trick is to know what you're supposed to do, what it is you do better than anyone else.

There are four criteria. There's something you love and something you're good at. When you combine those, that's your passion. When you combine something you love with something the world needs, that's your mission; that's what you're supposed to be doing.

It has to tie in with something you can be compensated for. When you find something you love doing so much that you'd do it for free, something you're good at even though you have to study and work harder, it's fun for you.

Getting better at it is the fun part. That's the stuff that gets you up in the morning, that propels you to the top of your game. If people need your skills, if they're looking for your help because you're the best at it and they'll pay you for it—when those four things intersect, it's why you're on the planet. That's your reason for being here.

That's success, when you find out what you're here for, you know you're good at it and you know you love it. You're so good at it that it comes easily to you. You love it so much, you'd do it for free and people want to give you money for it and the world needs it.

If you don't love the work, you might be rich but miserable, and that's not successful in anybody's book. You could be great at cleaning sewers—and we need people to do that and you can be well paid for it—but if you hate every workday, it's not successful.

Similarly, if you love it and you're not good at it, it's just a hobby because you can't get paid for something you're not good at it. It comes down to ikigai. When you get close to that reason for being, you're successful no matter what your bank account looks like because this is where you're supposed to be. You're doing all you can and the best you can.

Let's go deeper into that. What is your reason for being? What gets you out of bed in the morning?

In terms of training, I love being a fitness problem-solver. I've been excited by some of the obstacle course races because there's no standard protocol for them. We know how to get people strong for powerlifting. We've figured out VO_2 max for endurance training and the folks at Titleist Performance Institute have golf figured out. There's a model. Gray Cook and Lee Burton figured out movement and how to establish a baseline with the FMS. That kind of thing excites me; I like to find solutions. When someone has a sporting event with challenges, it creates something exciting to figure it out.

For example, powerlifting is predictable. If I get you strong, there's not much you'll have to react to. But when training an athlete for a team sport, there are intangibles to prepare for. It's problem-solving in real time, making adjustments, and that really excites me.

In the last few years, I've met some amazing fitness professionals who are absolutely world class at what they do. And they're broke. In terms of knowledge success, they're off the charts, but in terms of financial success and living their reason for being, they're not even close. It makes me uncomfortable to the point where I need to help. That part is easy for me to figure out—how to create a financial vehicle or some type of business or career for what they're supposed to be doing.

I get excited with a challenge. I wanted to be a good writer, then I got a *Men's Health* contract and book deals…and then I seemed to get bored. Then I became a good speaker and went on the Perform Better tour. And wondered, what's next? It's problem-solving. It's problem-solving and new challenges.

I like odd challenges, like training for a new sport I don't know much about, something that requires me to really investigate and go deep. It's the same with the fitness business. We had our coaching group in town for a couple of days. I'd wake up and as I made coffee, I'd be singing "I'm on top of the world, hey!" I'd do problem-solving every day if I could.

Is there a moment you can point to when you thought, "This is going well. We're pretty successful"?

We did a program-design seminar that I wasn't teaching. It was at a local hotel and I went to introduce our staff member, Craig Rasmussen, who was running it. He didn't like me watching him and threw me out of the room. We left while the seminar was in progress and went back to the gym, which was running smoothly. I figured I'd jump behind the desk and see if I could help book appointments or make shakes.

Our manager asked if I would get out of the way because I was slowing them down. I remember thinking, "I'm completely obsolete. This is a well-oiled machine. We've got great training in progress; the top guys are teaching a seminar on program design, and I come back and the front desk team is serving our clients at a level beyond what I can do."

I was actively hurting them by trying to help because they've got things down. It's a weird feeling. I remember thinking, "Wow, we built this." None of this existed until we showed up, until I said I was going to train people by myself in this little strip mall location. Rachel was going support us by working a paid job while I did my thing.

Rachel and I did a race with some of the obstacle course team the day after we'd finished our Mastermind. There was a sales seminar going on that our manager, Elias Scarr, was running. We had 30 people attending the seminar and we were coming back from the obstacle course race to run a workout with other people. The next day, we were doing the Certified Functional Strength Coach Level Two at the gym. I thought, "I'm going to the desert to do a race and everything is just trucking along. I'm not even worried."

Those were a couple of moments of feeling that things were right. My goal was to give other people a platform and have this thing be bigger than myself, and I had the realization I could go away and everything would just tick along.

It was a good feeling. I guess a weird feeling too, because these people are there because of me—their lives are in a different place because of me. It was one of those moments when you think, "Holy shit, I did it."

Some people might see feeling obsolete as a bad thing, but for you it was good.

You're right…some people wouldn't like that. The goal was not for me to go get coffee or go hang out, but this frees me up to take on new things. With the level we'd reached, I'd become obsolete. If the goal was for me to be invaluable so they could never work the gym without me, that's somebody else's success score. For that person, it would be a failure that I'm not needed.

But my goal was always to elevate people and do something bigger than I could do on my own. My job wasn't over, but everything was running well.

It's fine if you never want to be unnecessary at your own gym—you never want it to grow beyond you. If your goal is to be the highest paid one-on-one trainer in the country, that's absolutely fine. Don't ever move away from your own goals.

My definition of success was always to do something bigger than I could do on my own.

What are some habits that helped contribute to your success?

There are two things that almost sound opposite. I've always had an intellectual restlessness, where there's somebody else who knows more than I do whom I need to learn from.

There's always another seminar. There's always another book to read, another person to meet. It can be a weakness at some level, but I'm obsessed.

Craig Rasmussen tells me there's a primary question that drives everyone and mine seems to be the thought that there has to be a better way. I'm constantly refining things. But on the flip side, over the last few years in my career growth, I've developed the ability to trust others and focus a laser beam on the few things I do well and allow my team to do the things they do well.

With this idea that there has to be a better way, I have to continue to grow and refine and tweak and refine again. But also, this laser beaming keeps me from doing something that's not a great use of my time.

It's double-sided, this idea that there has to be a better way—that you have to get to a new level and figure out the next step. But there's also the idea of staying in your own lane. Don't become a jack of all trades and a master of none. Become a master of a few and an ignoramus at many.

I know a few things miles deep and have an inch of knowledge in others. I can have a conversation on most topics, but there are a few things I can talk about with the best in the world.

I know you set goals, but are they formal? Do you write them down and review them?

I write goals and then I like to break them down. If there's a big outcome I want to have—for example, if I want to have 50 new gym members in a year, that's about one a week. What does that look like? What's my actual action step this morning? It starts with a to-do checklist. Did I do that stuff on the list?

An outcome goal is important, but I've had more luck with process goals: Here's what I have to do today to move this forward. If you want to do 100 interviews for your podcast this year, that's two a week, so we'd better start scheduling a couple.

I'm outcome-driven and that's why some fitness stuff bores me. A training program is not just workouts—not to critique any system like that, but for me, it has to have a direction and an outcome. We have to know when we're finished that we achieved something. I want to solve a problem.

With everything I do, from financial to personal, I consider what success looks like. When do I know I've made it and I can check off this box…and what are the steps necessary to do that? What do the next 90 days look like, and of those 90 days, what do the next 30 days look like? What do the next 24 hours look like?

Tony Robbins tells us not to leave the site of a goal without making one step toward it. If you decide you want to write a book, let's spend five minutes sketching out the introduction so we're one percent closer to having it done. Take a forward step right away. Getting the ball rolling is hard, but once we get that ball rolling, we're solid.

There's science that says it's more beneficial to not just put goals in a Word document, but to physically write with a pen.

There's something in the stroke of a pen or pencil that triggers something a key stroke can't. Not to get metaphysical, but there's something about putting it on paper that makes it become real. Even if no one sees it, it's something that makes it serious.

And often things get a little scarier with a pen stroke. Now it's not just something you'd like to do; now it's an actionable step.

What's your morning routine?

Everything is about executing the steps. I'd love to say every morning is perfect, but what has to get done tomorrow morning starts the night before. I sketch this out the night before. I have a goal for each day: It's one thing. If I can get two or three things done, that's amazing. I try to get that single item done as early as I can in the morning. And once the idea is out of my head and onto paper, I can sleep better. Otherwise, I think about that thing all night long. I identify the one big thing that gets me closer to my goals. My morning routine starts before I go to bed.

Let's go into the dark side of being successful. Are there some sacrifices you've made to get where you are?

Some of that drive can be a negative. You can't switch it off. I heard Darren Hardy say, "All I ever want is to just stop wanting." There's constantly something else, another idea, another opportunity…and that can be a problem.

The whole work–life balance idea is bullshit. You're in balance over the course of your life, but not at any one time. You've got your career goals, and maybe you've got a hobby or fitness or athletic goals. You've got your relationships.

If you're training for an Ironman triathlon, you're probably not killing it in your career and it's not a great time to start dating someone new. All those years in college when you weren't at the top of your sport and you weren't focusing on your career, you were doing a lot of relationship activities. You had a lot of good times, hanging out and going on trips. Over the course of time, it all balances out. But at any time, there's always something you're sacrificing.

After I got diagnosed with cancer, I didn't speculate as to why I got it. Some people get it and some people don't make it, but you always wonder if your body's just out of balance. You spent too long in one area and neglected your health or your downtime. We're constantly making sacrifices, but I'll take the tradeoff.

You're always juggling a little. Your career and your fitness, or your career and your relationships—they're rubber balls. You can drop them and they may bounce back. But your health, when you drop it, it smashes. It's made of crystal and that's a hard one to drop.

You're constantly sacrificing. You're always struggling with balance and not everything will be perfect all the time. Sometimes your career will be on a downswing, but maybe at that time, you're training hard and your relationships are great. Imagine juggling three things. Not everything is at a high point all the time.

Was there a time when you felt like you wanted to give up, whether that was early on with personal training or during the cancer?

There's always a time. If you're running an obstacle course race, there's a point where it just hurts and your brain is strumming, "You can quit, you can quit." I was in a kickboxing match once and it was so hard, and I remember thinking if I just poked my chin up for a second, he'll hit it and it'll be all over and I could pretend I didn't see it coming.

But with the cancer battle, I never did…never. I owed it to my wife to fight. I've given up on things because I changed direction. I've stopped pursuing things that I didn't think were right for me, or maybe I wasn't prepared to do the work or because I realized it wasn't as important to me as I thought it was. Failure is when you could've done better and chose not to. That's something I couldn't do with cancer.

It's cliché now, but getting back to the "why" is important to be able to get through the worst of times.

What are three non-fitness books you think everybody should be reading?

This is hard to narrow down. *The E-Myth* by Michael Gerber was the first book to help me understand that business has very little to do with being good at something. It doesn't matter how good of a trainer you are; that doesn't mean you can run a training business. That was a real "wow" lesson for me, that there are different roles and you need a different skill set for each. Just because you know something well doesn't mean you should own a related business.

How to Win Friends and Influence People by Dale Carnegie is an excellent book about communication.

Start with Why by Simon Sinek is really good. It gets back to that idea of ikigai—that life purpose, why you're doing what you're doing.

You're getting four choices because I'm in love with Michael Hyatt. I'm in love with *Living Forward*. There's another book called *The Surrender Experiment* by Michael Singer that's powerful. Okay, that's five.

Another book everybody should get is *Think and Grow Rich* by Napoleon Hill. He was commissioned by Andrew Carnegie; he was a Scottish guy who moved to the U.S. I'm fascinated by people who weren't born into money. So…six.

Yes, *Living Forward* is another great book to help figure out the impact you want to make. Who are three people we should follow to learn from?

Richard Branson is a fantastic person to review, but you'll have to go back to some of his earlier stuff because it's harder for us to relate to him now. I've been fortunate to go to his private island—the deck outside his bedroom overlooks his other private island. It's hard for us to relate to that. But when you go back to how he started off running a student newspaper, that's someone to study.

Muhammad Ali was a fantastic person. He's remembered and highly regarded now that he's passed away, but he went through some real trials and was banned from boxing and was shunned. He came back as a United States Olympic champion, but he couldn't get a glass of water in a local restaurant in his hometown. It's depressing when you think about that racism, that ignorance, but he never stopped and he was on top of his game going through that.

The third person is a guy in the U.K. who's on a show called *Dragon's Den,* which is like *Shark Tank*—Duncan Bannatyne. He started selling ice cream out of a van and now runs a chain of health clubs. He's another guy I studied quite a lot. He's written a bunch of books on business, and now he has hospitals and hotels. There's something about a rags-to-riches story that makes me feel like I could do the same.

Muhammad Ali was talented. Richard Branson is talented and Duncan Bannatyne is talented. At some point, hard work starts to look a lot like talent, but it's actually hard work. I like stories of people who started from a lower level of income or who had to struggle because that shows I could do it too. There's something I can learn from them.

Alwyn, thanks so much for not only being one of my mentors on my journey, but for being an inspiration and guide to thousands of other fitness professionals. You have lived up to your core value of "changing the way fitness is done." Thanks for sharing your incredible journey to success.

BE LIKE ALWYN

"That's my morning routine; here's what has to get done tomorrow. I'd love to say every morning is perfect, but what has to get done tomorrow morning starts the night before."

THE EVENING OR WORK SHUTDOWN

Take 15 minutes at the end of either your work day or the evening to physically write what needs to be done tomorrow.

Start by looking over the schedule and see what appointments you have.

Schedule the whole day (also see Nick Winkelman's Be Like).

Make a to-do list of what needs to get done and prioritize them.

Don't be overwhelmed with 10 things; focus on the top three that will get you closer to your goals.

Once you prioritize them, you have an action plan in your head about what needs to get done first, the most important things you need to do.

Answer any email and return calls that need attention.

Leave with the peace of mind knowing you have a plan of action for tomorrow.

Do this every night and you will be more present at home and you will sleep much better.

Janet Alexander is a 35-year veteran of the health and fitness field and is co-owner of Pacific Fitness and Health, Inc. a private studio in Encinitas, California. Janet's disciplined and scientifically based approach to strength and conditioning has helped mold her into a knowledgeable fitness professional who has worked with a wide range of athletes in a variety of sports. Pacific Fitness and Health and Janet's progressive and pioneering program design has not only culminated in wins on the professional golf tours, but also has resulted in good hormonal health for her female athletes. Find out more at pacificfitnesshealth.com.

You have had success as a trainer, are a leader in our field and an educator. How do you define success?

Success depends on perspective and what type of success you're referring to: success in business, success as a friend or personal, spiritual or physical success. It's a huge realm.

Success is doing something you love that doesn't feel like work while still getting paid for it. For me, it's having a huge network and liking everyone in it and being surrounded by like-minded people who feel like family instead of just numbers. It's being able to share time, putting things forward and giving back.

You travel a lot for work, but you do find time for fun, whether it's on a bike or on a mountain? Do you make sure you have good work–life mastery?

I was born in New Zealand into a very big family—I had many role models. My mother was one of 14; she has eight sisters and five brothers. If my mom wasn't around, there was someone else who was a fellow mother. There was discipline; there were methods—in such a big family, there was a plan.

We just didn't go off and do stuff—they made a plan for the day and got it done. Tick the box and go on, and part of that was that we always had activities. When the sun came up, we were outside; when the sun went down, we came back inside. That would now be seen as bad parenting, but when we were kids, that's what we did.

It then became natural to look for a conference in areas I wanted to explore. I'll look for a conference in Prague because there's a mountain bike race there. If there's a conference in some area where I've always wanted to run, I'll go to that conference. It's not the other way around.

Maybe that's not the best way to do it, but that's how I plan.

What is it from a business perspective that drives you every day? What gets you out of bed in the morning?

It's just being alive and knowing I can change someone's world. It may not be a huge step, but giving a person the first step to change things, to making the world better, makes it easy for me to get up in the morning.

I have a special-needs sister; just knowing there are things she has to work for that I take for granted is my biggest motivator. She's older than me and has Down Syndrome. I'm always aware that my sister doesn't have the same opportunities.

Sometimes when I'm thinking, "Poor me, I've got a busy day," I remind myself, "Don't be such an idiot. You're blessed. Just get on with it."

One of the challenges with this project was to find the through-lines—what are some of the things successful people have in common. For me, one of the through-lines is people like you who are successful, who understand the importance of what we're doing and who understand how much we can change one person's world. Was that something you had to grow into or did you recognize that early in your career?

Getting into this profession started because I wanted to work outside—I didn't want to be at a desk. I went for a sports science degree and suddenly, the fitness profession came along with personal training and I got thrown into it. I didn't choose it. It was there and I had the sports science background so I decided I might as well do it.

I didn't go into it thinking in 20 years' time I'd be in a position to change people's lives. When I look back, I took all the correct steps without knowing this was going to become a "thing," that I would be working in the States where everyone works too hard, does too much and doesn't look after themselves.

I meet people where they are, and that might be my biggest success. I'm not going to push people over the edge if they don't want to go there. I've been successful at meeting people where they are and then cajoling them to take the next step. It takes 31 days to break a habit—just to start and you have to change things. If you don't meet people at least half-way, they're not going to change because change is scary.

I didn't think back then that I'd be doing what I'm doing now, but it's pretty cool.

There's story about JFK at the NASA Space Center in 1962. He went up to a janitor and said, "I'm Jack Kennedy. What do you do here?" The janitor said, "I'm helping put a man on the moon." That shows a powerful mindset and understanding of the importance of our roles.

My advice to a young trainer is to be ready to have some people not listen to you because you're not the right messenger at that point in their lives. The more people hear our message, the more they realize it's not just a fitness thing, that maybe they have to take control of their health.

With some people, you're going to be just a messenger—you're not going to be the person who enables them to make changes. You're the person instigating the little tweaks at the beginning. Others have already learned the tweaks from someone else and now you'll get to be the person who opens up their world. You have to be ready to be on that spectrum.

Janet, let's talk about the struggles you've had. You were in this business early on and you're a woman. This is always a weird thing to say; I don't look at you and think "woman." I think "educator" when I see you on stage or "trainer" when working with someone or "athlete" during your adventures. Where people have played into the "pink side versus blue side" game, you're just talking about training or picking up heavy weights.

This is such a young profession and you've been there for a good part of its growth. What challenges have you had coming up in the field?

I'm stubborn. I'm tenacious and don't like taking no for an answer. If you tell me I can't do something, I'll get it done. If you tell me I shouldn't be somewhere, I'm going to make sure I get there.

Being a woman was never really a problem because I figured out early that if I was going to be taken seriously, I didn't have to curb my personality, but I had to be neutral. I had to be prepared to lift heavy weights to be taken seriously. I wasn't going to be a "dolly trainer." I wasn't going to be wearing short shorts and tight tops. No disrespect meant to anyone who does, but that's not what I needed to do to be taken seriously.

I didn't want to be seen as just a physical female up on stage. In this world, in your five minutes of fame, too many people will take one look at you and quickly decide if they're going to listen. If you're trying to put across a message, it doesn't matter what you're saying—if you're not dressed appropriately for the moment, they're not going to listen to you. I figured that out early because I came into the fitness profession when it was starting. We made the rules.

When personal training first started in the mid-'90s, I was on that first wave. I'm lucky; we set the rules as women. Add onto that my personality and it was easier because if someone said something derogatory to me, I always had an answer.

I made sure I knew my stuff. I did all the research. If someone threw a question at me, I knew the answer or would own up and say, "I don't know, but I know three people who can tell me. Let me make a call."

That's a big thing about being successful—surrounding yourself with like-minded people you can call on. People know that if I don't know, I know someone who does. Part of having a successful business is having a huge network.

Janet, with all the traveling you do and your taking on the role of a leader, what sacrifices have you made to be successful?

To be honest, it's been my health. Many of my colleagues travel a lot. Our health takes a hit if we don't look after it. That's one of the biggest things. That's why we get so good at research because we notice the drop-off. I know what my normal is; I know where I should be. I know how I should bounce out of bed and if I don't, I have to take time off.

Your health gets in the way because when you're traveling, you don't have your routines. You don't have your normal foods. You don't have your standard of downtime because you're racing around. The other thing about traveling is that you're not with friends and family enough. You have to plan catch-up time and put it on your schedule. My husband's very good at making me do things like that.

Clients will ask, "Why won't you call me after 7:00PM?" It's because I'll get divorced—that's the witching hour. Once I'm home, that's it unless you're dying. And if you *are* dying, don't call me, call 911.

We have a problem with that concept in this profession, partly because we always want to help people and also because there isn't a shut-off point for health. There's no time when it's off.

I've gone out in the middle of the night because a client called and said, "I'm stuck on the floor. I went for a bike ride and I blew out my back. I'm stuck on the floor. What do I do?" I got in the car and drove to her. She ended up having surgery. That's different from someone calling with a headache. I'm not going to do that; it's different.

In our profession, we're not very good at saying no. We need to learn to say no more often—and not a "No, but." We have to draw a line and say, "I'm sorry. I can't do that. It's not good for me; it's not good for my health." If we're not at our prime, we can't be good for others.

When you're saying yes to your client, you're saying no to your husband. This came up often in this book. The quote is always, "For every yes, there's a no."

You're saying no to health or no to training—no to a letter you should have written or no to a birthday party. You're saying no to something. You get to the point where you feel like your life is not yours. Eventually, you'll realize, "I'm running around like an idiot and this is crazy. If I don't stop and put some 'me time' in there, I'm not going to be of use to anybody—friends, family or clients alike."

I was lucky because before I came back to personal training, I was working in a corporation. I learned the hard way what happens when you work 100-hour weeks and end up with health issues, being a skinny-fat person and not being your authentic, healthy self.

Janet, you mentioned a couple, but are there other habits that contributed to being successful in the fitness business?

Just coming from a small town with the desire to get out is what drove me. I wanted to see the world and wanted to leave the small town and the way to do it was through education. In my family, I was the first in my generation to go to university, but I had to work for it because I came from a poor family. I had to get a scholarship, which meant I had to work hard. I quickly figured out what I needed to do to get through university.

You learn pretty quickly to be tenacious and organized. In the fitness profession, it's easy to stand out because many fitness people aren't organized. It's also been good for me that my husband is military and is organized in math and physics. The two of us blend well and make a great team.

It's important to have cohesion, even with some of the fitness goals. You can't start trying to lose weight if your spouse isn't on the same food plan; it's not going to work.

Chris Maund, my husband, is a trainer who has a sports science degree. We work and run the business together, and we've still managed to be married for 24 years. The good thing is, his clientele is completely different from mine; it works really well.

Talk to us about goals. Do you have a formal process?

I have realistic goals for three months, six months, one year, five years and 10 years. The three-month goals are achievable and are keeping me on task.

I have the "musts," which are goals I have to get done. If I have five goals, I'll always get through the first three and then four and five aren't serious goals. They're there if I have time, but mostly what I'm doing is keeping myself on track to get to my number one goal or my five-year goal.

Talk to us about how you recharge.

I make sure to have a down week every 12 weeks. I have a "staycation" or a long weekend where I take off Friday, Saturday and Sunday. I'll ride a mountain bike for three days in a row with no work. I swim or bike or do something just for me…and there are no clients. That's quite helpful to bring me back to where I need to be.

I also make sure that my lunch is my time. Lunch is lunch. I don't run errands or do chores. I'll also take a half day off. I have to make sure it's not a half day off on a Friday afternoon because most of my friends are also off on Friday afternoons.

You have to plan those blocks in advance. We tend to want to put a client in that time block, but no, you can't because that's *your* time. It makes a huge difference, just having half a day off to get things done. That's how I bounce back pretty quickly.

I've learned this through coaching: not saying yes to all opportunities, not allowing clients to dictate my schedule, planning the weekends, having a workday shutdown and a cutoff point.

You have to have a cutoff point. My husband did a thesis on sleep, circadian rhythm and electromagnetic field. He wrote that in 1998 as part of his CHEK practitioner certification with Paul Chek. He did all the research, five years of research on that subject.

We have a cutoff time for the computer at night. It doesn't matter what time you're working on your laptop—your pineal gland is going to say, "What are you doing to me?" After 7:00PM, don't expect me to get back to you. For us, it's 7:00PM to 7:00AM; you're definitely not going to hear from me between those hours. It's too dangerous for health, because you just don't shut off.

It's easy not to shut off our work. You have to do it on purpose.

Let's finish up with two more questions. Name three non fitness–related books everybody should read.

Everyone should read *The Tibetan Book of Living and Dying*. That's an amazing book because it gives perspective on life.

Dr. Ben Lynch's *Dirty Genes* is the book I've been raving about lately. It's one of those books that even though it's not fitness, it's hugely influential in how we can help our clients. I loved it because it's about the personality traits people have because of food. Your genes express what they're fed, and that's huge.

Another book people should read is one of my favorite books in the world—*Our Lady of the Flowers* by Jean Genet; he's a French author. It has nothing to do with fitness and nothing to do with success. It's just a good read.

Success leaves clues. Give us a couple of people we should follow to learn from.

Oprah Winfrey is truly an amazing woman who has come from diversity. It's not just because she's a celebrity, but because of what she's doing and how she's giving back. She's been in a management situation and what she does and the way she lives her world is just insane. I think she's one to follow.

John Legend, the musician, is another—I love the way he lives his world. I like what he does in helping Black Lives Matter and kids in underprivileged areas. There are a lot of things to admire, not only as a musician, but what he does in the background.

No one will know my other suggestion, but she's unbelievable. She's one of my former clients, Tara Llanez. She was the world champion in downhill mountain biking and ended up a quadriplegic. She's now back doing mountain biking on a modified bike. It's remarkable when you see someone turn a life around from what could have been disastrous to what she's doing now and how she's helping others like herself. She's amazing.

She was such a badass downhill mountain biker and BMXer. I trained her when she was a professional athlete; she was going to the Olympics for BMX and she crashed and broke her neck. She's currently in tennis, and she's now made amazing modified mountain bikes for hand athletes.

When you see someone who has been such an amazing professional athlete and has an accident, you know she could have gone either way. I so admire her and people like her. She's also very motivational as a voice for the disabled. She's badass.

When you're around people who have that kind of dichotomy in life, you realize, "There's nothing wrong with me. I've got two arms, two legs. I'm good. I've got money. I can eat, sleep. I've got good water. What do I have to complain about? Zero."

That's very cool. Anybody who meets you knows how much passion you have and how much you care about this profession. I think *you're* very cool and I appreciate you sharing your journey toward success.

BE LIKE JANET

"You have to have a cutoff point. We have a cutoff time for the computer at night. After 7:00PM, don't expect me to get back to you. For us, it's 7:00 to 7:00. I might be up, but you're definitely not going to hear from me after 7:00PM. It's too dangerous for health, because as you said, you just don't shut off. It's easy not to shut off our work."

THE HARD SHUTDOWN

This is so important.

Too many of us bring our work home with us, especially those of us who have an online business.

Ideally, the Workday Shutdown (see Alwyn Cosgrove's Be Like) and the Friday Freedom Session (see Vince Gabriele's Be Like) will help with this.

However, we still need some ground rules to make sure we don't slip back into old patterns.

Start small. Pick a time you will absolutely not answer any more email, phone calls or texts from clients. You really want to move away from texting your clients at all because there's a different mentality with texting, where people think there needs to be urgency in a reply. Move everyone to email when possible.

Let your clients know about your cutoff time; they will understand and adopt to the new time.

Stay strong! Don't give in and start to expand into your time. Maybe your cutoff starts out from 9:00PM to 6:00AM. Start to slowly expand that time to get longer periods of time when you're offline.

Come up with some other rules as well:

Have cell phone, computer and TV shutdown times and stick to them.

Think about things that will ease you into getting better sleep (see Shawn Stevenson's Be Like).

When you're at work, you want to be all in. The same rings true for home and family time. You want to be present and get the most out of your downtime.

This will help tremendously your productivity…and your happiness.

VINCE GABRIELE

Vince is the author of the Ultimate Guide Fitness Business Book Series. He's a national speaker on helping fitness professionals grow their businesses and is the founder of Gabriele Fitness and Performance, as well as Fitness Business University. Find Vince at vincegabriele.com.

You've been successful in a lot of different areas: as an athlete, facility owner and consultant helping other people with their businesses. Talk to us how you define success.

I define success as living life within your core values consistent with the things you deem most important. There are people who have made tons of money who would be deemed financially successful. But when you look at the other areas of their lives, you probably wouldn't consider them successful.

I have three things that are consistent that I live my life by: family, growth and contribution. My life is successful when I have time with my family, when I'm making an impact on my kids, wife and parents. It's when I'm growing, learning, getting better and when my business is growing, financially—but also when I'm growing as a human being.

And finally, am I making a difference in the world? Is the work I'm doing consistent with the values I set? Am I leaving the world better? I'm working hard to do that every day.

That definition has evolved over the years, especially now that you have a bigger family and you're contributing on a more global level. When did you feel like you started to be successful, that you were starting to get this right?

I discovered that success recently. My dad had a stroke last year and it was bad. It annihilated the left side of his brain, which controls the right side of the body…and also the language centers. Everything was completely destroyed and it's still really hard. He can't talk; he can't really understand what we're saying, and he can't walk or move yet. It's a really challenging situation for my family.

I saw success when I was able to leave my business to go be with my family: He had the stroke and I just left. I didn't go into the gym at all, and my business ran and everything was successful. I got to be with my family and was able to help my mom get through a really challenging time.

If I wasn't successful, I wouldn't have been able to leave my business. We wouldn't have continued to grow and I wouldn't have been able to be there for my family. As much as this is such a terrible time and a terrible situation, I feel successful.

It's comforting—if something bad comes up, you're covered. As an educator, you're practicing what you're preaching. It's an important lesson for all of us to remember; things happen and you've got to be prepared.

From a fitness business perspective, what motivates you? What gets you out of bed in the morning?

I help the people in my community get healthy, but what gets me out of bed in these days are those young, struggling business owners trying to become entrepreneurs. If I can help them grow their businesses, they're going to have more members. They're going to help more people.

And that community will be healthier. I'm helping a community get healthier by helping a fitness business owner develop a better business.

That's what gets me going, knowing I'm not just impacting these owners' lives and helping them spend more time with their families. I'm also helping people in their communities get healthier. That's the end goal for me, to help the people in those communities— through helping the owners build better businesses.

In the beginning, we start building the business, but then we're thinking, wait a minute, I want to help people. I didn't plan to do accounting. What are some habits you try to instill in these business owners?

There are technical things you need to learn to grow a better business. But I think my biggest shift in mindset was reading *Mindset* by Carol Dweck, which taught me the growth mindset. All the mistakes you make and all the challenges and complaints in your business are just information and opportunities to learn. It's important not to take any of that personally and that's what a growth mindset teaches.

You can't own a business and expect everyone to love you and love everything you do. It's not going to happen. The biggest thing to learn—one of the habits—is to treat failure, mistakes and challenges ways to learn and grow and get better and to be excited. But it's hard to develop a mindset to be excited about problems.

There's a good video called *Good* of Jocko Willink, the Navy SEAL and author of *Extreme Ownership*, in which he talks about all the things happened in battle. He would say, "All right, good," no matter what happened.

The first bad thing happened, "Good;" second bad thing happened, "Good, we learn from it. When something bad happens, something good will come from it." That's a habit I practice and value.

But how do you respond in adversity? When you can respond calmly, knowing this is a problem you'll solve and you'll come out on the other side. That's the main function of a business owner—to solve problems. You'll be stronger and better if you don't let it break you. That's the first thing.

The second thing are people who don't understand enough about marketing and sales. There's so much focus and emphasis on the Xs and Os of training—the product. But how are you bringing people in to use that product? There are a lot of struggling business owners who have a great product, but no one to give it to. They don't understand marketing and sales.

You have to know what differentiates you from your competition. Honestly, there's not that much difference between most gyms. Most gyms have equipment, kettlebells, barbells and all the tools. Most gyms have trainers.

But the X factor comes down to how you treat people: It comes down to service. And it comes down to unfair advantage. Someone could come in with a gym identical to mine and park next to us. That facility will never be able to steal the way we treat our members. That's what you need to look for in marketing. What is your unfair advantage? And how do you communicate that?

I always said about the competition, "Nobody can steal my clients, but I can lose them." If you remember that and work to figure out what's unique about your business and communicate that, it can take you a long way.

Vince, talk to us about your personal habits. Do you have an unusual technique you can share?

I purchased a neuro-feedback machine called a Neuroptimal. I hook electrodes up to my head to measure dynamic neuro-feedback, which shows the brain a picture of itself. The brain is very smart and will self-correct. After I use it, I feel amazing. My brain's thinking clearer. It's a neuro-feedback drill that the readers should consider.

What about goals? What's your process for setting goals?

I've done it differently over the years and have boiled it down to not setting annual goals. For me, it's more of a 90-day world, which is something I learned from EOS—Entrepreneurial Operating System, a program I participate in where we use the idea of "rocks." Rocks are what you're going to accomplish in the next 90 days that are so important that if you didn't do anything else, it's a successful period.

We set annual projections and clearly set ideas of "What do I want to accomplish in the next period, in the next quarter, in the next 90 days?" We have a meeting every week to evaluate where we are on each quarterly project, but all we do is label it either on track or off track. We either moved the needle to finish the product or nothing got done on it, and if that's the case we ask, "Why didn't it get done?" And have a discussion. That's the thing we've shifted in our business, really focusing on those 90-day goals.

A year is a little long and you kind of get lost in there. But when you only do 90 days and you pick those things, you have to review them on a weekly basis. It's more urgent. It's really changed my mindset in terms of getting things done.

What about being organized? What are you doing to stay organized?

Growing up, my dad's brain was always firing and he was always thinking about something. We called him Spaceman because he was always staring off into space. He's a brilliant guy and his brain was always creating. But it disengaged him from things like the dinner table. I saw that and I started to see myself going down that path. I have three kids and on the weekends, my brain is wandering. This is hard to control.

I started doing something on Friday afternoons that helped tremendously; I call it a freedom session. It's a whole series of things where I download the week and upload the upcoming week. Sometimes I'll spend two hours doing this on Friday afternoon, but I won't leave work until I'm done. When I'm finished with that, I'm clear on things and can totally let go. And I'm ready to go Monday. Let's go be with the family for the weekend.

Having that freedom session on Friday afternoons has been a game changer for me.

My daily workday shutdown process is similar. I write down everything, make a to-do list and my three big things for the next day. When I leave, I let everything go. In the morning, it's all in my planner: I know what I need to do. It's given me a lot of peace of mind and helped me settle down and get more done.

What about recharging? We talk to our clients a lot about recovery and rest. What do you do to recharge on a daily, weekly or yearly basis?

I've dabbled in things like flotation therapy, which is when you lie in a big tank of salt water. It's called sensory deprivation; you lie in the tank and your body becomes weightless. It takes all the stress off your joints. Suddenly, some crazy stuff happens in your brain—you get out of that tank and your brain's on fire, coming up with great ideas.

The biggest things for recovery are common: getting good sleep and regular meditation in the morning. I've started sleeping with my mouth taped shut, which is interesting. It's a special tape you put on your mouth so all the oxygen you get is through your nose. That's helped a lot. The consistent things for recovery, like sleep and regular meditation, have helped the most.

Expand on taping the mouth shut for nasal breathing for us.

I'm no expert on this—I learned about it from Bulletproof Radio. When you breathe through your nose, you activate the diaphragm and it makes you more relaxed. Mouth breathing is more of the sympathetic response. If you're exhausted from a workout, you're going to breathe through your mouth; that's how to get the most oxygen. But that's not the best way to breathe when you're sleeping.

I was with my dad in the hospital, and the guy in the bed next to him had sleep apnea. He wasn't breathing in the middle of the night. His mouth was wide open; your mouth isn't supposed to be open when you're sleeping. Taping helps activate the diaphragm better by forcing you to breathe through your nose. When I tape my mouth, I'll also open my nose with the Breathe Right nasal strip. Don't consider this if you have problems breathing through your nose. It's probably best to check with your doctor first.

I've taped my mouth shut on a run—that's an interesting feeling too. You feel relaxed. It's a cool feeling.

What are some sacrifices you've had to make to get where you are?

It's really hard to have a social life when you have a six-year-old, a four-year-old and a two-year-old—at least that doesn't consist of birthday parties and princesses. I don't see my friends enough; I'd like to see my buddies more often.

The other thing is leisure activities. Working a lot and having a family, I don't do the things I like to do as often. I'd like to play basketball more. I like to fish. I'm terrible at it, but I really love fishing. This year, because of everything that happened with my dad, I didn't go fishing and that bothered me. I'd like to do more things like that.

As my business expands and I remove myself from day-to-day operations, I'll be able to do those things. But those are things I've given up and are in my sight to pull them back in.

Give us three non-fitness books people should read in their personal development.

I already mentioned the first one, which was *Mindset*.

The second book is an obvious one: *How to Win Friends and Influence People*. You can be really successful in life just by following Dale Carnegie's principles.

And with the third one, I'm going to give a shout-out to my good friend who a lot of readers probably don't know but should. His name is Ari Weinzweig. Ari owns Zingerman's Deli in Ann Arbor, Michigan.

When I say "deli," you're probably thinking of a little deli. No, it's a $70 million deli business. They're absolutely killing it. Ari wrote a book called *Managing Ourselves*, which is an outstanding resource for anyone in the entrepreneurial space.

Who are three people we should follow? Ari's one...who are some other people?

Ari is definitely one. Then I'm going to give you two names from the pastoral world.

I got the best marriage advice I've ever gotten the other night. I was watching a sermon by Andy Stanley. Andy has a church in Atlanta where he does leadership work. He has a good podcast called the *Andy Stanley Leadership Podcast.* His marriage advice was this: Expect nothing and owe everything and you'll have a happy marriage.

The other guy is Lin Winters, a pastor at a church in Chandler, Arizona, called Cornerstone. If you're interested in public speaking, these guys have public speaking down. When you have people showing up to church on Sundays, some probably want to go, but some don't want to be there—you have to be good. You can't be boring or the congregation is going to be empty. These guys have thousands of people in their services; there are stadiums for these churches.

The way they speak and make their message clear and simple is unbelievable. Anyone in the public speaking realm should be watching these good pastors own the crowd.

I'll tell everybody to follow Vince Gabriele after watching you help so many people. I've never heard anybody say anything bad about you. Thanks for sharing your journey into success with us.

BE LIKE VINCE

"I started doing something on Friday afternoons that helped tremendously; I call it a freedom session. It's a whole series of things where I download the week and upload the upcoming week. Sometimes I'll spend two hours doing this on a Friday afternoon, but I won't leave until I'm done. When I'm finished with that, I have my calendar loaded. I have all the projects coming up.

"I'm clear on things and I can totally let go. Let's go be with the family."

VINCE'S FREEDOM SESSION

My freedom session is one of the most critical hours I spend each week.

For me, this session takes place on Fridays and the sole goal is to empty my brain and be totally prepared for the following week by the time the weekend starts.

This gave me the freedom to be engaged with my family, knowing in the back of my mind my work life was in control.

Here is an outline of a process for a freedom session.

Block one to two hours at the end of your week. Put this session on your calendar and call it your freedom session. I schedule mine at 3:00PM on Fridays.

Positive Focus: Write five great things that happened that week. This gets your mind in a positive frame to have a solid session.

Clean up: Collect loose papers and materials from your backpack, desk, office, counter. Process the material by either tossing them in the garbage, shredding or filing them as necessary. Business cards, receipts, meeting notes—all of it gets processed Friday afternoon.

Get to ZERO: Get your email inbox and cell phone messages to zero.

15-minute mindsweep: On a yellow legal pad or journal, write everything you have on your mind in bullet point fashion.

Keep your pen moving the entire time. Go for quantity not quality.

Review the week's calendar

Review the upcoming week's calendar: One of things I look for is how many consultations we have scheduled for the upcoming week. If it's less than our goal, I'm on the phone with our sales and marketing team.

Review all to-do or action lists from the past week: Hopefully, you keep to-do lists of some sort; take a few minutes and look through them, then move all undone tasks to the next week's list.

Review your project list: Your project list is a list of all the projects you have in the works. What defines a project is that it takes multiple steps to complete.

For example, planning my current mentorship weekend has been a huge project that has many steps, including things like preparing the presentations, getting sponsorships, organizing the materials and booking other speakers.

I could never plan this in one sitting. In my freedom session, I check the status of the project and write the next things I need to do to move the project forward the following week.

Every one of your projects needs a desired outcome—the actual result you want from the project.

I normally have five to ten projects going at once.

Kevin works as both a performance coach and a massage therapist at Mike Boyle Strength and Conditioning in Woburn, Massachusetts. He uses his expertise in both strength and conditioning and massage therapy to help everyone from Olympic athletes to the average Joes move, feel and perform at their best. Kevin is also co-founder of Movement as Medicine, Massage and Movement Therapy and Certified Functional Strength Coach. Catch up with Kevin at movement-as-medicine.com.

You're becoming successful in a few different areas: training, your business, the certification. How would you define success?

For me, it's freedom and autonomy: I wake up every day and I do what I want. Although it's a long day and there's a lot of work, I love what I do. If I need to take a day off or to travel somewhere, I control that. I define success as having freedom over my life and being able to choose what I want to do and feeling comfortable doing that.

Success is also about enjoying the things you've built and having a will to want to get better. If you have something you love, you'll always have that. If you're pursuing education and trying to get smarter, you also want to get better. It's a balance between feeling a bit successful and also feeling like you're not good enough.

The most successful people don't say, "I'm successful." They say, "I need to be better." That's the paradox and that's the feeling I have on a daily basis. I'm trying to balance that with enjoying where we are now.

You have so many great people around you, which is a huge part of loving your job. But how do you create that? How do you keep from becoming stale and allowing this whirlwind to take over?

At one point when we didn't have any money, Brendon Rearick, Ana Tocco and I were living in what we called the "Strength Coach House." I remember looking at the statistics of how much money you can make as a strength coach and thinking, "I'm going down this path." I was committing to be a fitness professional and wondering if it was the right decision for my life's work.

Trying to think about your life down the line is a slippery slope. You make a career choice that might have seemed like a good financial one, but might end up hitting a dead end. I remember sitting with Brendon and saying, "We're going to do this and we're going to make a successful life."

You have to go head on into what you want to do and it gives you the fuel to work hard enough to chase that dream. Momentum in life is a real thing, especially when you're chasing a career you love.

You don't know where you're going to end up, but you have to push at it in the beginning. You have to be open-minded or you're not going to see opportunities.

I walked into Mike Boyle's MBSC when I was 20 and thought, "I'm just going to train high school kids." If you had told me, "Fast forward, you're going to be traveling and teaching courses. You're going to have a business and will have awesome opportunities," I wouldn't have thought that could happen. I just started coaching. But if you put yourself into it, things eventually snowball.

I made a commitment early on to treat education as an investment. Some people invest in real estate or the stock market. Why not just bet on myself? If I put all the money I'm making into education so I can be better, I can get that payout from my own work.

We were betting on ourselves. That's probably the safest bet you can make if you're willing to work.

When did you start to feel like the dividends were coming through?

When we brought Marco Sanchez and Scott Georgaklis into Movement as Medicine, I began to feel a bit of stability in the business. Then, with the CFSC moving up a level, I was feeling like, "I've taken this knowledge and experience I've gained and built a product—not just my one-on-one service and not just the group coaching in therapy. Now, I have a product even more people are interested in and that can help more people."

There were many nights when we were in massage school from 6:00 to 9:30PM. Brendon and I were dozing off after work and then scheduled at MBSC from 5:00AM. I would wonder, "Is this the right investment?" We invested about $12,000 into massage school. I can now see after a few years doing CFAC that investment is paying off. It was a good investment of my money and time.

There had to be times when you wanted to quit and go back to being a trainer. What got you through those times?

It helped to have people doing it together. Brendon and I were going through the same things at the same time. We weren't making much money; we were working a lot and were tired, but we knew we'd get through it together. It also helps that we're both competitive and hard-headed. Neither of us was going to give up; we weren't going to let the other down. It helps to have friends who believe in the same things, especially when you're doing something challenging.

If you're dreaming big, people might think it's the wrong idea, that you should get a safer career. People often think you should pursue something better financially in the short term. However, it helps when you have people around you who think the way you do. This is something we really wanted.

What is your "it" that gets you out of bed in the morning?

I always have another thing to work toward, something I can do better. I want to have better intakes; I want to have a better way to keep my clients doing their homework—just little things about my business. When I wake up and before I go to bed, I write a list. If I don't, it's either going to escape my head or I'm going to think about it all night. I make notes on Sundays for the upcoming week and I do a purge at night before I go to sleep.

When I get up in the morning, I know my big tasks, and I always seem to get them done. I think about what's next and balance that with taking time to be grateful for what we have.

Kevin, let's talk about your goals. Is there a formal process? Do you sit down at the end of the year or do you do it on the fly?

Rather than the calendar year, I take my birthday to review the year. I review my goals; the big rocks I wanted, did I achieve them? I reflect on how I feel about everything: personally, professionally, internally, spiritually. Then I reassess for next year. What do I want to take on? I look at where I made progress and think about what's next. Am I happy with where I am at this point in time?

I think about Steve Jobs' quote, "If you wake up every day thinking you're not happy with what you do for a living, you have to change." I always think, "Am I happy doing this?" Thankfully, it's been yes in recent years.

We read studies that say all successful people write goals, but the most important thing is the action steps. You have to plan your action steps because when you get busy or you get down, you need to commit yourself to a goal. As Tony Robbins says, "Do something that immediately commits you toward your goal."

I note all the continuing education I want to do because once I get busy teaching and coaching in the gym, I could schedule myself out of attending courses. When I have all that emotion about what I want to do, I book and pay for flights to get to them. That commits me toward those educational goals.

Just take action steps to commit yourself toward a goal. That's the biggest thing that commits me toward the goals I set.

I love the idea of identifying a bunch of "whys" behind your goals. Why do you want this goal? That keeps you on track to remind you; sometimes you have to remember why you wanted it.

When I think of that, I hear Mike Boyle say, "The problem isn't too much information. It's filter failure."

And for goals, it's the same thing. There are so many things we could be chasing career-wise. You have to focus on the best decision for your career. If you don't go back to the why, you end up chasing a lot of rabbits. And you go home hungry.

It's important to have clarity and to write out your goals so you can check back and know when you're off track. Talk to me about recharging. How do you recharge on a daily, weekly and yearly basis?

Proactively, I look at the calendar for all the upcoming events. I can see which events I want to do and which I have to do, and make sure I'm not sabotaging myself from the onset. I don't want to be the person backing out due to over-commitment.

I look at the travel weekends and the weeks I'm home; I have to balance those. I set myself up for my travel schedule to be successful. I have to be at MBSC and also at Movement as Medicine to make sure things are running well.

If I don't exercise, my energy and productivity falls, especially while traveling. Initially, I fell in the trap of going from one thing to another to another, and I'd miss a week of training. It's not about the intensity of training; it's about the regularity and the psychology. I have to make sure I commit to get off the plane and go do something, even if it's just 20 minutes.

That helps me energize and stay in a routine. I like having routines and when I don't, my energy is low.

Committing to that and making sure I have hobbies is essential. We sometimes get so committed to this career, we start cutting off everything unrelated. I make sure to have something I can completely put my head into that has nothing to do with strength and conditioning or massage.

I've begun to take more naps in the last few years. I'm a pretty sound sleeper at night, but I've learned the value of naps too. *Sleep Smarter* and *Take a Nap, Change Your Life* are two books I read that made me think about valuing naps more. When I heard Mike Boyle say we need to take more naps, I knew I should start napping. I didn't picture him as a napper, but it turns out he's a big nap guy.

You've had to make sacrifices to achieve your goals. What are some other habits you feel have helped you along the way?

I always get up with extra time in the morning, which sets me up to be successful the rest of the day. If not, I'm always reacting. I don't want to react to things—I want to prep. I'm a big planner and I like to be early for things. I like being prepared. That might not sound like a big hack, but it's a simple habit to always think ahead and plan.

When I was in massage school, I didn't focus on how long it was taking, how tired I was or how much money it was costing. I was grateful for the opportunity. I was thinking about how I was going to build a business and I was reminding myself why I was doing it. There were many times in massage school when I might have felt a class wasn't going to apply to what I'm doing, but I reminded myself of the outcome. I continued to think of how it fit into the plan.

Sometimes what you need to do is not what you want to do. Do that first so it's done and you don't have to fight with yourself over it.

What are some things you feel you've sacrificed that were important to getting you where you are?

Early in my career, I was really busy and didn't see my friends and family enough. But now I have more freedom and can spend more time with them because I've built a platform under me.

People call that "the delayed life plan," but everything takes sacrifice. Everybody has to do that; you have to be okay with understanding some of the tradeoffs you're going to have to make as an entrepreneur. People often don't realize the amount of energy and time that go into building a successful business and career.

Most people are willing to do a certain level and then after that, it's not worth it to them. You have to be able to push longer. There were times when I worked seven days a week, day in and day out—and I still do sometimes. Sometimes the people who think you worked too hard are the same people who say, "I wish I had the opportunities you had." They don't know all the work we had to do to get here.

I try to picture where I want to spend my time when I'm 40. Where does my time want to be spent when I'm 50? Projecting in advance, I can think, "Am I on the right path?" If not, I need to do more now so I can be there then. When you are on the right path, remind yourself to keep doing what you're doing.

You're a big reader. Give us three non fitness–related books people should read for their development.

Let's start with *Letters from a Stoic*, which is Seneca. Stoicism is pretty popular in the fitness world. Marcus Aurelius' *Meditations* is great, but I really like the Seneca book. That's the one I keep by my bed to read a page here and there.

Another suggestion is *Deep Survival* by Laurence Gonzalez, a book of survival stories about people hiking or skiing. It's about the psychology in decision-making that goes into why someone might survive a plane crash or a climbing accident.

I just read a very good book called *Memory Rescue* by David Ayman—it's about long-term brain health. It's about things you can do for long-term brain and memory health. Alzheimer's is a disease found in my family, so it's something I was personally interested in.

How about people we should follow to learn from?

I've been enjoying Doug Kechijian's podcast and tweets. He's a physical therapist and performance coach. I've enjoyed a lot of what he's put out recently.

Ben House has interesting nutrition and lifestyle information. I'm interested in the overall health and impact of both exercise and nutrition. He has some good information for us.

Both of them are active on social media.

You've done so much in a short time. You're a good model for how things should be done, working hard but still understanding balance. It's great to watch this journey—thank you for sharing it.

BE LIKE KEVIN

"I wrote down all the continuing education I want to do because for me, once I get busy teaching and coaching in the gym, I could schedule myself out of attending courses. I hate that because I love continuing education. Right when I had all that emotion about what I want to do, I booked and paid for flights for all of them."

SCHEDULE YOUR VACATIONS, CONTINUING EDUCATION AND EXPERIENCES FOR THE YEAR

Kevin is a planner. It's what helps him not only stay organized, but also be able to balance what's important for work and for his life experiences outside of work.

Make a list of all the things you'd like to do during the next year.

What continuing education do you want to attend?

What events do you want to attend—concerts, sporting events, festivals?

What places would you like visit?

What experiences do you want to have?

Just keep writing.

For now, don't worry about how much something will cost or how long the event lasts.

After you make the list, prioritize the items. What's the most important to you?

Depending on your budget, pick two to three of your top choices—ideally a vacation, an experience and some continuing education—and put them on your yearly schedule.

Write as if you're going. Make it a priority.

Commit to something: Pay for the course, reserve a hotel room or get an airline ticket…get a friend involved, do something to make a commitment.

Prepare on some level beforehand: Do some research, get a book on the subject, watch some videos. This will keep it top of mind and keep the excitement alive.

Rachel has co-owned Results Fitness since 2000—it's one of the top 10 gyms in the USA as named by Men's Health Magazine. She's the bestselling author of The Female Body Breakthrough and Drop Two Sizes; she's a columnist and is on the advisory board for Women's Health Magazine and was named IDEA Personal Trainer of the Year in 2012. Rachel is a highly sought after speaker on topics such as strength training for women, creating your dream fitness business and fat loss programming for your female clients. Rachel's work can be found at rachelcosgrove.com.

You and I have had conversations about women in this profession. For this book, you were the first woman I thought of because of the impact you've had, not only on businesses, but also in working with women. I want to start by asking how you define success.

Success is having the freedom to do what you want when you want—the time freedom, the money freedom. If you love what you do and you want to work, work as long as you can. Or if you want to travel or be there for your family, it's a matter of getting to a point in your career where you can make those choices.

I go to the gym every day, but I don't have to be there. I love connecting with the clients, seeing our members and being a part of their journeys. But I don't have to be. My definition of success is to have that freedom.

The masterminds or workshops at Result Fitness University always start with the vision of a perfect day. I love the story Alwyn told about someone who wanted to make more money. But after he did the exercise, it turned out he was making plenty of money for his perfect day.

That's why we start with that exercise in our masterminds and mentorships. So many people haven't taken the time to think about that. When you think about what makes you happy and what you love to do, sometimes it doesn't cost a lot of money. That person you were talking about said, "I'd love to play video games all day."

We asked, "How much does that cost?" and the answer is…not a whole lot. He built his business so it could pay him enough that he could stay home and play video games. He got that, but it got old after a while and he decided he wanted to do something else.

Who are we to judge if that's his definition of success? If you want to play video games and that's what you want to do, cool. Set up your life so you can accomplish whatever success is for you.

This next question is a tough one because people in this field are so driven, and we don't stop to celebrate our successes. You've been a successful author. You have a successful consulting group and a successful gym. When did you start to feel, "I'm starting to get this right?"

Alwyn and I just got back from trips where we met up in New York. He was there speaking at IDEA. I was doing a book photo shoot in Philadelphia and took a bus to meet him in New York. It was one of those weekends where we both had a moment of, "Here we are; you're speaking at a conference. I'm at my book photo shoot. I'm just going to come in and meet you for the weekend."

I was shooting *The Big Book of Exercises* with Adam Campbell. It was one of those experiences where you're thinking, "Look at me—here I am in New York City. I'm just going to go meet my husband while he's speaking at a conference. Then I'm going to head back and work with Rodale."

Some of the moments of realizing we had a successful company were not so much during the fun parts, but when things happened in our lives, like when Alwyn was diagnosed with cancer. I was able to step out and be with him at the UCLA med center and not worry about the business or finances. I had the freedom to be there.

We've had the gym for 18 years and during that time, things have come up in our family. I've been so grateful our company is set up the way it is and we've been able to grow and be at the point of success so I can drop everything and be there for my family if they need me.

Often when people talk about success, they talk about money and fancy cars. But really, success for me is about those moments when you're able to be there for your family when they need you the most.

Is that what motivates you to get out of bed in the morning, to keep that freedom?

If you aren't excited to get out of bed in the morning, it's probably time to make some changes in your life. I'm always ready to hit the ground running in the morning. I'm excited about what we do. I'm excited about our next idea to help more people, change more lives, or whatever it might be that we're working on at the time. That's what gets me out of bed in the morning.

Alwyn and I are married, and we're business partners; we're always talking about new ideas. It's hard for us to switch off when we've been talking about our next idea to launch something exciting. As we're sleeping at night, our wheels are turning. I wake up in the morning excited to get going.

It's exciting to see our profession change. It's changed a lot since we've been involved. Trainers are starting to be seen as professionals and are working to set a standard of being healthcare professionals. That absolutely drives us.

It's fulfilling to create a place at our gym where our trainers can have a career. The trainers can support their families; they have health insurance and a retirement plan. We've grown our team to 22 people. That's as rewarding as seeing a client accomplish a fitness goal.

When we opened Results Fitness, "changing the way fitness is done" was about creating a place where trainers could have a different work experience, but it was also about our clients. We now have affiliate gyms all over the world changing the way fitness is done. It's exciting to see that come to life—it's less about a financial goal and more about the mission. How many people can we help?

I don't want a client to move to another city and not be able to work out at a gym similar to ours. We've had people decline a move because they don't want to leave the gym. That's wonderful to hear, but Results Fitness shouldn't be the exception; it should be the norm. Everybody should be able to work out at a gym where they get the customer service we give and experience the science behind our programming.

That's our mission.

We've made some progress, but we still have a long way to go in changing the way fitness is done. That's definitely part of what gets me out of bed in the morning; it's that mission.

When you get up in the morning, is there a routine you perform every day to set up your day?

That's my time to think about my day and what I have going on. Writing and journaling are how I can sort out the thoughts in my head. Some people need to talk; some people need to think. Writing is how I sort out my thoughts. I might be struggling with an idea and if I just sit down and write, I can probably figure it out. I've always journaled. I started journaling when I was in junior high, and that's been something I've always done. Writing and journaling are, really, how I can sort out the thoughts in my head.

Many of us get so busy being busy, we don't make the time to create a vision, to have that open space—it's really brain space to create the things we need to create to be successful. So many people wake up in the morning and immediately check their phone and their email. You have to be careful you don't become reactive. That's the hard thing about checking email—you might end up on someone else's agenda. I guard my email box pretty tightly. Most people don't have my email address; they have to go through our office manager…bodyguard.

As a business grows, you definitely have to put up boundaries. People don't have my cell phone. That's not something I give out freely because giving that out is giving out my time. If you're letting anybody text or email you at any time, you're saying, "My time is worth nothing and I can do whatever you want me to do." You end up becoming more reactive than proactive.

Goal setting is an important part of what you do in your coaching group. Talk to us about your process for setting goals.

Goal setting means deciding what you want—deciding where you're going, the direction of the path and figuring out the action steps you need to take to get there. If you're not setting goals or at least thinking about what you want to create, what success is to you or your vision for your ideal day, as Jim Rohn has said, "You're going to end up somewhere in a year; you're going to end up somewhere in 10 years. You might as well decide where that is."

You might write down a goal and maybe that goal doesn't end up being as important as you thought it was. But it will get you going in a direction you can then adjust. If you have something pulling you, write it down. There's a reason for that urge. You never know where it's going to take you, what you're going to learn from it or what person you're going to become because you set the goal.

I love vision boards because I'm a visual person. Think about how your goal makes you feel and why you want to accomplish it. Then find pictures that illustrate the goal so when you look at the pictures, they remind you of the feeling of achieving it. That's where a vision board comes into play. Put it somewhere you'll see it every day so it reminds you to take action toward the goals.

It's crazy how that plants into your subconscious. Whether you think you're moving toward them, you're probably nudging in that direction because you wrote them down and thought about them. Even if you aren't disciplined about moving closer toward your goals, many times you'll end up taking movement toward them because they stick in your sub-conscious. It's powerful stuff.

Rachel, we're always talking to our clients about recovery and sleep. How do you recharge daily, weekly or on a yearly basis?

Everyone has to find something that recharges them. For me, it's competing. I love to compete; I've done everything from powerlifting to triathlons. Right now, it's Spartan races. I've found when I'm training for and competing in something, I'm fired up. It's my escape. When I take that time for myself, it's something that also gets me ignited… recharged. Having goals and focusing on improving physically charges me up and keeps me motivated.

Plug into people who challenge the way you think or who challenge your ideas. That's something every successful person surrounds themselves with—people who get them fired up. Once a month I meet with a group of women; we call ourselves The Brainstormers. Being a part of a group you connect with and letting your guard down about your business and sharing ideas are good ways to recharge.

I've never been a big meditator—I haven't mastered it. But when I go to a dance class where all I can think about is the steps I'm learning, that's meditation. I take a dance class once a week because my brain gets that distraction; I can't think about the meeting with my team that afternoon. In classes like that, your brain has to work differently and you become the student.

What do you feel are some sacrifices you've made to be in your position?

Sacrifice is interesting wording. When I look back, I don't feel I sacrificed anything be-cause everything I did was a choice. I didn't have to do any of this; no one forced me to work the way I work.

Anybody who's opened a business has been through the grind where you're working insane hours. You're not making any money and it can test you. It can physically and mentally put you at that edge where you begin to think you're not sure you want to do this. It can be tough. But it's a choice. I would never call any of it a sacrifice.

Many times when people identify the "why" of what they are doing, it helps when times are tough. This business is sometimes tough. How do you get through your worst times?

Burnout is real in this business, especially because we give energy to people all day long. When you're a personal trainer, your job is to fire up your clients. Many of our clients walk in with low energy and that means we give, give, give. It can burn us out over time.

You have to know there's good ahead, that it's going to be worth it. You have a vision. You have to think about where you're going and that you're not going to be doing this forever. This isn't for the long term. This is a get-through-the-grind phase, until you can get to where the business is successful enough that you don't have to work these long hours. You can eventually build a team and start to delegate. Then you can start to create the freedom that means success for you.

Having a vision is what pulls you through the tough times. Getting clear on that is like a magnet. If you don't have that, you don't have the magnet to pull you through those hard times. If you have that, you look back and can realize, "I don't know how I got through that, but I never really thought about quitting because I always had that magnet pulling me through it."

You need a stronger "why." The book *Start with Why* by Simon Sinek will be helpful in this. If you know why you're doing something, you can get through anything. You can pull yourself through it.

When you have that "why" as a magnet, it's amazing the resilience you can have as a business owner.

I know you're a voracious reader. Give us three non fitness–related books people should read.

When anybody comes into our mastermind groups, *Start with Why* is one of the books we have people read.

Delivering Happiness is a book by Tony Hsieh, the CEO of Zappos; he's been a big influence on us. Along with your mission and your "why," you also have to think about your values. If you don't have your core values solid and don't know what you stand for, things can get tough.

Decisions can get tough, and you just can't use your backbone. Setting your core values is another key part of success.

The last suggestion is *How Successful People Think*, which is a great John Maxwell book. It's an easy read and something I read over and over again. I definitely recommend that one.

***Delivering Happiness* changed a lot of the way I did and thought about things. It does a great job of breaking down the process. Rachel, let's talk about some people you think we should follow on social media.**

There are people who are better at social media than others. When you think of social media successes, Gary Vaynerchuk is one of the people who comes to mind. He knows social media inside and out. He started off with a brick-and-mortar wine company. Then he went into consulting, and now he's very creative on social media—his lessons are great.

He can be raunchy, harsh and in your face. But he has good messages. Today, you can't grow a business without understanding social media, building your brand and gathering a following on the different platforms. Gary V is someone I would definitely follow to learn more about how to do this.

Darren Hardy is someone whose work I love. I get his daily video email, Darren Daily. He provides great tidbits of success-minded ideas and getting your mind in the right place. It's a two-minute video that will produce a shift in your mindset.

Marie Forleo is great. She's doing great work and has interesting ideas. Lisa Sassevich is somebody I follow.

Of course, everyone should follow Richard Branson—I love his approach to how he runs his business.

With all of the recent catastrophes in the Virgin Islands, I've been watching how he's approaching recovery and how he's handling things. It's really cool to see somebody like that; it's not even about him. Yes, he lost everything on his island—it's wiped out. But he doesn't care; his focus is on how to help other people.

The more successful we are, the more we can help people. He exemplifies that. He's always looking for ways to use his wealth and what he's created to help other people. He's somebody I would definitely follow.

Like your core values state, You and Alwyn are "changing the way fitness is done," which means you've changed many people's lives—not just those trainers and those businesses, but the people who are going through those gyms. You're doing good work. Thank you so much for sharing your journey to success.

BE LIKE RACHEL

"I've always journaled. I started journaling when I was in junior high, and that's been something I've always done. Writing and journaling are, really, how I can sort out the thoughts in my head."

JOURNALING

Too many people make the mistake and think journaling is about writing a book every day about everything that went on in their life.

Some journals like Michael Hyatt's *"Full Focus Journal"* are all set up for you and ask you a bunch of questions that you just fill out.

There are also apps like "Day One" if you feel like you want to go digital.

It doesn't have to be complicated. You can just use a notebook for now.

Pick a time that you know you will have limited distractions, either very early or right before bed.

Make it easy. Keep the notebook and pencil in a spot that is easily accessible and a place that you will see it.

Start small and out just do it for five minutes every day.

Keep it positive to start. Make a list of five questions to answer. Some samples:

> Write at least five things you're grateful for.
>
> Write three wins that happened either yesterday or today.
>
> How are you feeling?
>
> Write something funny that happened recently.
>
> Write your quarterly goals and why you want to achieve them.
>
> What are some accomplishments you had recently?
>
> Write about someone you admire and why you admire the person.
>
> Write about ideas for your training or business.

Just keep writing—it's not being graded. Don't be hard on yourself.

Like fitness, the key here is consistency. Challenge yourself to do it for at least 30 days and you'll see how easy it becomes.

Wil is an athletic performance and weightlifting coach in Bloomington, Indiana. He has coached 100s of athletes to Division One scholarships, dozens of All-Americans and national champions and has been invited to five weddings…so far. He has two kids and a beautiful wife; his family means the world to him. Learn more at wilfleming.com.

Wil, you've had success as an All-American track and field athlete in college, which you've continued as a masters weightlifter. Your facility has thrived as well. How do you define success?

We can talk about monetary success or reputation, and it probably all ends up hand-in-hand. To take a cue from Pat Rigsby, we each have an ideal business or lifestyle. I don't know if we can ever reach it, but success is just taking steps toward that ideal lifestyle, whatever you have in mind.

The biggest thing for me is free time and time with my family. There have been many times in life when I could have made a choice to do something in pursuit of increased reputation or more money in my bank account. But since I've been married and had my son, the thing that determines success for me is my ability to spend time with my family, to be a good husband and dad, and to make sure things are functioning in the home.

There's a phase everybody goes through in the rise and grind. Eventually, you make a choice whether family is more important. When I look at social media posts from successful people I know have a family—if I never see their family, if they're posting on Instagram at 6:00PM and 2:00AM and again at 7:30AM, we're not after the same thing. That person and I differ in a significant way; that's not my idea of success.

You've had success across different areas, but when did you start to consider yourself a success in the fitness business?

The progress toward being successful is incremental and step-based. You may have a moment where you feel you've impacted somebody, but that's different than feeling successful. For instance, people come up to me at continuing education events and say something I wrote impacted them. That's a great feeling.

I have an Olympic lifting technique poster; a kid emailed to say, "I qualified for nationals and I've never had a coach. I just used your poster." I felt like I was making an impact. But none of that would make me think, "I'm successful."

All of those add up to a reflection that I've been successful at what I'm trying to do, which is to impact our athletes and help coaches elsewhere impact their athletes.

What is it that motivates you to get up in the morning?

It's connection. There's a trend in the fitness business to move everything online and release a product because there's a huge untapped market who want to buy things online and want to connect. But I need that coaching aspect—I still want to impact people toward achieving something they didn't think was possible.

I wasn't a particularly good athlete when I was younger, but I had good coaches who helped me develop. I had doors open to me that otherwise wouldn't have been open. Had those coaches not given a lot of effort toward me, I wouldn't have been recruited for track and field or football in college, nor lived at the Olympic training center.

That connection—that ability to help people achieve things they didn't think were possible or thought were at the edge of their possibilities—that makes me most excited. I couldn't go a day at the gym when I didn't get to coach somebody. I love human contact.

We have online training people, but it's still connecting with them through text, Facebook or email. Even though the connections are more shallow than a face-to-face connection we can make in person, I can still help people do things they didn't think were possible.

In order to be an All-American athlete and school record holder at Indiana U, be a top masters champion and own a business, you have to have good habits. What are some of the habits that helped get you to where you are?

I'm pretty persistent in terms of how I set and strive for goals. It's better to chunk things and maybe that's most apparent in training since I'm still competing.

"Hit singles, not home runs." That's my motto. I'm always trying to get a little more and not go to the point of failure. That would be a good metaphor for how I approach business, making a little bit of progress toward something better every day.

I always try to find the brighter side. Even in moments I've had failures, whether that's competitively or in business, I try to compartmentalize. When I'm at home, I'm going to focus on my family. When I'm at work, I'm going to focus on work and not bring anything negative back home.

By compartmentalizing, I'm able to find those positives that help me get up the next morning and go back to it even after what would be a perceived failure.

"Hitting singles, not home runs." There's that progression, that idea about getting a bit better every day.

I remember when I was 15 or 16, I came back to training with my coach and said, "Coach, I figured out if I do one more kilo a day, every time I come in, which should be pretty easy because I've been doing two to five kilos more every day so far, I should have the world record in just a couple of years, right?"

He said, "It doesn't always work like that, but let's try it for as long as we've got."

I'm glad he didn't knock you down on that.

He said, "Let's reframe that a little."

That was a goal you had when you were a kid, to be a world record holder. What about now, in terms of setting goals, is there a formal process?

In terms of business, there's a yearly goal I like to see complete by the end of that year, or launch this new program…improve revenues by this amount. Working on business goals might take a day. I'll sit down with two people from the management team at my gym—that's my wife and our general manager and we'll map out those goals, then break them down quarterly. We'll discuss the actual steps. Each month we'll break things into something more actionable.

I'll keep the big goals written and every time we readjust the monthly goals, I'll put them in front of me every day so I'm making sure I'm making progress. I try to turn that into something actionable each day or at least each week.

A couple of years ago when I wrote my book, I needed to get 500 or 1,000 words on a page every day to make the progress I wanted to see. I chunk things out, and that's the same in training, where I work backward: Here's the big goal at the end and here's how I'm going to measure progress. At this point, I should be *here,* and at that point, I should be *there.* Even if I hit something big along the way, I don't readjust. I just keep progressing toward the goal.

Being an athlete and having had that experience makes me look at the final goal and know, "Here are the benchmarks I need to reach at each stage to accomplish this." I'm realistic. I'm 35 years old—I'm not going to improve my snatch by 40 kilos in the next three months, but five kilos is a reasonable goal. I take that same approach when it comes to business; most great things have happened by incremental steps rather than one great thing at one time.

You mentioned you're 35, and you're not going to improve "x" amount. Some people might say that's a limiting belief. But we need to be realistic about our goals. Have you ever regretted limiting yourself or thought you could have pushed yourself more?

Yes, certainly, but the feeling of, "I had a little more in the tank. I think I could have done more" is a much better feeling than, "I set myself up for failure with that choice."

I'm in the sport of weightlifting for the long haul. It's more valuable for people to have miniature successes as opposed to a big failure followed by a big success followed by a big failure followed by a big success. That big failure is when a lot of people say, "I'm going to hang it up."

I try to set my athletes up for long-term success. If you want to go out on a bang, go for it, but my goal is to be good at this for a long time, whether that's my business or weightlifting or whatever sport I choose. We can make analogies between the physical performance, whether that's weightlifting or track and field, but the big thing is, don't get hurt.

As Dan John said, "At some point, there's going to be the last injury you will ever have," where that's the last time you'll get hurt because after that, you're done. You never want to get yourself to that phase. You never want to get to that last big failure where you permanently stall your progress.

Maybe I have an aversion to loss—somebody could be diagnosing me right now—but that's my thing.

Can I have a bunch of small successes and continually have small successes over a longer period as opposed to just going for broke? Yes, let's do it that way.

In training, ultimately we want the right amount of stimulus at the right time if we want to reach our pinnacle. It's much better to go with less stimulus than more. Overtraining can sink a person—and that goes in all parts of life.

You're a busy guy, not only with the facility but with some other obligations and being a dad and still competing. How do you stay organized?

The overarching thing is having a priority list. I go to church every week: God first; family second; business third; coaching fourth; training fifth—those are the top five on my list at any given time.

During the eight to 12 weeks I usually take to get ready for a meet, training might bump up to four and coaching comes down to number five, but the top three stay relatively the same at all times. That orders my day. It gives me some overarching sense it's going to keep me on the path.

Being in the fitness profession, we're always talking to people about recharging. How do you recharge on a daily, weekly or yearly basis?

Each day, the time with my wife and son in the evening recharges me. Some days your kid doesn't want to listen to a thing you say and it takes 10 minutes to get on a sock—you're exhausted. Still, every night when my wife and I go to bed, we marvel at some of the things he's doing.

Even though it feels like everything's scheduled out pretty well all the time, Sundays are a weekly recharge. I don't work out on Sundays. I spend the day with family, my wife and son or my brother, sister and dad, and that's on a weekly basis.

I love you've been proactive about making sure you spend time with your son, and it's great your business is established so you're able to do that. What sacrifices do you feel you've made to get where you are?

When you make a choice to pursue anything, you sacrifice something else. A good analogy is if you pursue health as a goal, general fitness would be a second goal, maybe mobility is a goal and strength is goal. If you go after strength, then mobility and fitness and health are probably going to decline a bit.

You're not giving as much attention to those as the other. If you want to be the most limber and mobile person in the world, your strength is probably going to decrease. You make sacrifices along the way.

With a choice to spend more time with family, I sacrifice on the monetary side of having a successful business. If the revenue isn't at its max every month, as long as certain thresholds are met, that's okay with me. Weigh all those things and that idealized successful life—I'm more interested in time with family than I am with making a ton of money.

Being a trainer, being a business owner—were there any mistakes you've made that you regret to this day?

I said yes to too many things, getting spread out too thin. Getting too far from whatever you're good at is a mistake. If it's two or five or 10 percent away from your ideal, you probably shouldn't do it.

We shouldn't try to be all things to all people as opposed to dialing things in and being ourselves. When you say you're all things to all people as a growing business, you're spread too thin. Focus in; dial in who you are and what you do well and embrace is better rather than saying you'll do everything. When you do everything, you don't do anything well.

I've made those mistakes. Hopefully the readers can learn from my mistakes.

Sometimes we chase the dollar, especially as business owners. My facility, Five Iron Fitness, was geared toward golfers and I had to be discerning of whom I chose to train. I would sometimes get people who just wanted to lose weight; they weren't golfers. Unless I knew they were friends or family of my current clients, I pointed them in another direction because I would have had to spend too much time with them. You have to focus on who you are and stay true to it.

Give me three books that people need to read to become better people.

Smarter Faster Better from Charles Duhigg is really good. There's a cool section I liked a lot where he was talking about goal setting. It was along the lines of classic SMART goals, which are specific, measurable, action-oriented, reachable and time specific.

He talks about the idea of making stretch goals that make you rethink what you're doing, and then do everything differently to reach those goals. Don't make the goals so big they paralyze you with fear or set you up for failure. Don't make stretch goals that aren't accomplishable— just a hair out of reach. We use that idea in training and also in business, that there are smart stretch goals that end up being smart goals.

Legacy by James Kerr about the New Zealand All Blacks is an outstanding book. I enjoyed it and the whole idea of "sweeping the shed" and taking pride in what you do.

I'm going to give you two more: One is *Seven Principles for Making Marriage Work* by John Gottman. If you read *Blink* by Malcolm Gladwell, you'll remember Gottman as the guy who had the lab where he could determine with 90-percent accuracy within 15 minutes whether a marriage would work. It's important in my life to make sure I have a good marriage; I got a lot out of that book.

For new parents, a book called *Happiest Baby on the Block* is probably the single most impactful book I've read in my life. You get a baby handed to you and you're expected to know what to do. It turns out not everybody does—I didn't—and this book helped me. I can quiet any crying baby due to ideas from that book. It's a really good book.

Will, it's been great talking to you about the journey through all your successes in different endeavors.

BE LIKE WIL

"The overarching thing is having a priority list. I go to church every week: God first; family second; business third; coaching fourth; training fifth—that's my top five."

PRIORITIES

Part 1—The Priority List

One way to help make decisions about things in your life and your business is to get clarity on priorities.

What are your top three to five priorities in your life?

1._____

2._____

3._____

4._____

5._____

Use these as a guide to help make decisions.

To use Wil as an example, he puts family ahead of his business. He has decided seeing his son until 9:30 every morning is more important to him than checking a few things off the to-do list or adding revenue to his business by getting to the gym earlier. His priorities justify his decisions.

Part 2—Make a Quit List

Identify some things you can quit or limit to free up time for what's really important to you.

When I did this exercise, I realized a podcast I was doing wasn't worth the time I was spending on it. Although I loved doing it, it wasn't adding value to my target demographic and I wasn't generating any revenue from it. I decided to stop doing it.

Another thing I was doing was visiting the gym in my building in the late morning to talk shop with some of the trainers. I loved doing it, but it took away from my productivity. I decided to stop going there every day.

I also made a list of people in one-sided relationships who were taking too much of my time. That can be hard to do, but it was game changer for me.

Make a list of some activities, projects, tasks or relationships you might want to get stop that are taking you away from your priorities. Even if you can't quit them completely, try to cut down on the time you spend on those things or those people.

GERALYN COOPERSMITH

Geralyn started in fitness as a group exercise instructor and personal trainer and evolved her 28-year career into leadership roles with Equinox, Nike and Flywheel Sports. At Equinox, she was the Senior Director of the Equinox Fitness Training Institute and founded the Equinox Academy. As the Global Director of Performance and Fitness at Nike, she supervised the re-creation of the Nike Training Club App and oversaw the Nike Trainer Network. Most recently, Geralyn was the Chief Talent and Content Officer for Flywheel Sports, managing almost 500 instructors nationally and launching the Fly OnDemand at-home bike. Today, Geralyn provides customized learning and development and marketing expertise for some of the industry's best brands with her firm, Coopersmith Consulting and educates and inspires the next generation of fitness professionals with her website, fitnessprobootcamp.com.

Geralyn, besides being an extremely successful trainer yourself, you've trained and coached thousands of trainers on how to make it in this profession. What's your definition of success?

Success is not fixed; it's a constantly moving target. I don't consider myself a success because there's the idea that with success, you get there and it's over. I'm constantly evolving and going to a different place—on the journey, as opposed to actually getting there.

Success is a feeling that your passions and talents are in line with what you're doing and getting compensated for, at whatever level that may be. Hopefully, it's at a level where your basics are covered and you're not stressing about your bills and are living your passion on a day-to-day basis.

You say you don't consider yourself a success, but was there a time when you started to think things were happening and you were beginning to excel in this business?

I was on the right path and things were working around 1997 when I was starting grad school and was a full-time trainer in New York. I had zero time, was completely booked, had a waiting list of people who wanted to train with me and was profiled in New York Magazine as a "trainer to watch." At the time, the idea of success was external things, like seeing my name in print or enjoying other people's affection; in that context, I thought I was on the right track.

I always want to feel content to the extent I can in my life, but I never want to feel complacent. Those are at odds with each other. Be where I am now and feel good about that, but don't think where I am now is the be-all end-all, and that there's nowhere for me to evolve into over time.

What motivates you to get out of bed in the morning? What's the "it" that drives you?

On both the micro level and the macro, I like to know I'm making people's lives better. If I pull up higher to a 30,000-foot view, I like seeing that the bigger picture is getting better. That's the hardest thing to see; that's a bit like turning the Titanic. Is it moving? I can't tell.

Over time, you realize you've moved more and faster than you expected. When you're in the middle, it seems really slow. Feeling able to change people's lives for the better has always driven me.

As a trainer at the beginning of a career, you might not feel like you're making much of an impact. Sometimes we have to look a little deeper into what we're doing.

As a trainer, it's very easy to get into a situation where you find yourself counting to 12—standing with a clipboard counting reps. That's when you get stagnant. You're just dialing it in. We've all been there where you just don't have it the way you should. But to the extent you can "bring it" every day, you really need to.

You also need to have different things outside of work to keep you moving. Whether it's building a website, writing a book or developing your ability as a speaker, we need other things that force us to grow.

It's definitely an evolution. For me, it started out as training one on one; then my schedule was filled and I opened my own space where I started doing semi-private and group training. It was great to impact more people, but it was in doing the *Strength Coach Podcast* and *StrengthCoach.com* that I started to see the impact on people all over the world. Working with you on the Nike Training Club app and reaching millions of people empowered me to keep doing what I was doing and look for more ways to do it.

What are some of the traits you attribute to how successful you've become?

I work really hard and I try to give more than 100 percent in everything I do—100 percent is just doing the job you're supposed to do. I love this quote from Brian Tracy, "Your success in life will be in direct proportion to what you do after you do what you said you were going to do."

People will say, "I did what I was supposed to do." That's just the bare minimum. I'm always thinking, "What's the additional 10 or 20 percent minimum I'm doing over and above what's expected?" If I can do more, great. That's the biggest thing that has helped me stand out. It made people take notice.

I believe in putting people first, being kind to people and really thinking about how I treat every single person. Things like saying good morning to everyone and treating everyone at every level of the company with the same respect. I'm always watching how other people treat people, especially people in positions considered "less important" in the company. When I see other people talk to them in a rough way, I make a mental note, "Not really a nice person."

Mike Boyle talks about being a Certified Nice Person. This is a very close profession; I can't tell you the number of people I've worked with who say, "That person is a jerk and I never want to work together again."

On the other hand, you hear, "That person's gold. She'll have your back; you want her in your foxhole."

I'm always on a path for self-improvement and self-reflection; I'm very conscious of it. I practice metacognition—I'm always thinking about my thinking and trying to be detached and an observer to check myself. Am I right or do I just think I'm right? And if I'm wrong, own it. I can choose to be wrong, but I want to own my choice.

What are some of the sacrifices you've made to get where you are?

Picking up my family and moving from coast to coast is a specific instance of a sacrifice I was very apprehensive about. Nike was a really good opportunity for me, but it was hard telling my son—who was in the middle of his eighth grade year during that initial move—that we were moving across the country and he had to leave his friends. I had to hope it was worth it and I wasn't screwing him up.

A lot of the sacrifice has been time. It's the most precious commodity any of us have. I have to be very thoughtful and constantly balancing whether things will be worth the time and effort.

I went back to work full time when my son Logan turned four. I wasn't going to be the PTA mother; I wasn't going to be at every bake sale and recital. I haven't been and I can't be. I'm not the lead parent; I was for the first four years of his life, but I'm not now. Sometimes, especially as a woman, that's a little heavier.

People say, "You can have it all," but you can't. You have to figure out what's taking the lead in that moment and you have to be really thoughtful.

If you're choosing not to be here, is it worth it for the greater good? Do you have to be here? Could you reschedule? If not, you're not going to be at that event and you have to be okay with that. That's a lot of personal sacrifice in terms of time spent prioritizing things.

At least your son had those first four years. A lot of kids with both parents working don't have a lead parent the way he did during that time.

It's funny because he doesn't remember it. I believe it formed who he is and it's one of the reasons he's so balanced and mentally healthy. He doesn't remember me staying at home.

Every once in a while, he'll say something about being proud of me. His idea of what women should be is different than what a lot of kids might think. He assumes a woman would work hard and succeed in her field. It will be an interesting orientation for him to have as he goes through life and has his own relationships with women.

You've dealt with the ups and downs of being a trainer, the stress of management in a big corporation and a lot of frustration educating trainers in a profession with a high turnover rate. Was there a time when you wanted to go into another field?

I've had those moments in every iteration of my career. When I was an independent personal trainer working in August when nobody's around and I was worrying about which flavor of Ramen noodles I was going to get for the month, it was a constant inner struggle.

I went through it again as part of management at Equinox when I didn't agree with the direction the company was taking. Sometimes you can influence that and sometimes you can't. When I had to enforce something I didn't believe in, I used to have to say, "This is the game we're playing; we're all suited up to get out on the field. Should you choose to join us, these are the rules of the game. I may not like it, but this is where we are."

More recently, at Nike, it's a big place—as an individual, you're only going to have so much impact on an organization with 40,000 people. If you're not cool with that, it's easy to get frustrated…and at times I did. You want to make an impact and you can't always have that.

One of the things that drove me to Flywheel was a greater opportunity to make an impact. Flywheel is a 1,200-person organization and I reported to the CEO. There were fewer layers of filter to go through to make something happen. When you feel you have almost no chance of moving the ball forward, it's hard not to get to a point where, irrespective of the income, you think about doing something else.

I don't want to feel like I'm just going through the motions and not getting anything done. That makes me crazy. If you can push past that, there's usually something better on the other side. But in that moment, it can be a miserable place to be.

Anyone who knows you or has worked with you knows the impact you had on every level in this field. It helps the rest of us to know that even the most successful people feel that way sometimes.

You're an avid reader and book listener. What are three non fitness–related books that can help us in our development?

I'm obsessed with self-improvement books and learning. If I get one idea out of something, I'm ahead of the game. I love a paradigm shift, but that's rare—even one takeaway is worth the time reading a book.

For specific recommendations, *The Element* by Ken Robinson is amazing. It's about finding your passion in life. It's the element where your aptitude and passion meet. Everyone has to find their own element.

Feel the Fear and Do It Anyway is an oldie but goodie by Susan Jeffers. I read it when I was in my 20s. I don't know many books that have had as much of an impact on me. The whole idea is that we're always uncomfortable and we're always stepping into spaces we don't know. That's life—get used to it, embrace it and just go forward with it. That's a great book.

The Eighth Habit by Stephen Covey is a really good read. People always talk about *The 7 Habits of Highly Effective People* because that's what he's most known for, but *The Eighth Habit* is about leaving a legacy and understanding how to elevate other people. There's a huge leadership component to it. That was a very important book in my life.

Give us three people to follow we can all learn from.

Tony Robbins has been a huge influence in my early thinking about what I wanted to be and how I wanted to go about my life—a huge, huge influence.

Jack Canfield is another person to follow, because he makes things simple, tangible and user-friendly. He's great.

Marianne Williamson gives us an embraceable way to think about spirituality, an idea of manifesting in a way that makes sense.

I really love Joseph Campbell's work. He was a philosophy professor at Sarah Lawrence College for many years. He talked about following your bliss— I love reading his stuff. A lot of what you hear in *The Element* was informed by Joseph Campbell.

Geralyn, you have been instrumental in the development of many trainers and coaches in this profession and your impact has been felt worldwide. Your efforts helped move the needle in such a positive way for all of us. Thanks for sharing your journey.

BE LIKE GERALYN

"I'm obsessed with self-improvement books and learning."

READING (AND LISTENING) IS FUNDAMENTAL

Earl Nightingale said, "One hour per day of study will put you at the top of your field in three years. Within five years you will be a national authority. In seven years you will be one of the best in the world at what you do."

Pick a number of books you want to read or listen to over the next year.

Try for a minimum of 24. That's two a month.

Schedule time every day to read or listen—at least 30 minutes—and focus on sticking to that schedule.

If you have a commute, use audio books. If not, make reading part of your morning routine.

Don't just pick training-related books. Try to think outside the box: Personal Development, Motivation, Business and Biographies.

After each chapter, write a takeaway or try to teach someone what you learned.

Make what you learned a topic of conversation with people you speak with. Try to teach them what you learned.

Both writing and teaching are great ways to increase retention.

DAN JOHN

Dan is a senior lecturer at St. Mary's University, Twickenham, London. He's a National Masters Champion in Olympic lifting, discus and weight pentathlon and has coached since 1979 at every level. Dan's the author of multiple books, including the bestseller Never Let Go. He's active on social media and writes a blog on his site, danjohn.net.

You've had success in different areas of your life as a student, athlete, teacher, trainer and writer. How do you define success?

I think I'll steal the answer to this one. During the dark night of my soul, which would have been 1985, I was struggling. I went to the library and there I found a cassette called *Lead the Field* by Earl Nightingale.

I was living on a foldout bed in a basement and my car was always broken. The bumper was held together with a weightlifting belt, and the backseat was burned because I put books on it—the battery was there and it started a fire. I was a school teacher and I was ill with live parasites from the Middle East.

I listened to the cassette series and Nightingale's definition of success hit me across the face. It's the progressive realization of a worthy ideal. He continued, "And school teachers are probably the most successful people in society because of their ideals." That entirely changed my worldview and my paradigm.

I stopped and thought, "I sleep on a foldout bed; it's cold at night because the heater isn't very good, and it's a struggle with my illness to work every day." I slept up to 12 hours a night, but you know what? I'm okay; I have this vision of things and I'm marching toward this ideal.

People are going to miss this very important part. I'm not talking about goal setting; I'm good at both setting and getting goals. My wife Tiffani will tell you I've had goals that didn't mean that much to me—she could see it in my eye. But whenever I've focused on that thousand-mile journey, that step-by-step journey toward something that's bigger than how many commas are in a bank account number, how far you throw or how much you lift, but instead the vision behind the vision—that's when I'm most successful.

There's certainly science behind the idea of happiness and the progression with movement toward that ideal. As an athlete, especially a high-level athlete like you, these small progressive movements toward the goal make the difference.

John Powell used to have the world record in the discus. He made a point when I first met him in 1975, but I didn't fully grasp it at the time: "Yard by yard, it's hard, but inch by inch, it's a cinch." It didn't make sense until my life changed—when you're young that just pours over you like water. You don't get it.

The idea is, if I make a pound of progress every day, at the end of the year, that's 365 more pounds on my lift. People totally under-appreciate how much can be done a little every day. That has become my worldview.

Arthur Schopenhauer's great comment was that when you're going through life, you just bump into things. There are always accidents, but when you look back on your life, you can see it's a straight line.

When did you consider yourself a success? When did you to start to feel, "I'm getting this life thing right"?

I can tell you the day almost exactly. There's a picture of me standing next to my old silver pickup truck, smiling. I was holding the first copy of my book *Never Let Go.* That's the first time I ever breathed a sigh of "I made it."

Forty years ago, my team won the California state track championship, and I also won the discus. But as an athlete, you don't celebrate because there's always something else coming up. When I got a scholarship to Utah State, I was so happy, but then I had to step up to the Division One level. When you're done with that, you have to step up to the national level, then the international level. There's always a bigger level; when you're in the middle of it, you can't see very much—you're blind.

Holding that book was the moment for me because so many things in my life intersected at that point. I'd overcome so many things. So…2009, holding the book *Never Let Go.*

One of the most important lessons I've learned this year with one of my coaches is the idea of not celebrating enough, not taking time out to look at an accomplishment and rewarding myself for it. If you don't do that, you forget. Do you feel like you should have taken a little more time?

I have one regret: I didn't celebrate well enough.

I was always somewhere else and never celebrated things. I didn't give myself even the decency of a personal high five. These days, I take celebrations much more seriously. When I have a book coming out, I tell people I'm going to be at Brio in Fashion Place mall here in Murray so we can meet. Sometimes I sign copies for everybody, but sometimes all I have is a single book and I don't care: I celebrated. I'm very focused on making sure I celebrate things now.

In fact, on my Facebook page, you'll find a video my wife took of me breaking the state record in the snatch. I had this massively goofy smile. I celebrated on the platform and then I celebrated later. It's something I regret that I didn't do enough of in earlier years.

I don't know what year it was when I got your first DVD, *Everything's over My Head,* could have been 2009. I remember specifically saying, "How did I miss this guy? Where has he been?" In this profession, we're thinking you've had this great impact in this field—things you were doing and saying and teaching. That needs to be celebrated too, that impact.

I wish I would've done a better job of promoting myself. This is straight-up stuff, I invented the goblet squat; the words "suitcase carry" came from me—I can show them to you from old articles in *Men's Health.* No one used the words in that context before. There was the slosh pipe—that was Greg Henger's great invention and I wrote the article that brought it public.

Most people don't realize it, but then they'll see something, and all of a sudden, they realize, "Wait, that was you in that video from 1991?" *Bigger, Faster, Stronger* has videos of me lifting, and people say, "I saw those in high school! That was you?" It's just funny—what else can I say at that point?

I'm not saying, "Look at me, look at me," but one thing I didn't do is sell stuff very well. I should've named the lifts after myself. I'm joking. But yes, I've been around.

I mentioned your success in different areas as a teacher, athlete, trainer and author. Just pertaining to the fitness industry, what motivates you to get out of bed and get moving in the morning?

I do things a little differently. I'm sticking with this idea of the worthy ideal. My wife and I have a mission statement for our family: "Make a difference." I want to leave a legacy. For example, Tiffani, my daughters and I have an endowment we use to donate money to schools and organizations.

One of the things that gets me to write first thing in the morning is that I want to record the lessons I've learned in strength, fitness, longevity, health and performance sports. I'd like to leave that information documented. If someone decides to go on a journey of athletics, longevity, health or reasonableness, there'll be a canon of books they can refer to with this crazy psychopath maniac's ideas.

The next thing that gets me out of bed in the morning is that I don't make any money unless I write and do my college class work. The other thing that rolls me out of bed is the excitement of being able to work out with my friends every morning.

I love that you're building a "canon" of books. Is there a routine for your mornings?

The mistake most people make is that they try to make first thing in the morning the start of the day. I use the *Genesis* model: a day starts with the night before. The night before is the key to a good morning. I imagine a dog going in circles, getting ready to go to bed.

I've also learned that the morning routine starts the night before. Everybody's different, but having a workday shutdown process as opposed to an evening routine sets me up for the next day.

In theology, the night is before day. It sounds weird, but a successful day starts the night before. Nothing new here; successful people have been thinking this way for 5,000 years.

If you start thinking, Thursday starts on Wednesday evening, you're preparing for a better Thursday by getting more sleep, eating a healthy meal, winding down. You'll tend to be a lot happier and more successful with this brand-new 5,000-year-old idea.

What are some other habits you attribute to your success?

Woody Allen said, "Ninety percent of success is showing up." I'm very good at showing up. I have all kinds of certifications. I go to things. It doesn't matter what competition I've ever won in my life, someone will say, "You won because Bob Jones didn't show up that day." Well, everyone knew the discus throw was 9:00AM on June 26th. How did he not know that?

I'm going to keep that national championship because I showed up.

Show up. Don't quit. Ask questions. I read that for the first time, probably somewhere in the 1980s: Show up. Don't quit. Ask questions. I know someone who recently claimed to have invented that phrase, but I saw it in an article in the 1980s. Those are the three secrets to success.

I hate to call them habits, though. It's the idea that if you want to go on a fat-loss program, just start and…then keep going. That sounds too simple, but it does work.

I have a couple of other habits. One, I have a shopping list—I think a shopping list might be the most important thing to have in life. You go to the store with a shopping list because you have a menu. I've written about my menu in almost every book I've written and people still miss the value of it. Monday night we eat steak and salad. Tuesday nights, we have Viking enchiladas. Wednesday night is jambalaya. Thursday night is breakfast for dinner. We've been doing that since the girls were babies. Then, we shop to that menu. I always know what to buy and it extinguishes all that clutter.

The next thing to note is a chore list. Monday was white laundry. Tuesday was dark laundry. Wednesday was bathrooms. Now that it's just my wife and me, it's a little different—it's a lot easier. Now Wednesday is laundry day. I'll be folding laundry right after we finish this interview.

When we had the girls in the house, we had white and dark laundry baskets. If I went past the white basket on Friday and I saw it was full, I just dismissed it because I knew Monday was white laundry day…not Friday. It didn't even seep into my brain space that I had a full basket of white laundry.

Make yourself a menu, a chore list, a shopping list, a monthly checklist for the home, a car checklist. When's your car registration due? You know it's coming, so plan it. If February is when your car registration is due, on February first you can knock that thing out of the way. Clean up that mental clutter; the upside of all this crazy stuff is that it cleans up your brainpan so you have extra space to do the things you want to do in life, not what you need to do.

I first heard the idea from Craig Ballantyne that structure will give you freedom because you don't have to think about those things. It's a hard thing for people to grasp; they don't get it, but once you start doing it, you understand how effective it can be.

We fought with our daughters when we sent them to Catholic schools. Every Catholic school student complains about how ugly the uniforms are. What they don't understand is what a total pain it is to have freedom from uniforms. They were both seniors, and they both said the same thing. Having a uniform is great; you sniff the shirt to make sure it doesn't smell too bad. You throw on the pants or skirt; you're done and you walk out the door. You know everything matches because it's a uniform.

All that mental space that would be spent on whether you should wear the blue dress with the pink pants—it's out, done. People get on my case because I wear the same thing every day. I have 16 of the same black polo shirts, and why 16? That's all they had in North America. I wear Barbell brand jeans every day. I have six pairs of Nike Frees. I wear the same thing all the time. People say, "Dan, how can you write so many books?" It's because I have 16 of the same shirt.

"No, no, no, what do you do to write that much?"

No, you missed it: Every minute you spent looking at your shirts, I was, well, not necessarily typing—I might have been just drinking coffee and staring out the window, but my brainpan was freed up. I'm probably the most habitual person you'll ever meet in your life.

There's a lot to be said for fighting decision fatigue. Steve Jobs, Mark Zuckerberg… the list goes on of people who wear the same clothes. There's no decision there.

Talk to us about your process with goal setting, whether you review them—give us a look into that process.

In 1971, I threw the discus 103 feet—which is fine. I got the book *Track and Field Omnibook,* where in the original edition it talks about Ralph Maughan at Utah State University being a great discus coach. I told my sister, "I want to go to Utah State and throw the discus for Ralph Maughan." There I was, a 118-pound discus thrower.

Six years later, I got a phone call: "I'm Coach Ralph Maughan from Utah State University, and I'd like to offer you a full-ride scholarship."

When I set goals, very often they're those kinds of goals; they're big and beautiful and multi-year. I also tend to make shorter-term goals, like to get ready for a contest…and that would be a little different. With those, I use an idea from Pat Flynn called "pirate maps."

Here's the mistake some people make—they write a goal, but they don't write a plan. A pirate map is this: Go to St. John's island, find the white coconut tree, take six paces to the west, dig down six feet and find the buried treasure.

The pirate map for my last weightlifting meet was this:

Number One: Honor my sleep routine.

Number Two: Wake up and be grateful. If I'm not grateful when I wake up, I didn't get enough sleep.

Number Three: Do a one-minute meditation every day.

Number Four: Olympic lift three days a week; do mobility work three days a week.

Number Five: Eat eight different vegetables every day.

If I follow this every day, I put myself in place to be successful.

The other thing I do with goal setting is when I want to compete in a contest of any kind, the first thing I do is register for the contest. I extend my membership for the group—U.S. weightlifting or U.S. Track and Field or the Highland Game community…whatever. I start sending checks out on day one.

The contest might not be for six months, but when I write that check, put it in the mail, I'm beginning to gear up. I haven't even exercised yet, but I'll book the hotel room and buy the flights and if I have to rent a car, I'll rent a car. I'm six months out, but I'm pushing things forward.

Tim Anderson always says, "It's that last snowflake that makes an avalanche." I'm trying to prepare for the avalanche by dropping snowflakes. That's how I do it.

Once I slide into the pirate maps, every time I eat a meal, I'm looking for a different vegetable to add because it's good for me. Yes, it's good for you to eat vegetables. Yay for me, but here's the thing: It also puts me on the platform every time I'm looking for a vegetable.

Several times a day when I'm eating, I'm mentally throwing the discus or lifting weights on the platform. Where I am in my career, the most important thing I do is simply show up for competitions—that's the big one. I have to plan it to do it, and that's how I plan.

Are there things you do within the year to recharge?

I block out time for bigger things. Tiff and I take at least a month a year to go to Ireland; we rent an apartment in Galway and stay there. I write, we walk, we swim in Galway Bay, we laugh, and that's very important.

I used to cross out June for discus camp, but that doesn't exist anymore. In December, I try very hard not to travel much. I also have a tradition—I got this from a friend who's a Benedictine nun. She told me, "You should block out an afternoon every day of the week when you just read." Between traveling in planes and that afternoon a week, that's when I do most of my reading. If I could make the world a happier place, every Wednesday afternoon we'd set it up so everyone stops working and reads for three hours. We'd all be happier—and smarter.

Dan, there's wisdom as we get older, but sometimes we do things a certain way when we're younger. On this road to trying to get where we are, we have to make some sacrifices. Do you feel like you've had to make sacrifices to get where you are?

The only joints in my body that haven't had surgery are my ankles. Every other joint has had surgery—fingers, wrists, elbows, shoulders, knees, hips. I didn't have sex on purpose for a long time—years in fact—because I wanted to be a great thrower and I had this idea that dating, sex and all that would stop me. I'm proud of it in a way. I look back, and it's like, "You're a brave man."

I didn't drink alcohol; I didn't celebrate at all in school until my senior year in college. How many celebrations have I missed being on the road? It's a lot.

I've had to walk away from some friendships. Sometimes you wake up and you realize a relationship isn't good for anybody. I know this is going to sound awful and I hope some of my friends don't hear it. Tiff and I both noticed that when we finally hit our stride financially, it was tough to be around some people.

What sacrifices? My body, probably my long-term health, friendships, time celebrating. I don't have those stories about that time we got drunk and threw up on each other. That story about picking up that chick at that thing, and doing whatever…I don't have those stories. Do I miss them? Sure!

I wore a tie seven days a week through the late '80s, '90s and into the 2000s. I told my daughters when I hit a certain level of income, they'd never again see me in a tie except for a funeral or a wedding. Once we were at an event, and my daughter walks over and says, "You're not wearing a tie," and I said, "Nope, I'm not." She said, "You did it," and I said, "Yes, I did."

It's important that I don't need to prove anything or to fit in. There's no way to say this without coming off a bit snarky, but I don't need to impress anybody anymore. If I don't get a job because I'm not wearing a tie, I'm okay with that. If someone notes, "He's not wearing a tie," well…shut up. That's not important to me.

Being a lifelong athlete, think about those times when you realized, "Damn, I can't lift for x amount of time; I can't compete," which is important to you. How do you get through those times?

This is going to be an odd answer, but I've had two doctors tell me I'd never compete again, once was the wrist I broke really badly and the other was after a total hip replacement. I also took a discus in the head that gave me a six-month blackout.

But Maurice Ravel has a piece of music called the *Bolero,* and during my worst times, I'd go "bolero" on things. *Bolero* means "tun, tun, tun, tun, tun, ta ta ta, tun, tun, tun," and the song is going to take 26 minutes for the whole rest of the orchestra to resound and play along with that. My mental image was *Bolero.*

True story: I was in a walker after a hip replacement, hobbling down the hall in our apartment building, and I hear a little girl across the way say, "Mommy, is the nice man okay?" I thought, "I'm using a walker today, but I'll be on crutches tomorrow, and on a cane next week, and then I'll be running hills in a year." But God, give me that year.

The thing is, I've had my journey in the darkness. But you realize it's going to build back up—you just got to give the song the 26 minutes. You have to give me the year. You have to give me the six weeks, that's all I'm asking, and that's how I've done it my whole life.

Dan, you're a prolific reader. I know this will be a hard one for you, but give us three non fitness–related books people should read for their development.

We can be here for days. I'm going to give you three books I read at different times in my life. I'd have to say the *Sword in the Stone*—if you read my *Wandering Weights* newsletter, you'll know I'm going paragraph by paragraph through the book, reviewing the lessons I've learned from every chapter. *Sword in the Stone,* especially if you can find the 1938 edition, is a book that embraces education. They throw their arms around education, and to be honest with you, there's a whole bunch about lifting in the book too. It would have been 1970 when I first read it.

Probably about 1985 or '86, during that dark night of my soul, the movie *Dune* came out, which was terrible, but because the movie came out, I read the book. It's such a leap of imagination. He builds an entire war of the universe with such interesting insights of things; I recommend *Dune.*

Oddly, I didn't read this book early on; it came out when I was young, but just a few years ago, I read *The Godfather.* One thing you'll discover about these, they're all modern epics—modern, big stories, epics. When I teach epics, I always start the lecture with, "Let me explain what an epic is. An epic is big." These are big stories.

Now name three people we should follow.

This is going to sound like a weird list. The first is J.K. Rowling, the author of the Harry Potter books. She said something that just stopped me in my tracks: She felt that "rock bottom" was the foundation she built her career on, and I thought to myself, "You just can't do better than that."

Study J.K. Rowling, study her story of how she was struggling; she has a daughter and they were just struggling. This thing called *Harry Potter* pops into her head and she takes out pencil and paper and diagrams the entire seven parts that all just tie in; she diagrams them first. I love it.

The next person is another author, Rick Riordan. Probably the most famous of his books is the book *Percy Jackson*, but he also does the one I just finished, the Jason Grace series. He retells demigod stories.

Rick Riordan has a son who has dyslexia; he decided that instead of moaning, "It's a terrible thing," he'd write about it. The stories are that Percy Jackson has dyslexia because he's a demigod and he's not wired to read English; he's wired to read Greek. The books are delightful.

Then the final person is the Stanford professor, BJ Fogg. His idea, which he calls "Tiny Habits," completely changed my vision on how we coach and develop athletes and, really, how we should work with everyone.

If somebody had asked me why I think you're successful, I'd say, "I don't know if there's anybody who's as accessible, who can listen as much as he likes to talk—he can listen like nobody I've ever seen."

I've seen you in conversations where you were involved with people you don't even know who came up to you to ask a question. There's a sense of humor and that genuineness that you can't fake. That's why people respond to you. They love you.

I wish my mother and father could have heard that; that's quite a statement. I really appreciate that. I really do.

Dan, thank you for sharing your journey to success. We appreciate your life lessons.

BE LIKE DAN

"I have one regret; I didn't honestly celebrate things well enough. Now, as Tiffani and my friends will tell you, I celebrate all of life's little victories."

CELEBRATE

First, start by writing three of your "wins" down each day during your "work-day/evening" shutdown (see Alwyn Cosgrove's Be Like).

Ideally, the wins will be related to your goals, but they don't have to be. It could be as simple as "Had a great lunch with _____" or "Took a nice bike ride."

Whatever they are, just write them down. This will put you in a great frame of mind remembering the good things that happened that day.

When you write our your goals, make sure to include how you will celebrate.

For example:

Goal: "I will get 10 new personal training clients by September 1st."

Celebration: "Going to dinner at the expensive new spot in town."

It's important to make sure it's something you really want, and you also have to make sure you don't reward yourself if you don't achieve it. If you went to the dinner anyway, the goal and celebration combination doesn't mean anything.

Like Dan said, "Be sure you're celebrating things worthy of celebrating."

When unexpected things come up that you worked hard for, make sure to stop, smell the roses and celebrate them too.

You work hard, you deserve it!

BRANDON MARCELLO

Brandon is a high-performance strategist who takes forward-thinking organizations and elite athletes to the next level of their games and careers. Having extensive involvement in both the applied and research worlds, he has implemented successful high-performance training programs for professional, Olympic and collegiate athletes. A recognized author, researcher and international presenter, Brandon routinely speaks around the world on a number of topics pertaining to elite-level training and human performance. Continuing his work with the U.S. Department of Defense, Brandon has recently been tasked with defining the future of soldier performance. Keep up with Brandon via his site at brandonmarcellophd.com.

You've been in this field for 22 years, a true overnight success. How do you define success at this point in your career?

It really comes down to being happy with your life's work and what you're doing. And does it allow you to do all the things you want to do? Your life's work is never complete. That makes it worthwhile. Are you making a dent; are you helping people? Are you doing what you want to do? And are you happy?

A common theme among a lot of these interviews has been progression, moving forward and keeping that momentum going—not only to progress a career, but to keep helping others and making an impact.

You can get caught up in trying to be successful. It's almost like looking at a dysmorphic image. When people look in the mirror, maybe they want to be bigger, but they see themselves skinny, and they have to gain more and more. They're not happy with who they are.

People get caught up in a success model of never being happy because they don't feel they've attained success. I'm not saying we should be complacent. I'm saying it becomes obsessive, and that's a mistake.

When we're younger we sometimes don't understand that. When did you feel you were starting to become successful?

I don't know that I really am. I look at so many people in our profession who are extremely successful, which means they're able to reach and help more people. I'm still working on it.

It's not an overnight thing. I've been screwing up for 22 years. And that's what a lot of people miss. Mike Boyle has done amazing things for our profession. People want to be Mike, but they want to be him *tomorrow*. Or I want to be a Gray Cook—I want to be Gray *tomorrow*. But these people put in their time.

We live in a world of immediacy. If you want an answer, you can google it. If you need money, you can go to the ATM. If you want something ordered, you can buy it on Amazon and it can be at your door tomorrow. In a world of immediacy, we get caught up in believing that overnight success is a real thing. There's such a thing as overnight success, but it's just the start of something, which takes a long time to accomplish.

Is the idea of moving forward and staying on the long tail of greater reach what gets you out of bed in the morning? What is it that keeps you going?

There are a couple of things. First is my family. And the other is my mentors. There's an extreme responsibility to do good by your mentors. You're a reflection of family, and you're also a reflection of your pedigree and your mentors. That's part of it—I'm trying to do a good job for all those people.

I've always stood by that "Poor is the person who does not surpass his master" idea. Mentors should want you to do better than they've done. If you're guiding and mentoring people, you have to be comfortable that, comfortable knowing they're going to be better than you—and you want that to happen. If you're only in it for yourself, you're really not in it for the profession. And that's not being successful; that's being self-centered.

The last element would be colleagues. I want to continue to interact and work with colleagues and learn from them.

A common theme among everyone I have interviewed is a mission to make an impact. If that doesn't come across to the readers, they're not reading it closely enough.

Let's talk about your morning routine. Do you have a routine in the morning?

My morning routine is to take my daughter on a morning walk; I wrap her up in a blanket and we go on a walk, sometimes 10 minutes, sometimes a half hour. She loves to go outside and look around at the birds. It's just interacting with nature, probably something we should all do a little more. It's our quiet time together.

Certainly, taking a walk is something a lot of people incorporate to get the creative juices flowing.

When I was at Athletes Performance, I used to walk a couple of miles to work and some mornings, the athletes would say, "You walked in this morning, didn't you? You seem different when you walk in compared to when you drive."

It gets the creative juices flowing. There's science there, too. We know that walking at 1.2 miles per hour actually stimulates creativity. The purpose of our walk isn't to stimulate creativity, but it's a side effect I'll take.

As the Director of Sports Performance at Stanford University, being part of setting up Athletes Performance, being part of the USA Softball at such a high level, there have to be some habits you've done that contributed to helping you get to where you are.

We read books and articles about how successful people operate. There's a four-hour work week; some people get up at five in the morning and have their morning routine or the opposite, some people stay up late. Everyone has a different recipe for success.

And that's the thing: understanding which recipe works best for you. I don't sit down well to work straight four hours in a row. I work in 30-minute increments—that's my thing. I work 30 minutes and then take a break for five, maybe walk around outside for a bit. I'm still thinking about what I'm doing, but I'm not devoted entirely to the task. I'll go back and work for another 20 or 30 minutes, and then take another break.

But I also know people who can't work that way.

Everybody works and learns differently. Some people like offices; some people like coffee shops; some people like to work from home. Find works to be productive, be fruitful and to achieve what you want to achieve—that's the key.

There was a time when I thought I had to be in the office, that I had to be there early and had to work all day. But I wasn't getting done what I needed to get done. I was stale. And then finally, I decided to try it my way. All of a sudden, things were completely different.

Those "how to work" books are great because they give people structure and people do well with structure. Sometimes people are looking for a spark or an idea, and sometimes those books are what they need to realize, "I never thought about getting up earlier and knocking out email and then sitting down to read for 20 minutes. That would be great."

That's great for some people, but you have to be careful not to paint everybody into that picture. Those ideas are fantastic for general guidance. But sometimes we put them in these buckets of absolutes, which is a mistake.

That's what I'm trying to do with this book project, to give readers a well-rounded view of the most successful people in this field. We have such a diverse group. There are 50 action steps in this book (the Be Likes). I don't want everyone to do all of them. I want them to find what works for them. There are so many roads to the path of success.

What about goals? What's your process for those?

I have endgame projects. I work in projects, rather than goals. I reverse engineer, just like I periodize a program. I write thoughts and ideas of when I'd like to accomplish "this" by.

And other things have deadlines I'm pinned to. Maybe I'm doing a presentation for Perform Better and Chris Poirier needs the slides by a certain day so they can print the handout. Maybe I have a project for work. I have deadlines I have to achieve. But for other goals, some don't hold my feet to the fire. They're loose goals that have a rough range of what I'd like to get done.

I found the book *The One Thing* to be phenomenal in terms of organizing. The whole premise is, "What is the one thing you can do that makes everything else either easier or unnecessary?" hat's been helpful in terms of project or goal management. And we have a vision board at home too.

A lot of people think *The One Thing* is going to be about finding the one thing you could do every day. But in the book, there's an excellent way of reverse engineering long-term goals.

That book is how I used to teach program design. I'd say, "You have an athlete who comes in or somebody trying to achieve a goal. You have three minutes. What do you do?" And they'd pick that one thing. Then, "Write that down. Now, what if I give you five minutes, what would you do?"

We go 10 minutes in, 12 minutes in and then 15 minutes in. The next thing you know, they've built a full program based on priorities, that one thing, and building upon that.

What about staying organized? How do you stay organized?

There are certain parts of my life where I have to be extremely organized, and there are other parts where I'm a complete disaster. Like my desk—forget about it; it's a mess. But there are other pieces, like I want the car clean…garage, clean…the house, clean. The kitchen is spotless. It's weird. I have different compartments where I can be very dishev-eled, and these other compartments where I have to be very clean. In my home life, I'm very clean and then my work life is cluttered like you wouldn't believe. I don't know if that's a good thing or a bad thing.

You're one of our go-to experts on sleep, naps and recharging. With all that you've learned, what have you incorporated into your life?

I monitor my sleep every night. I wear a Fatigue Science ReadiBand and every morning, I look at my sleep record. Last night, I got 7.1 hours of sleep. I woke up three times and lost 40 minutes to awakenings. The ReadiBand comes with a little effectiveness score as well.

If I'm a little under where I'd like to be, sometimes I'll sneak in a nap. I don't always have that luxury, but I would if I could. I'm a big fan of naps and if I can take them, I will. My big thing is to try to get the bulk of my sleep at night; I go to bed early. I read at night and then I shut it down.

What are you trying to do with that sleep data?

There are a couple things I do with it—one, just in the near term, I look at my nightly sleep. How did I do? I also look at it also across the seven-day average. Did I average seven hours of sleep? That's my arbitrary number: I should average 49 hours of sleep in a week. If I can achieve that, I'm in a pretty good spot. If I'm under it, I might need to take a couple more naps or I might be hurting myself. I also look at consistency. Am I going to bed at a consistent time?

The other piece I look at it is how many awakenings I had through the night; obviously we want to keep those down. If I wake up a lot during the night, maybe I have something on my mind—it might be indicative of something I've got to clear off my plate.

Often, when you want to be successful in this business, it's very hard in terms of own-ing a facility or consulting with a team. There's a lot of travel involved, especially for somebody like you, who's speaking all over the world. What are some of the sacrifices you've made to get to where you are?

It's a give and take. Right now, in terms of sacrifices, I'm giving up time for family when I'm traveling so much. I travel 12 to 15 days a month. I sacrifice being home. At the same time, when I'm home, I'm home.

Early on, I made sacrifices in terms of personal life. I thought I had to work and work hard—and you do. But you also have to take time for yourself, which I didn't do. I wasn't very good at that, and I realized later it didn't have to happen that way. Nothing you can do about it then, but you can correct it for the future.

Was there ever a time when you thought, "I've got to figure out something else." What did you do to get through those hardest times?

Anytime I have a hard time, I lean on family. They can give a great perspective. Or you can lean on mentors, because they have insight. If you have a tough decision or you're having a hard time, it's important to reach out to people you trust.

"Trust" means people are looking out for your best interests…and you know they are.

That's the important thing I've done in the past when I've hit hard times. I reach out—reach out to family, reach out to mentors and use their advice to help me, to guide me through the quagmire.

Give me three non-fitness books we should read to help in our development.

I have tons of them. I have a 50-page rule. I'll give a book 50 pages, and if I don't like it, I'm out.

I just finished reading *The Happiness Track*, which was good. That was about tapping into your inner happiness and reframing your thoughts.

I read *Verbal Judo*—that was fun. It was the recommendation of Gray Cook; we were chatting about books and he said, get *Verbal Judo*. It's about using words to disarm people and situations. And it was a really fun read.

Checklist Manifesto is a book I just picked up so I can't give you a good review of it yet—I just started it. A friend of mine sent it to me and said, "Here's something you need to read." I just started reading it and am enjoying it so far.

This is going to sound crazy, but I just read a book called *No Bad Kids*. I read it because I have a little one, and it talks about toddler discipline without shame. Let me tell you, some of these things really transcend what we do in my world in dealing with athletes. Some are really good, valuable lessons. What it comes down to is, you would never talk to an adult the way you would talk to a child.

I also am a big reader of *Time* magazine. I get it every week. I try to read very little from the profession, believe it or not.

Give us three people we should follow from any field.

Cheri Mah is one of the "sleep" people to follow. If I have a sleep question, she's who I go to for the answer.

I follow the Dalai Lama. I follow Chris Mohr for nutrition—some others are David Tenney, Bill Knowles and Stephen Colbert.

A lot of people I rely on are not present on social media, so I have to call them, which is pretty interesting. They tend to hide.

Thanks for doing this, Brandon. You're certainly one of the people we look to as a role model and for information.

BE LIKE BRANDON

"I have walked myself into my best thought," ~ Soren Kierkegaard, Danish philosopher

A QUIET WALK

"When I was at Athletes Performance, I remember I used to walk the two miles to work some mornings and the athletes would say, "You walked in this morning, didn't you? You seem different when you walk in, compared to when you drive. We know that walking at 1.2 miles per hour actually stimulates creativity."

Thomas Jefferson did it. So did Charles Dickens and Ludvig van Beethoven.

Silicon Valley executives do it. Steve Jobs was famous for his walking meetings around Palo Alto. LinkedIn, Google, Facebook and Nike all incorporate walking paths on their campuses.

There are so many advantages to getting in a good walk, but it's something that we often overlook. It can stimulate creativity, help reduce bodyfat, clear your head, improve circulation, reduce stress and the list goes on.

Is there a time you can carve out to go for a quiet walk? Maybe it's only 10–15 minutes to start but that's okay. Try to eventually make it consistent 30-minute walks.

If you can't make it part of your commute, make it part of your morning routine or lunch break.

Schedule it into your day (see Nick Winkelman's Be Like).

Be present during the walk. Turn your phone off or even leave it behind.

Try to look for (architecture, trees, birds, people), listen for (birds, people, dogs and cars) and even smell things (local bakeries, flowers, trees and grass) that you don't normally notice when you are rushing around.

This is a time to take a break, reflect and just be present in the moment. You will wonder how you lived without it.

Greg is the co-founder of the Titleist Performance Institute (TPI) in Oceanside, CA, and is the co-host of the Golf Fitness Academy sponsored by Titleist on the Golf Channel. He's an Advisory Board Member for the National Pitching Association and is a Certified Chiropractic Sports Physician and Fellow in the International Association of Clinical Acupuncture. You'll find many of his videos and articles at myTPI.com.

Greg, you've had success in many different areas of your life; you've been an entrepreneur, you owned a golf performance facility before you started TPI and you've had amazing success in different areas of your life. How do you define success?

Everybody defines success differently, but success is really simple: You're successful when you can do what you want…period. There are times when everybody does what they have to do, but when you get to the point where you only do things you love, that's success. If you're able to take care of the people you love at the same time, that's 100-percent success.

I've heard the story of how you came to be a chiropractor—you went to engineering school, then you were golfing with chiropractors. Was that the start of deciding "I'd rather do this" and was that when you started to feel that was the road to success?

I'll tell you two parts of that story. I was going into civil engineering at the University of Maryland, building roadways and homes and structural engineering. I was doing that because that's what my dad's company did. But after the first year, I could tell I didn't want to be an engineer. It wasn't something I loved—more that it was something I thought I had to do.

To gain experience, I began working for an engineering company two times a week while going to school and they put me on a job site at a golf course. The superintendent asked, "Have you ever played golf?" I answered no, and he told me, "For this business, you really want to learn it. You're going to have a lot of meetings on a golf course."

The University of Maryland had a golf course and I decided to learn to play. I always say one of two things happens when you play golf; either you become completely addicted or you absolutely hate it—there's no middle. I became addicted; I loved it. I thought, "This is great; I suck at it, but I love it," and then, "I'm only working two times a week. I can probably pick up some other hours if the golf course needs help."

I went to the head pro at the course and said, "I'm an engineering student. I'd love to play more golf; I can't afford it, but I can definitely work here and you don't have to pay me. I want to play for free." He hired me on the spot.

I was the guy who picked up the range balls. I'd go out there to hit the balls in the morning before we opened and then go out and pick them up. One day, I realized, "This is so much more fun than engineering. I wish this could be a job."

After a year in engineering school, I made friends with three chiropractors and we began playing golf. One day, one of the guys asked why I was doing something I didn't love. That was the first time somebody made me think hard about this. I said, "It's the family business and it's what I'm supposed to do."

He said, "That's pretty stupid. You only live once; you should do something you love."

I told him, "But I don't even know what I love," and he answered, "Why don't you come to my office and follow me around?" I didn't know what the hell chiropractic was, but I followed him around for a day. And…I'd found my passion. Maybe I just hated engineering so much that anything would have sounded good. I never looked back after that. I thought, "I'm going to try to live this life the way I want and if chiropractic is it…"

You never know what you're going to be when you grow up. You have to recognize the things you like and go for them. I went to chiropractor school thinking I was going to love that. I still love chiropractic, but I discovered along the way that I like golf more. When I graduated in 1995, I decided to open a chiropractic practice just for golfers. I thought it would be a dream to combine two things I love: chiropractic and golf. Everybody told me I was crazy, but I think I've proven them wrong.

I was once assigned a speech in college about _What You Believe In_. Everybody else's speeches were about abortion or gun control. My speech was about my belief that everybody should take a mandatory year off after high school to travel and work different jobs so they can meet people outside their neighborhoods and see what other jobs are like.

When you're young and you're not doing what you love, you should just get used to saying yes. When people ask you to try something, say yes—don't say no, because you never know what you're going to love.

That's such a great idea—just keep saying yes. What about now—what is it that drives you from a business perspective, from your mission and vision?

The key to success—and this is what separates the boys from the men and the girls from the women—is that whoever works the hardest wins. You could win the lottery, but that's usually not what happens. People who are successful work 10 times harder than the people who aren't; they eat, breathe and sleep work.

I've always believed I'll outwork anybody, that there's nobody I've met who wants to work as hard as I do. The reason successful people can do that is because it's not work; it's what they love.

When you ask what I do to motivate myself when I get up in the morning, it's more like you have to tell me why I need to go home—I love what I do. The hard part is creating balance with a family because I don't feel I'm sacrificing anything to go to work. I love what I do.

I always want to make sure there's balance and include family, but I have a great family who knows this is what I love and they participate in it with me. If you have to look for something to motivate you when you get up in the morning, you're in the wrong job.

From your perspective, what is it that you're "doing"?

As you alluded to in the introduction, I have multiple businesses. Most people don't realize this: I have six businesses. When people ask me what I do, it's hard to put into one word, but to put it into as few as possible: We help anybody in the field of performance get better at what they do.

Whether you're a coach, fitness or a medical professional, we've spent over 20 years studying how to make you better at what you do. It could be making a medical professional better at diagnosing a problem or making a coach better at helping a young kid develop motor skills. That's what we do in a nutshell.

Many of the people we work with are in the sporting world, so we often help sports federations or governing bodies help their people get better. But we do a lot outside of sports, such as the work we do at FMS with the military and regular people walking down the street. We're more B to B, not B to C—at FMS, we're business to business. We're not direct-to-consumer, although we do advertise to show consumers why they need to go to one of the businesses we educate.

We help anybody in the world of performance help the people they work with get even better. Whether you're with the Navy SEALs, the Seattle Mariners or the local business down the street, that's what we do.

Many people think you're the golf guy.

Golf is my passion; that's what I love the most. I think that's why we've had so much success in golf. But, through the Functional Movement Systems, we touch almost every sport. I have a company that does nothing but help federations increase children's participation in sports, which I'm passionate about.

Whether we're talking about working with Junior Golf or working with the Mexican Football Federation for soccer—it doesn't matter—I love working with kids. I love working on improving performance and seeing how much we can extract out of human performance. I love the challenge.

Have you made sacrifices you felt you had to make to be where you are?

Absolutely, and if anybody tells you they didn't sacrifice, they just didn't have anything to sacrifice. When my daughter was younger, I didn't want to be the dad who wasn't there so I took her with me. One of her first years in school, she missed 31 days, which is why she's always been in a private school. If she were in public school, she'd still be in first grade.

She was on five continents by the time she was six—that's a great education. As kids get older—12 or 13—they might want to play on a sports team and it's hard for them to commit to a team and not be there. She's 16 now and she probably wants me gone. A 16-year-old daughter doesn't want her dad around.

I have a rule for my wife and daughter: They're invited on every trip. I have so many flyer miles—I can get them a ticket. I already have a hotel room. They can pick the trips they want. My schedule is their schedule. For some reason when I go to fun cities, they're there. But if I go to a "bad" city, they don't want to come with me. There's a good balance; there's nothing wrong with a little distance every once in a while too.

Because you travel so much, are you able to set a routine?

No, I'm thinking about it now that you're asking me, and honestly, I don't think so. If it's a seminar or we're teaching a class, we have a routine—what time we get up, where we meet. It's almost like we're preparing for a round of golf. We have our pregame routine—we definitely have that for seminars. But personally, it's about creativity, which I love. I'm a creator. I love creating, and if in the middle of the night I'm having a dream about something I'm trying to create, I'll wake up and start working. I don't have a routine where I say, "It's 7:00AM; I'm going to go answer email." I don't work like that.

Sometimes it doesn't take discipline when you love what you're doing. What are some of the habits you've had that have helped get you here?

My number one habit is work ethic. Habit number two—missing this one is a mistake many people make—you have to surround yourself with people smarter than you. I'm going into war in business and I want to come with the best weapons, not the cheapest. I try to build a team around me who can answer all the questions I can't, which is really important. That's a definite habit of mine for every company.

And, if you put people on your team and realize they're not the right fit, get rid of them immediately. Don't delay that.

For our software, we use a development system called "Scrum," which is a form of managing product development. Scrum comes from the rugby world. Every morning we have a morning scrum where everybody involved meets to talk about what we're doing that day. What are our goals? We call them sprints. That's what the Scrum management does—one-week sprints.

Everybody knows what we need to accomplish for the week. At the end of the week, we have a sprint review, "Did we get to where we wanted? What are we doing next week?" That routine in business is one we copied for all of our businesses.

TPI resonates with the idea of building your team—knowing the other lanes, but staying in yours. Everybody around you sees how valuable you feel that is and that it's coming from a genuine place.

That's the "sphere of influence." Figure out what people, what organizations and what things could influence your work. Build that sphere around you and you'll be successful at whatever you're doing.

It's cool to be exposed to different people from different fields. That's another thing with successful people; they don't just stay in their field. They try to learn from anywhere they can.

In fact, I'd say get out of your lane. Physical therapists who only go to physical therapy seminars or chiropractors who only go to chiropractor continuing education—don't you think you can learn something from the other profession too? Get out of your lane and broaden your horizons. You have no idea where you're going to pick up a gem.

Do you have a formal process for setting goals?

I'm sure everybody you've interviewed said the same thing: Having a goal is incredibly important. Thom Plummer, a business consultant, always talks about creating a 10-year plan, which is so important. Most people I know who are successful have done that.

You have to write your goals, but people don't dream big enough. For me, part of goal setting is making sure to set the right goals. People set goals that are either unattainable or are so freaking easy—I don't understand why it's even a goal.

I like 10-year goals where we say, "Where's our company going to be in 10 years? Where am I going to be in 10 years?" Make sure that's where you want to be because if we're going to set this path, that's where you want to be.

Nobody can just sit down and write a goal this big. It should take you a month to come up with where you want to be in 10 years. Then you should be able to quickly decide, "If I need to be here in 10 years, here's where I need to be in nine years; here's where I need to be in eight years." Then, work your way back seven, six, five…and it'll tell you what you need to do this year and every year forward.

But the goals most people have are: "I want to own my gym and I want to be successful, making half a million dollars in my gym by year 10."

Then we say, "Let's move backward," and they say, "I need to have my gym, making $400,000 in year nine." By the time you get back to year four, you realize, "I can do this in six years." They didn't think big enough or didn't realize their goals were just too easy.

Dream a little when you create your goals. Goals are goals. People sometimes confuse goals and dreams; I put them together. To me, a goal is a dream. Let's say I want to win the Masters; I'm going to set the actions that to happen to reach that dream. I can't control if I'm going to win the Masters, but I can sure control my actions. I have a target; I pinpoint my goal, and then identify the actual steps I need to take to reach the goal. Then we lay those out into our sprints.

I put goals and dreams together because I want you to think bigger.

Break things down into actionable steps. Give me the solution, give me the steps we're going to do, and if we do these, hopefully a million people will be clicking on our website by the time we're done. The goal might be "Let's get a million clicks," but that doesn't tell you what to do. You have to create the action steps to get to that goal.

We are always talking to people about recovery, sleep and nutrition. How do you recharge on a daily, weekly and yearly basis?

I have a set routine on how I recharge and it's unusual—I am a fanatic gardener. I grow almost 70 percent of the food we eat. It's one of the reasons we live in San Diego and literally, I do everything myself. We live on an acre of land, and I go out into the garden at least an hour a day.

Most people think that's hard work; to me, it's complete escape. It's a mental recharge when I'm out there, and it's another thing I love. It's my quiet place and when I'm out there, I feel great. If I travel for a few weeks and don't get that garden time, I need to recharge my brain. Some people meditate; some people go into a steam room or sauna. I go into my garden. That's what I do.

As much as things have gone well for you, there are times when things don't go well. How do you push through the rough times?

I've had businesses that failed and I've had businesses that have been incredibly successful. In the bad times, you have to remember that whoever works harder is going to get there and it'll work.

You have to always stay honest. Always stay true to what you do. Stick to what you believe. Do not compromise, and if it doesn't work out, don't change. Just try it again in a different location, a different setting. Trust what you believe—that's the best you can do.

You read a lot, so it may be hard for you to narrow this down. Name three non fitness–related books people should read for their development.

The first is one I always thought was the easiest choice: *The E-Myth* by Michael Gerber. Every person should read that before going into business. It stands for the entrepreneurial myth; it's important.

I would 100 percent say my next suggestion is *Motor Control and Learning* by Richard Schmidt and Tim Lee. They have two books, *Motor Control and Learning* and *Motor Learning and Performance*. Understanding how humans learn new skills is incredibly important for the fitness profession.

I like *The Art of Learning* by Josh Waitzkin. That's a great one. I'm all about learning. I like to learn new skills. When you're going to start a business, you have a lot to learn.

You've brought so many amazing people to our collective attention. Name three people, from any field, whom we can all learn from and we should follow.

I'm going to answer this differently; I'm not going to name anybody. But what I would tell you is just because people are on the internet or on Instagram or YouTube and a lot of people are following them, doesn't mean they have the best information.

I'm always on the lookout. I like fresh minds.

If people are trying something different that makes people call them crazy—those are the people I watch at our seminars. I love something about the "under 35." They tend to be more creative and think outside the box.

Instead of falling on one person, be on the lookout for young talent. Don't stay away from them because you think they don't have any experience. That's a big mistake.

That's great advice because you're right, you have to be open-minded.

You just said the key word there: open-minded.

Many people are close-minded; they believe what they believe and they're not willing to listen to other people. If you learn one thing that becomes part of your day, it was worth it.

I'm going to a running seminar this weekend; I don't even run. But the people presenting the material are young; they're innovative. They have cool ideas. I don't know what parts of the material I'm going to use, but I'm sure going to use something.

The Functional Movement Screen is a great example. When people talk negative about it, I'll ask, "When did you go to the workshop?" And I'll often get the response, "I've never been there, but I've seen all of this stuff on FMS and in some research."

You just brought up a great point: There are two types of people. Some people take the word of other people and some people investigate for themselves. I trust other people, but I want to build my own opinion.

People will quote research and say it's evidence based. But they're citing the abstract or the conclusion, which is the subjective opinion of the data from the researchers. They've never looked at the data. And half the time when I look at research, I don't agree with the written conclusion.

Don't give me abstracts; don't give me your conclusions. Give me the data and I'll see what I discover.

Great advice. Greg, thanks so much for your time. It's been great to see you impact the profession the way you have. We really appreciate you doing this.

BE LIKE GREG

"I'm going to a running seminar this weekend. I don't even run. But the people presenting the material are young; they're innovative. They have cool ideas. I don't know what parts of the material I'm going to use, but I'm sure going to use something."

GET OUT OF YOUR LANE

Pick a workshop or seminar that will teach you something out of your scope of expertise.

Get out of your comfort zone and go learn something that will help broaden your perspective.

If you want it to be in the fitness field, choose something you don't know anything about or that might not be related to the things you are teaching now.

Bonus: Go by yourself.

Christa is the owner and founder of Tuff Girl Fitness in Hamden, Connecticut, where she coaches with her husband, Mike. In 2017, nine years into Tuff Girl's wild, word-of-mouth success, Christa and Mike's six-year-old daughter, Lea, was suddenly diagnosed with DIPG, a fatal, incurable brain tumor. Lea died nine months later, leaving the Doran family devastated, but—with Lea's bravery as their guide--a new story of strength to tell. Now, in addition to inspiring hundreds of women to feel stronger in their bodies and minds, Christa is teaching the lessons Lea taught her: that bravery is being present; that power comes not from avoiding pain, but from naming it and living unapologetically as you are. Christa lives in Hamden with Mike and their daughters, Livia, 10, and Keira, who is five. Lea would be seven now. You can learn more about Christa's mission at tuffgirlfitnessct.com and read about the love and loss she experienced at lessonsfromlea.com.

The idea of how to define success evolves for everybody, and it's certainly evolved for you after a major family issue. How do you define success and how has that evolved over the years?

I have a folder on my computer titled "Success." In it, you won't find revenue reports or bank statements. Rather, you'll find messages from clients who have opened up about how Tuff Girl and I have helped them change their lives for the better. You'll hear about getting out of an abusive relationship to opening a business, to jumping out of a plane, to asking for a raise, to leaving an employer who wasn't respectful.

This is how I define success: by impact, by success stories, by changing people's lives. On a business front, my success is gauged by reach. I also value referrals, because if people are referring their friends and family, it means they're happy and sing my praises. Business-wise, that's how I measure success—by my ability to impact people's lives and make them better.

Personally, success has meant being present. This doesn't mean Instagram followers and how many people liked a post; it means I'm the best version of myself to the people who love me. Am I putting my best foot forward as a leader to Tuff Girl and my team?

Success has been waking up every day and, regardless of what's going on in my life, choosing to be the best version of me that I can be. Every day looks different and I have to honor that and surrender to what life has thrown me and realize I have a choice. Often, people don't want to own their choices; they want to place blame onto circumstances. I try to teach my team that we need to own our choices—we're responsible for them and can change them. We can make different choices if we're not happy with the way our lives are going.

At one point, you were getting too busy and that also presents a problem. If you don't understand your mission, you won't recognize too much success can be a problem.

When my daughter was diagnosed with a fatal form of brain cancer and given nine months to live—let's just say you realize where your priorities lie. It was with my family and my business took a backseat. All the things I thought I wanted…I didn't. And when I think about what was most important to me, all my decisions now reflected back to this mission and vision.

Earlier, I was influenced by what people told me I should do: "Tuff Girl is so incredible, you need to franchise; this apparel is so amazing, you need to sell it everywhere." At what cost does that come and does it really matter to me?

Now I'm in a position where my apparel line is smaller. I'm doing limited online work. My business is off the charts. We're at an all-time high because I'm delegating and trusting people and leading from a different place—and am still able to be the support I need to be for my family. I've had to restructure my life. When you have to do that, you realize what's truly important. For me, it was going back to this mission, and the mission gives me purpose.

One of the reasons I'm able to work despite tragedy is that I'm so committed and connected to this purpose. Regardless of the struggles in my life, I love this. There can be days when tragedy in your life can make you not want to get out of bed, but I still have a purpose. I have family who need me, and then I have this business that gives me a reason to get out of bed. These people want a better life and they're coming to me for help and I have to deliver on that.

Your purpose is one of revolutionizing self-image for women, but how do you articulate that mission?

My mission has always been to empower women to see what they don't see for themselves. As a coach, I'll look at a woman and think, "She doesn't realize how powerful and strong she is," and I want to help her see that.

The tools I use as a strength coach are strength tools. One of my favorite things is to have people push a heavy sled. They'll ask, "How much does this weigh?" And I'll say, "I'm not going to tell you until after you push it all the way down the turf." And they'll push it all the way down the turf and I'll say, "That was 400 pounds." They'll look like they want to cry. If I had said that sled weighs 400 pounds before the push, they probably wouldn't have even attempted it because they don't know they're capable.

When you show women they're stronger and more powerful than they realize, it unlocks their potential. My goal for women is that they leave my doors and wonder where else they're not working to their true potential.

"Why am I letting my boss mistreat me—disrespect me, not pay me well enough and harass me? And why am I settling for a job I hate; why am I in a relationship where I'm not respected or loved? Why am I not going for the promotion? Or why am I not doing something on my bucket list that I really enjoy but scares me?"

Every day, we set opportunities for women to be brave, to be scared…and then to do it anyway. We help them realize their strength and power. I want to empower women to see what they don't see for themselves so they live better lives, fully immersed in their strength and power and believing in their capability. We've been taught we're not capable; we need somebody to take care of us, that we're not enough. I want to help change that.

That doesn't mean we don't want a partner; it means we want to partner with somebody who treats us with respect. And it doesn't mean we don't want to work with men. It means we want to be respected, to be paid the same and that our talents are recognized.

A lot of women don't understand their gifts, what they're capable of. We help them see that for themselves.

It's incredible what that empowerment can lead to. What are some of the other things you need to do to help empower them?

A lot of it is in the words we choose. All my coaches are trained to empower and build people up. I hear stories of people going to other gyms where coaches will say things like, "I know you ate a donut last night. You need to work that off." Or "Bikini season is right around the corner." Or "Don't you want to get rid of those love handles?" They're motivating from a place of self-deprecation; they're saying, you're not enough; you need to do these movements so you can become what society deems is acceptable.

We don't coach like that; we coach from a place of seeing a body as something that has purpose. We have purpose-driven goals, not aesthetic goals. I'm not saying reducing bodyfat or weight loss are bad goals, and we certainly help people achieve that. But we help people shift their thinking. Those are not the only goals. There are more.

The goal can be a bigger deadlift or showing up at the gym three days in a row and let the training be enough and not think we have to do more. We work with women to shift their thinking from a place of believing the body is something to be looked at to seeing it's here for a purpose. Your body is strong and powerful and capable. The messaging we give while they're training has to be powerful and impactful.

You will never hear one of our coaches talk about somebody's appearance; you will only hear them talk in a positive way about performance. While we have to give constructive feedback because we're dealing with technical movements, there's an empowering way to do that to help people feel good about what they've done.

We deal with women at all ages and stages of their lives, but there are similarities. When you walk in the door, we're going to greet you with a smile and tell you we're so glad you're here. And when we see people hurting and rushed, we're going to say, "Take a breath and just be present. Fully immerse yourself in this hour."

Then when they leave, we're going to tell them to think about something they've done that made them proud. Women don't take enough time to think about what they're proud of—they only think about what they could have done better, that nothing is enough.

These daily little reminders help them shift their thinking—this can take years. It wasn't learned in a year; it's not going to be undone in a year. But we can chip away at this, slowly and surely, so that five years down the road, a woman is in a completely different place in her life with a new appreciation for her body, happier in her skin even if she's not 120 pounds with 15-percent bodyfat. She loves herself more and appreciates what she can do.

Let's talk about the struggles of success. Your husband Mike has a gym next to yours and worked with you on other parts of the business before that. Including the family has been a great way to make sure you were able to spend some time together. But what are some of the sacrifices you made to make Tuff Girl as successful as it is?

I was a one-woman show for two years in the beginning—you sacrifice time with your family, time with your friends, free time. As a business owner, you can never be off; you don't get to clock out, turn it off and go home. You're not always working, but if you're not producing and creating, your business is not going to thrive and grow. My goal has always been to grow and impact more people.

You sacrifice other things that people with steady jobs don't think about. You sacrifice a regular paycheck; you sacrifice benefits. I gave up a corporate car. Mike gave up great benefits, a 401k and more. For me, it was sacrificing that safety net, sacrificing time with my family and friends. I'm able to have a little more flexibility now that I have a team.

When a lot of businesses start, it's just you—you do everything, clean, manage email, market, coach. You learn the business really well in those first few years, but it comes at a cost. If you don't love what you're doing and are not connected to that mission where it doesn't light you up, it's probably time to rethink what you're doing.

At the two-year mark, people often keep going on their own. And that's a big mistake. As an example, when your six-year-old daughter, Lea, was diagnosed with DIPG, a fatal brain tumor, if you hadn't set up your systems and built a team, life would have been even worse. Although we all go through tough times, it doesn't get any worse than what you're going through. How do you push through this?

I get asked that question a lot. The first thing that helped was surrendering to my situation. This is what it is and this is awful and it sucks. Then just giving it up—this is the card I've been dealt. I can't whine and cry about it and stay in bed, although I do cry. It is what it is. The cards I've been dealt suck, but they're my cards right now and I've got a plan. That definitely helped me. I have very strong faith and am leaning on that. I have a great network of family and friends that helped get me through this awful time.

The most important thing in our lives is our relationships, but in most cases, they're what we spend the least amount of time on. We spend hours and hours at work. Sometimes we love it and sometimes we grind away at jobs we hate just to make money, to plan for a better future. But in the end, we're neglecting the most important things in our lives.

Relationships are important and deserve a high priority and my time is now spent more with them. I've always had a strong network, but these days it's even stronger. People have come out of the woodwork—they're dragging me out of the house; they're taking me out for drinks. My parents have moved in to help me be able to still work and take care of Lea. That network is powerful and has really lifted me up.

My job gives me purpose; I can't imagine doing a job I hated with the magnitude of what's happening in my personal life. Being able to go to work and feel so connected gives me an amazing distraction from the reality of my life, like I get to sort of forget about it for a little while. I'm so immersed in my work and I love it so much that it turns that part of my brain off for a bit, for which I'm really grateful.

I started a personal blog and love to write, being vulnerable and transparent. Having people email me things like, "You've changed how I parent. You've changed how I look at my work," is incredible and gives me even more fuel to keep writing.

The last thing is my training: I'm committed to training and being a role model and being emotionally and physically strong. Training physical strength has translated to me being emotionally strong; strength training has taught me I'm stronger than I realized. Anyone who's ever done a heavy squat knows the feeling of "Am I going to be able to get up from this?" And somehow, you do.

That analogy—consistent practice of training strength and pushing through difficult training regimens—has helped me realize things can suck. And I embrace the suck and keep moving forward. One step, one day—sometimes, one hour at a time.

I had an older brother who committed suicide. The reason I say "committed suicide" is because committing suicide has a totally different element in it—it's not a regular death; there's so much crap that comes with it. When people who haven't seen us in a while ask, "How's your brother doing?," I answer, "My brother took his own life."

My wife sometimes asks, "Why do you say that? Why don't you just say he died?" My response is, "Because he didn't. That's really what happened." I need to be honest about it. I need people to know. I didn't want anyone to feel sorry for me. Sometimes it's good to have that, but at the same time, I felt this is the reality.

You surrendered to the situation. People can connect with you better because you're putting this out there publicly. Vulnerability is a huge piece—to put yourself out there instead of hiding.

Unfortunately, in our field especially, we see an image of perfection—the perfect diet, the perfect body, the perfect hair. There's the idea of physical perfection: I never miss a workout; I never have a cheat meal; I never eat a cookie.

We really do ourselves a disservice here. With this idea of perfection, you alienate yourself from people—you distance yourself from people when you put on an air of perfection. It's not connectable. Nobody can relate. It's not reality.

One of the biggest things that transformed my business was when Lea was born. Before that, I only wanted to show the good side of life. But then, I realized I'm going to share the shit; I'm going to embrace the suck and show the reality of life.

What happened was incredible. Business exploded because I was more real and more connectable and people didn't think I was a perfect person who never drank wine and always worked out and had perfect workouts and perfect abs. I attracted more customers; people are intimidated by perfection—they were staying away! As much as they might want to look at perfection, they don't actually want to be coached by it; they want to be coached by a real person they can relate to.

When I started being vulnerable, more women were attracted to me and Tuff Girl. Now it's just who I am. I've always been an open book, but it's liberating to say, "This is me and if you don't like me, that's okay. I'm not for everybody, but here I am in my raw state. Take it or leave it."

It's liberating as somebody who was so hard on herself for so many years to just say, this is who I am and I love myself, with makeup, bad day, good day, bad workout, good workout—at whatever bodyweight, whatever size. It's such a freeing place to be; I hope I can give that to my children and other women. Vulnerability is something that connects us.

What do you think helped get you to such a great place that made you successful? Early on, what were these things?

Sometimes people want to look at habits and think, if I do these, I'll be successful. Because I started a business at the same time as I started a family, I didn't do that. My schedule and routine and habits were all thrown up in the air like confetti because all bets are off when you have an infant. You're up all night and you have no routine and no schedule and you're piecing work together as best you can.

But there's a set of things—guiding principles for the business—that I abided by then and still do now. When I talk to people starting businesses, they always want to know what my secret was. There's no secret.

I was successful according to other people's standards when I had no gym, when I had no staff, when I had no equipment. When I was working in a park, I had 125 clients and though I was a good coach, I was nowhere near where I am today. But there were things I did then that made a huge difference.

Now I have a team and a nice TVs and check-in systems. The things that remain the same are a commitment to excellence—and that's excellence in every single area of business: from the way we greet our clients when they walk to the door to how we interact with them, using their names, the communication we send out, how frequently, what it says, how we brand ourselves on social media and on the website…and the kind of experience we give when they're with us.

Part of what makes Tuff Girl special is that we're together in the gym, but we also do things outside the gym. That community was there from the beginning. We'd go out for coffee after class with our kids. We'd occasionally go out for drinks or get our nails done. I built this community of people who knew me outside of the gym and who were connected. It wasn't work for me because I really wanted to build a community.

Today it's the same. My coaches are trained to greet people at the door with a smile. This field we're in is intimidating and our target market is people who don't like how they look. They're walking into a place where they feel they're going to be judged, where other people have a "better" bodies. They look at me as a coach who's strong and fit; I can be intimidating. How can we not make people intimidated?

I want to meet people where they are and help them on their journeys and make them feel as comfortable as we can in the process. Going into a gym when you're overweight and out of shape is uncomfortable; we have to make it accessible. We have to make them want to come back. Otherwise, we can never help.

This commitment to excellence is in every area of Tuff Girl—from the cleanliness of the bathrooms to the social media, to how our coaches speak to people, to the leadership. It all has to be the excellence standard I hold myself to. There's no wiggle room there.

And what's truly been a testament to our success is that people love how they feel when they're with us. We give them a feeling they haven't felt before and they want more of it. That's when they come back; that's when we can start to change their thinking and help them become more empowered.

Daniel Coyle wrote a book called *The Culture Code,* in which he discusses "belonging cues." You do an amazing job with belonging cues—like including in your bio that you love pasta and wine. People respond to that connection.

People want to have fun. We already do enough in our lives that we don't enjoy. Our training should be fun. That's where, say, dancing comes in…music and just being silly. There's too much seriousness; I'm not taking myself too seriously. I take training seriously, but also I want people to have fun because if they're not having fun, chances are they're not going to come back.

I love that saying, "Don't look at it like a workout; it's training," because it's not just about today, when you come in when you don't feel well and have a crappy workout. I had a client who used to say the same thing when he was tired at the end of a session: "You know what, Ant? At least I was here." I told him I was going to get that on a plaque over the door where people could see it as they were leaving. That taught me a lot over the years.

Let's switch to some ideas about goals. Do you set goals? Is it a formal process?

I used to be more rigid about goal setting. I used to set goals at the beginning of each year when I'd set a physical performance goal, a business goal and a personal goal. But now, they're a bit more flexible.

My personal goals are to be present in my life and to be kind to myself. When I feel like I can physically and emotionally handle another personal goal, I'll take that on. But right now, it's a steady goal of showing up. I've let myself relax a little over the years, and it's definitely served me well. Some of the rigidity is gone and to be honest, I'm a happier person because of it.

Let's finish up with a couple non-fitness books people should read to help in their personal development.

There are two books that changed the way I lead and live. The first is *Thrive* by Arianna Huffington. She talks about sleep and how we're always plugged in and working. She really helped me set boundaries—to unplug and shut down and gave me strategies on how to do that. That really changed how I look at my work and my life and how I manage everything, from a place of wanting fulfillment and not wanting to feel like I got dragged through the mud every week.

The other is *Daring Greatly* by Brené Brown. That was one of the books I read when I decided I was going to be vulnerable, be real and put it all out there. I'm going to air the dirty laundry, share the shit. Her book was transforming; it helped me with sharing struggles and connecting with more people. It also helped in getting rid of the illusion that as a trainer, I have to put on an image of perfection. I always like to hear what she has to say.

Those are the two books that really impacted me the most.

They say success leaves clues. Who are three people we could follow to learn from?

This might surprise you: The three people you should look to and learn from are your customers, your team and those you admire and aspire to be.

When I want to learn something about my business, I ask my customers because they're the people supporting it. What do you want to see? When I want to get better and to learn how I can be a better leader, I ask my team: How can I grow—how can I get better?

I also look at businesses I admire. From a customer service standpoint, Tory Burch and Zappos are two businesses I really appreciate. I try to model our customer service at Tuff Girl on these businesses. That's whom I learn from.

We don't ask enough of our current customers about what's going on or what they like or dislike. There's so much to be learned from the people we're working with

and who are supporting us. There's a reason they're there, and we should make sure we know what it is.

And if people leave, I want to know why and what I could've done better. And if they stay, I want to know why. We often look at businesses and think we need to be like them. As I've become more confident and self-assured, I'm recreating what makes sense and not thinking I can take best practices from businesses that have been successful. I'm going to put it on and make sure it feels good to me and make sure it works with our mission.

There have been times when I've let people tell me a policy had to be in place because other people have done it. But we have to go back to the vision. If it doesn't feel right—regardless of what anyone else is doing—I'm not going to do it. I might rewrite the rulebook because I'm writing it according to what I want for Tuff Girl.

As entrepreneurs create and grow businesses, they have to be consistent with their mission, vision and values. If they're not, they're going to get themselves into trouble. When somebody asks why something is in place, I can give the reason with confidence. It's not because they did it down the street; this is why we don't do other things a lot of places do.

So many people have learned from you and what you're bringing to the table. It's inspiring to see how you've reacted to everything in your life. Thanks so much for doing this.

BE LIKE CHRISTA

"I thought about what was most important to me and all my decisions now reflect back to this mission and this vision:
To empower women to see what they don't see for themselves"

WHAT IS YOUR MISSION; WHAT'S YOUR PURPOSE?

Christa talks so much about her mission. It came up many times in our conversation and you can see how it directs everything she does.

It's not an easy thing to figure out, but if you're intentional about it, you can start to shape it.

My mission and purpose is to "Help fitness professionals realize their own vision of success and to help them make an impact in the world."

Do this exercise once a week for the next four weeks:

Think big (see Charlie Weingroff's Be Like); don't hold back and go into "painstaking detail" to shape your mission. See Mark Fisher's Be Like for a similar exercise to follow up.

It's 2028. You're at your favorite restaurant, celebrating some of your accomplishments with family and friends.

What have you achieved?

What are you proud of?

What do you want people to say about you?

Where have you made an impact?

Who have you impacted?

Turn it into a sentence that will help guide your decisions in your business and your life. For example, Christa's mission statement sentence is "To empower women to see what they don't see for themselves" and mine is "Help fitness professionals realize their own vision of success and to help them make an impact in the world."

Giovanni is the owner and operator of Roselli Health and Fitness and is a nationally recognized fitness coach, author and presenter. He serves as a Master Instructor for ViPR PRO, Kettlebell Athletics and Core-Tex Fitness, providing both introductory and full-length workshops. Additionally, he has mentored many trainers and coaches and considers those interactions among his proudest accomplishments. The former WWE professional wrestler, known to fans around the world as "Romeo," has also professionally acted alongside some of the world's top actors including Tina Fey, Mickey Rourke and James Franco. Learn more about Giovanni's programs at GiovanniRoselli.com.

You've had success in a few different areas, specifically as a WWE wrestler, as well as success in the training business in a relatively short time. But how do you define success today?

The older I get, success now is putting my head on the pillow every night and being satisfied with how I spent my time, my day and being able to know I got the most out of that day.

I just heard something about the psychology of happiness: If we're making a little progress every day on our journey, we're going to be happier. Knowing you did all you could is important.

When I'm going through each day or when I'm winding down my day, I'll ask myself, "Did I get a little better today?"

At a young age, you started wrestling; you were determined and driven and became a WWE wrestler. You then got into the fitness business and advanced rapidly. When did you start feeling like you were a success?

I still don't consider myself a success. It's weird having this conversation about success because I feel like I'm just at the tip of the iceberg even though I've had 10 years in the fitness business, have done some pretty cool acting jobs and was a WWE wrestler. But that's a characteristic of successful people. They never settle and never have a feeling of, "This is when I got to be a success. This was the moment."

I started to become driven toward success in high school. It was very simple and it's probably a story we've heard many times. I liked basketball, but I got cut from the team and I said to myself, "I'll never have that disappointing feeling again. And no matter what I do, I'm going to give 110 percent." And the switch flipped. From that point, I was tunnel-vision focused. I was completely driven; I can't pinpoint when I felt like a success, but that's when it started.

In the wrestling world, I could say my success was debuting at Madison Square Garden and having Hulk Hogan and come over and introduce himself. That was surreal, considering I was a kid growing up watching him at Madison Square Garden events. Here I was debuting in Madison Square Garden—I could put that on my bucket list; not many people can say, "I performed in front of a sold-out crowd in Madison Square Garden." That was another defining moment for me.

Another characteristic of people who are successful is comfort saying when they're wrong. It's okay to say what I was doing wasn't the best, but I'm trying to get better. We learn from everything and hopefully what I'm doing now is better than it was six months ago and six months from now what I'm going to be doing then will be better than where I am now. We're always looking to get better. There's nothing wrong with looking back and wondering what the heck we were doing. You just try to do the best you can now.

What motivates you to get out of bed from the fitness business perspective? What's your "it" in this business?

We are all extremely lucky to be here and to be alive. We have such a short amount of time, there's no reason I wouldn't make the most out of every day.

I have a beautiful young daughter now, Juliet Rose. Fatherhood is absolutely amazing and she's just great. It makes the schedule harder, but it gives my "why" a little more oomph. In addition to making sure we raise her as best we can, we want to lead by example.

Thomas Plummer reminds us that we don't want to be sitting in a rocking chair one day wondering "what if?" I never want to sit in my rocking chair and say to my grandkids, "I wonder what would have happened if I had tried to be a WWE wrestler. What if I'd tried to be a fitness professional, if I had tried some acting. I wonder what would've happened." And I can honestly look back on my life so far and say I have no what-ifs. I feel like I'm staying true to myself.

You're one of the most disciplined people I know. What are some other habits you attribute to your success?

Perseverance may be the most important quality anyone could have because it will get you through anything and will drive you to anything. People who don't have perseverance will quit. If an obstacle gets in their way, they'll just say, "I guess that's it." The people who have perseverance really get on in this world.

Consistency is another obvious attribute. You have to be consistent in your practices and how you're going about your day, setting goals and getting to wherever you want to end up. The last element is intensity. Intensity is another way of saying you have to have fire in you. If you really want to go far, no matter what the goals, you need intensity, some form of inner fire. Intensity, perseverance and consistency helped me tremendously.

Let's talk about sacrifices. Your body's been beaten up with the wrestling and the travel and time away from family. What sacrifices have you made to be successful?

We all make sacrifices every day depending on how motivated we are. Every decision you make every day of your life is setting you up to get you closer to where you want to be. There's a lot of sacrifice with time, money and energy. It always ends up as time.

One of my clients always used to say, "You can work around mother nature, but you'll never beat father time." And it always goes back to sacrificing time, whether that's studying, taking certifications, traveling to certifications, reading…I consider sacrifices worth it when you can look back and say, "That paid off. That's what got me to where I am today."

The sacrifice of moving to Florida means I'm spending less time with my family. But this was a decision made to hopefully help me and my family in the end. I had an audition in New York where I flew up from Florida; I did the audition for one minute and then flew home. To me, that's a sacrifice—and there are plenty of similar examples.

Then there's wrestling. When you're starting out as an independent wrestler getting experience, you wrestle as much as you can, wherever you can. You end up driving 12 hours to show up in an armory where there might be a hundred people watching you wrestle for maybe 15 minutes and then drive back home. And you might get paid 20 bucks. That's the life of an aspiring independent wrestler.

Looking back, that made me who I am. It made me stronger and made me driven. I look back at all the sacrifices as successful endeavors.

Talk to me about whether there was a time when you felt like it was time to give up. Was there a time when you had to mentally push through?

There were quite a few times like that in wrestling. I've had major shoulder injuries and my shoulder kept dislocating when I was wrestling. I got it surgically repaired, went back to wrestling and then a year later, dislocated my shoulder and tore my labrum again. When I was wrestling, mostly everybody asked, "Can you stop?" And once I started getting injured, it got worse. It was paining them to see me injured. That was definitely a crossroad.

In that respect, that's when I started turning to reading about successful people. I found— whether it was an athlete, a politician, a celebrity or anybody who was successful—they faced trying times, but persevered.

I knew if this was still in my heart, I needed to persevere. And in the end, it would only make the story sweeter.

We often hear it's more about the journey than the destination. The times when you want to give up but don't are when you become stronger and you have more in you to use in the future.

The one thing I look at would be my shoulder history and it haunts me. I still have a cranky shoulder that creaks a little and reminds me when I move it that it's noisy and has arthritis. But I don't regret anything. I was able to do everything I've set out to do so far and I can sit back in my rocking chair and know that instead of giving up, I persevered and did everything I set my mind to. That's satisfying.

That shoulder will always remind you of the good times too. Give me three non fitness–related books everyone should read.

I'm in the middle of reading *52 Cups of Coffee* by Megan Gebhart. She went on a quest to have a weekly cup of coffee, meeting with a different person every week. The power of relationships and the lessons you can learn about life, careers and personalities is remarkable. It's a very interesting read, motivating and inspiring.

Grain Brain by David Perlmutter is somewhat fitness-related, but not exactly. It makes you think even more about what you're eating. It's eye-opening when he discusses exactly what you're eating, what it's doing to your body, what it's doing to your brain, what it's doing to the future of our genetics. That's another great read.

I'll go a little fitness-related again because I'm a big fan of his: Read anything by John Wooden about leadership. I read a lot of his books. There are so many lessons about leadership qualities and characteristics.

It's said that success leaves clues. Give us three people to follow we can all learn from.

The first person who comes to mind is Abraham Lincoln. Year to year, he was faced with problems. He lost Senate races. Family members passed away. His girlfriend left him. He lost more Senate races…more things happened to him. He applied for school and got denied. Take a look at a timeline of what Abraham Lincoln had to go through in his life.

And then at the end of that timeline it says, "Elected President of United States." Look at all the times he was defeated in the Senate and all these things that happened to him and all the times he could have quit. But he persevered. There's that word again: perseverance. I really admire what he was able to do.

Eric Thomas is another person to consider. He's a motivational speaker, a former school dropout out who grew up in a rough neighborhood in Detroit. Now he has a PhD and is one of the most popular, sought-out speakers in the world today. He tells it like it is.

Gary V—Gary Vaynerchuck—is another person who's very popular on social media and on the 'net. He's very popular; he breaks things down: What do you want and what are you doing to get it?

But in the end, all the big successes end up saying the same thing and that's what I gravitated toward.

One of the things Gary said that really stuck out was the question, "What's the alternative?" I constantly ask myself about the alternatives, especially in the tough times.

The three people you mentioned really exemplify a big work ethic. Eric Thomas and Gary V talk about how much work it's going to take and that you've got to keep pushing on. Giovanni, we really appreciate your sharing such a great story of success and perseverance.

BE LIKE GIOVANNI

"Perseverance may be the most important quality anyone could have in this world because perseverance will get you through anything and it will drive you to anything."

GOAL PERSEVERANCE

Can we develop perseverance? Research shows we can if we're intentional.

A few things to do:

Write down a few instances of when you persevered through tough times to reach a goal. Put those top of mind to remind you you've been here before and you can do it again.

Set goals that excite you (see Todd Durkin's and Charlie Weingroff's Be Likes). When you set your goals, make sure they're attainable, and also that they're a little out of your reach. Make them something you can say, "It would be amazing if I reached this goal."

Write down as many "whys" for the goal as you can. Keep the paper in a place where you're going to see it often. Commit the list to memory. Summon the "whys" when you're feeling down, when you want to quit. The "whys" will bring you back, slap you in the face and remind you how important this goal is.

Don't get caught up in all the details of the goal. Focus on what you have to do today, which will get you closer to your goal next week (see Brett Bartholomew's Be Like)

Each night, write down one win for each goal (see Alwyn Cosgrove's Be Like). What was one thing you did to get you closer to that goal? It doesn't have to be a big thing—remember, we just want to keep making progress toward that goal. Focus on the gain, not the gap (a Dan Sullivan concept). Don't focus on what you haven't accomplished; focus on what you have accomplished. Keep it positive!

Self-talk: Don't allow those voices in your head to bring you down. Keep telling yourself you're going to get this accomplished. This is where you belong; you're smart enough and work hard enough to get this done. Tell yourself that you're someone who gets things done. You take action!

Keep pushing. The bottom line is that when you set all of the above up, you still need to keep pushing. Take it one step at a time and don't beat yourself up for lapses. Tomorrow is a new day.

You got this.

Alan is a coach, speaker and author with an expertise in improving organizational performance, cohesion and accountability. He spent over 15 years working with the highest performing basketball players on the planet… including NBA superstar Kevin Durant. He now travels the world teaching organizations how to use the same strategies in business that elite athletes use to perform at a world-class level. Learn more about Alan at raiseyourgamebook.com.

You're writing a book, going into the corporate world and speaking. Your success in fitness and basketball is a stepping stone to other things. You never know where you're going to end up. But how you define success?

I look at success as being synonymous with happiness. I use happiness in my heart as my guide for a lot of my decisions. I certainly look to make decisions logically, as well, and to weigh the pros and cons. But I usually go with my heart.

Success is serving others and making a contribution. I'm the happiest when I'm serving others and pouring into other people. It doesn't matter if we're talking about my three children in my role as a father or if I'm working with basketball players or speaking to a group of executives to help them improve their leadership.

Success comes back to contributing to those around us, being a servant leader and doing what makes us happy. Being able to live life on your terms, doing what you want, when you want and with whom you want is really my overview of success.

When we're younger, we often look at external factors and then we gain a new perspective. When did you begin thinking, "I'm getting this right"?

If we had this interview earlier, my answer would have been completely different because it would have been based on those outside metrics. I would have put a dollar figure to it—how much money I was making, what type of car I was driving, where I was living. I had a narrow view of success.

I've learned through maturity never to play the comparison game because if you let other people define your success, especially with outside metrics like money, you'll always lose. I can walk outside of my apartment and throw a rock and easily hit somebody who makes a lot more money. I would never want that to devalue myself. It was only within these last few years that I've had the maturity to gain a broader view of success.

As far as considering myself a success, that was a problem. No matter what I achieved earlier in my career, I never felt successful. It wasn't until I reframed success my mind that I can say proudly but with full humility that I consider myself successful because of the new definition. But that doesn't mean I'm content or that I'm not still striving to improve.

I lay my head on my pillow at night feeling proud of what I'm doing and knowing I enjoy what I do; that enjoyment and fulfillment keep me going. To answer your question, it's probably only been in the last couple of years that I made that mind shift. I'm now at peace with what I'm doing.

Tell me about this idea of serving and contribution: Is that what gets you motivated to get out of bed?

It is the servant leadership side, helping people become the best versions of themselves. That's what drives me. What gets me out of the bed in the morning is the opportunity to become the best version of myself. While I'm making progress and am better than I was a year ago, I certainly hope that a year from now I'll be better than I am at present.

What gets me excited is the opportunity to work on myself, but then to share those tips, best practices, mindsets, disciplines and habits with others so they can become the best versions of themselves. It's been a nice jump to go from basketball to the corporate world because I'm still sharing the same overall ideology.

In order to be the most effective leader in your company, you have to be the best version of yourself. To be the best basketball player you're capable of being, you have to be the best version of yourself in every area of your life. Excellence is not something you can compartmentalize. You can still achieve certain things if you don't aim for excellence in other areas of your life, but you're not the best version you're capable of being unless you aim for excellence.

This helps me in every area. It helps me in business, as a speaker, a parent and a leader. That's really what gets me going: Every day, I have an opportunity to work on myself, to grow and to develop, to sharpen my sword and master my craft and to take things one step further. I'm very fortunate I get to share that with people.

Habits and disciplines are an important part of sharpening your sword, mastering your craft and becoming the best version of yourself. It takes a lot of discipline in the beginning for some people and then it becomes a habit. You're a guy who has worked with many youth athletes and you're trying to instill those habits in your athletes. What are the habits you attribute to your success?

From a coaching standpoint, the foundation for being able to help create a habit in others is establishing trust and a connection. I was able to be successful in the fitness and basketball space because I always lived by the mantra that you connect first and coach second.

Whether I was working with a soccer mom looking to lose five pounds or an elite-level basketball player who wanted to play in the NBA, the most important part of our relationship was to make a human and emotional connection first and to build trust. Once I was able to build trust, I could coach and be the practitioner to teach them what was needed to achieve their goals.

I am a big relationship guy. I don't know if we can quantify that as a habit, but I've always put my power in the ability to connect with people. If you connect with the right people, you'll learn so much. You also want to be able to make connections so you can share and pour into other people. For those two reasons, developing, forging and maintaining relationships is a pillar of everything I do. It's gotten to the point where it's a habit for me to progressively seek new relationships with people who might be influential in my life.

As far as actual habits—and this is newfound—there's commitment to the process. I used to be outcome-based. It didn't matter what it was, whether I was trying to bench more weight or make more money, I was always focused on the outcome. And I often got lost in the process. I now have such a stronger respect for the process of anything I'm trying to attain.

As far as habits in general, I'm a simple guy. I love the fact that I live my life and I run my business based on a handful of core principles. That something is basic doesn't mean it's easy. Most people think those are synonyms and they're not.

In fitness, what it takes to change the human body are basic principles. But to change the human body is anything but easy. You need a commitment to a good diet and to working out. Those are hard. But they're basic in principle. Having an appreciation for and sticking to the basics is extremely important.

Relationship-building is a habit because otherwise the books *Never Eat Alone* and *How to Win Friends and Influence People* would have never been written. Those are active, conscious things we need to do. They're definitely habits. We talk to our athletes a lot about goals, but let's talk about yours. Do you have a formal process?

This comes down to almost a bucket-list concept. I have certain goals and metrics in place. Writing a book was a goal of mine and I have that underway. But above and beyond goals, I'm a relationship and experience guy. There are two experiences I want to have this year. One is to see Tony Robbins speak live. I've been devouring his stuff for years in a variety of forms, but I've never seen him live. That's an experience I want to check off. That's different from a goal, but it's on my list.

Ever since I saw the movie *Couples Retreat*—this is going to sound really out there—when I saw those huts on stilts in the water, I've always wanted to go there. Most of those are either in Fiji, Bora Bora, the Maldives or Bali. I set another bucket-list item—an experience goal—of going to one of those places, not for business. It'll be just a time for me to get away and reset.

From a goal standpoint, I want to be able to scale my message and have other avenues to disseminate information so I'm not tied to being a corporate speaker. Writing a book and creating some online programs, courses and curriculums are probably my primary vocational goals for the year. The goals are the outcome and I do have them so I know where I'm going. The actual process steps are most important to me and are where I put my focus.

That's definitely a cool way to vacation. Let's segue that: How do you recharge?

People are often surprised because I've spent my entire career in the public eye, as a speaker, coach and trainer, where I'm with people and pouring into people. But I'm actually introverted. I recharge my own battery and refill my tank and bucket in complete solitude and privacy. I need to have time completely to myself, whether it's for a workout or to read. As much as I love people, I recharge in solitude.

I take digital detoxes at least once a week, and that's a big one for me. I'll take an afternoon and not look at my phone or any screen, just to get away from it. I have some type-A, borderline OCD tendencies, and I'm tethered to my phone 24/7. I often have to take a purposeful step back to realize that's not a healthy approach. Once every month or two, I'll do a digital detox for a full 24 to 48 hours to get away from everything and let other areas of my life be recharged by getting off technology.

That's challenging. When I first started doing that, I had anxiety about not checking my phone every three minutes. That's when I realized this had become an issue. I grew up without a cell phone. I know I'm capable of living without one. But it's amazing how mentally and emotionally dependent we become on technology.

It's important for people to understand it's such a recharge to get away from that dependency. You have to take baby steps, and it's all about progression.

And there are so many parallels to that in fitness. Think how many times you've come across someone who had been sedentary for a few years and was not in great shape. It happens all the time with New Year's resolutions. In their minds they say, "I've been sedentary for the last two years. I haven't been working out; I've really let myself go. But starting January 1st, I'm going to work out two times a day, hire a trainer and completely revamp my nutrition."

No, you're not. That's not going work. You need to inch in. Maybe starting January 1st, just make a commitment to go for a walk, 20 minutes a day. Just that—that's the only thing you need to focus on. Don't worry about anything else. Once that's part of your routine and has become manageable and easy, you can stack something on top of it.

Getting off of your phone for an entire Sunday afternoon is a baby step. You'll be able to grow that to one weekend a month, to be off the phone for the whole weekend. And grow that to maybe once a quarter, take a three- or four-day vacation and not be on the phone the entire time.

It starts with sticking your big toe in the pool first to get the temperature. Find what's right for you. Don't play the comparison game of worrying about what other people do. Because someone else takes a full-week digital detox once a month doesn't mean that's right for you. You need to find what's appropriate. And that takes self-awareness.

What are some of the sacrifices you feel you've had to make to get to where you are?

I'll set the context: I'm 41 years old. I'm amicably divorced and am great friends with my ex-wife; she and I make terrific co-parents. I have three children, seven-year-old twin sons and a five-year-old daughter. My children live with their mom, but they're with me half the time. I put that on the schedule first and I build everything else around that. My time with my kids is non-negotiable. The only caveat is if an incredible opportunity comes up when I'm supposed to have my kids, I may switch nights with my ex-wife.

When I don't have my children, I schedule whatever I want, whenever I want, with whomever I want. It'll sound counterintuitive, but being divorced has actually helped me in that area because when I was married, I did a poor job of finding harmony between my work life and my home life. And I didn't find myself being present with my kids, either in mind or body, because work tended to always come first. I certainly sacrificed some connection and presence with my children early in their lives because I was so focused on work.

I'll use the word "regret" here, but only because that's what most people would associate with it. I've forgiven myself and give myself some grace to know it was part of the process. I certainly would do it differently if I could do over again, but I don't beat myself up about the past. I have so much better harmony now; I'm able to still pour into my children and be present and connected with them. But I'm gung-ho, fast-forward, 100-percent going toward what I'm doing vocationally now.

In your website bios, it said you're amicably divorced. I love that transparency. We're all dealing with different things in our lives. There's vulnerability there.

I appreciate that. A lot of people go through divorce. I'm in that age bracket where I'm meeting a lot of people who are in a similar boat. I came to the conclusion that my sons would grow up learning how to treat women by how I treated their mother. And my daughter would grow up learning how a man should treat her by how I treated her mother. I made the decision the moment I knew we were getting divorced—regardless of how I felt emotionally on the inside—I was going to be kind and respectful to my ex-wife, no matter what, for no other reason than to set an example for my children. I'm extremely thankful she made the same commitment and has always been kind and respectful to me.

We were able to take ourselves out of it, take our egos out of it, take any spite, disdain or frustration out of it and decided we need to be good to each other for the kids. When we both made a pledge to do that, a real friendship started to bud between us. And it's been a neat experience.

That would be my only advice to anybody going through that who has children, put your own pride and ego aside and treat your ex with respect because it's going have a profound impact on your children.

Talk to me about when you were going through that in the beginning and starting to realize you weren't present with the kids and the relationship was falling apart. Was there a time you felt it was important to change gears, maybe you needed to get out of this business? And how'd you get through those times?

Therapy and counseling: I went to a therapist weekly for two straight years. That was the most pivotal time in my life for reframing my mindset. I have the before-therapy and after-therapy sides of my life.

What first started the downward spiral was was letting outside metrics determine what I thought was success. As an example, thinking I had to work the McDonalds' All-American Game because that's a badge of honor to help build my reputation. It didn't matter if I was going to miss something important with my children; going to the All-American Game was more important because I was letting other people define my success.

When I look back on my life and legacy, what will be more important—an event I could spend with my children that may never happen again or going to the All-American Game? When I live by better values and principles, it makes my decision-making easier. It doesn't mean I won't be disappointed when I don't get to attend an event, but at least I know I'm making the right decision.

I was living in a fog where I was never fully present wherever I was. I wasn't fully present when I was with my kids because I was thinking about work. And then I'd go to work feeling guilty that I wasn't with my kids. Once I went through therapy and started to get some clarity, I learned being present is one of the most important things we can do. The trigger I use for defining "being present" is to be where your feet are: Wherever your feet are, that's where your head and your heart need to be.

While I haven't mastered that, I've made some great strides. Right now, I'm fully present with you having this conversation. My head, heart and my feet are in one place and you have my full, undivided attention. I'm not folding laundry while we're talking. I'm not checking an app on my phone. You have my full attention.

Later this afternoon when I pick my children up from school, they'll have my full attention; my head, heart and feet will be with my children. And I won't be worried about anything else. That's really made all the difference in the world, but it's still a struggle. I'd never pretend I'm present every moment of every day.

There's a chance when I'm with my children today, my mind will revert to this conversation, and I might be replaying some of the answers in my head. Or I might start thinking about a talk I have to give to a local group tomorrow. But I now have the awareness to trigger that and say, "That'll come when it comes; be where your feet are."

Therapy is what put me on the right path toward that. I'm very open about that because there's a stigma in society about going to see a therapist, especially with men, and unfortunately, a lot of people see that as a sign of weakness. I can't tell you how many people said something to the effect of "What are you going to do, go talk to somebody about your feelings?"

Yes, that's exactly what I'm going to do because I need help with this. It's getting out of control and I'm not managing this to the best of my ability and all areas of my life are suffering. Yes, absolutely, that's what I'm going to do.

I look at that as no different than being a coach or a trainer. Someone hires you for fitness training because they need your guidance and expertise to do what's right in the world of fitness. I was hiring a coach, who just happened to be a therapist, to help guide, push and teach me what I need to do to manage my life. I still to this day have several coaches in different areas of my life. I have a speaking coach. I have a writing coach. I have a coach who helps me with sales. And I consider a therapist just an extension of that, another spoke in the wheel…someone who can help me become my best self.

Here we are in a business where a lot of us are selling our coaching services; it's a little hypocritical not to have coaches ourselves. If you believe in it and you're selling it, you should be buying into it as well. I have the name of your next book: *Be Where Your Feet Are.*

I don't know if Oprah was the first person to say that or if she got it from somebody else, but I'd heard that in therapy. It rang true to me.

Alan, give us three non-fitness books everybody should read.

Leading with the Heart by Coach K: I'm a diehard Coach K, Duke basketball fan. That book's probably 20 years old, but I still consider it the bible when it comes to leadership.

There's a new book I just started reading, *Own the Moment* by Carl Lentz, a pastor in New York City. I'm bringing that up because of your appreciation for "Be where your feet are." It's similar in that regard.

For the third, let's go with *Toughness* by Jay Bilas. Jay is a good friend, a college basketball analyst at ESPN. The book talks about the difference between mental and emotional toughness and this fake male bravado of physical toughness a lot of people think is tough.

Being able to stay present, be disciplined, focusing on the process—those are actual signs of toughness. It has nothing to do with if you walked into a bar and could kick everyone's ass. That's not real toughness, yet that's what society tends to think.

Real toughness is being able to put into practice the mindsets and rituals and routines and habits we've been discussing.

Success leaves clues, so give us three people you think we should follow to learn from.

Gary Vaynerchuk—Gary V—really makes waves and is a modern entrepreneur. The thing I love most about Gary is his transparency and his self-awareness. He's been preaching self-awareness for a long time. Gary's "go, go, go, constantly grind, never stop moving" mindset doesn't work well for me—I'm not trying to adopt his mindset…or his schedule, for that matter. But I love the fact that he has the self-awareness to know what works for him and where he's in his sweet spot. Gary is definitely someone to follow.

A friend of mine named Jon Gordon is a speaker and an author; he has written really solid material. The reason I like his books is they're all short-story fables. Jon puts out really positive stuff. His whole angle to being an effective leader is based on positivity and filling other people's buckets and pouring into other people. Jon Gordon is definitely a must.

Finally, look up Michael Port and *Steal the Show*. Michael is a former actor who's turned into a public speaking coach. His work is extremely important, even for people who don't do public speaking. He says we're all performers. If you're an author, if you're a fitness coach—whatever you are in life, you're a performer.

That mindset might sound a little "out there." When I was reading *Steal the Show*, I was reading it for the sole purpose of becoming a better speaker. But there were so many things in that book I could apply to different areas of my life.

Alan, I love this journey you've been on, in terms of working with athletes, in the fitness world, the basketball world and transitioning this into a bigger message in the corporate world. We really appreciate your sharing your journey.

BE LIKE ALAN

"Just being able to say I'm going to get off of my phone for an entire Sunday afternoon is a baby step. I'll be able to grow that to one weekend a month, to be off my phone for pretty much the whole weekend. And then grow that to maybe once a quarter, take a three- or four-day vacation and not be on my phone the entire time."

DIGITAL DETOX

This goes in line with what Sue Falsone suggested, limiting emails and social media to certain times of the day.

This might be a little harder, so it might be a good idea to start out with Sue's Be Like first.

Once a week, take a digital detox for a certain period of time. Make it easy for yourself to start; we want this to be successful and, like training, we are going to slowly progress.

Pick a day you have off so you won't be tempted to check email as much and feel there is some urgency to answer them. Try 12 hours at first. If you are really dependent on your devices, start out with six hours.

Tell your friends and family, maybe even make a social media post that you will be offline. People will get used to it.

Use auto-responders to let people know you will answer them the next day.

Shut your phone down so you won't get any buzzing or notifications, and it will make it more of a pain to try to slip back on.

Leave the phone with someone with instructions not to give it back until the time you agree on.

In James Clear's book, *Atomic Habits*, he talks about going as far as having someone change the password to his phone for the weekend and not giving it back until Monday!

Be creative with the idea and do whatever it takes to keep progressing.

Set a goal to do what Alan does: Once a month try it for 24–48 hours.

But remember, "Just because someone else says they take a full-week digital detox once a month doesn't mean that's right for you. You need to find what's appropriate."

Shawn is the author of the bestselling book Sleep Smarter and is the creator of The Model Health Show—featured as the top health podcast on iTunes with millions of listener downloads each year. A graduate of The University of Missouri St. Louis, Shawn studied business, biology and kinesiology, and went on to be the founder of Advanced Integrative Health Alliance, a company that provides wellness services for clients and organizations worldwide. Shawn has been featured in Entrepreneur, Fast Company, Forbes, The Dr. Oz Show, ESPN, CNN and many other major media outlets. Visit his site at themodelhealthshow.com for more information.

You have a bestselling book; your podcast is in the top 10 in Health and Fitness on iTunes. You've had success in a lot of areas. Talk to us about how you define success.

It's ever-evolving for me; there's always another level. I equate success with growth. Every day, my modus operandi is to get just one percent better. If I can achieve that, it's a successful day. I chalk it up to marking off those successful days as equating to a successful life.

In his book *Legacy*, James Kerr talked about "Kiwi kaizen." It's all the little things getting better in different areas. There's been a lot of science covering happiness and it comes down to progress and growth…when you can see the needle move a little.

People have heard the statement, "If you're not growing, you're dying." But this is a biological phenomenon because life itself is about movement; it's about growth and development. And the opposite is true when we start to lose life—lack of life is specifically a lack of movement. There's no movement; there's no life force.

There's a constant trudge toward growth and development, even as we get into our elder years and continue to grow and become better, at least in how we think and relate to people. We find some way to continue to get better. We're bringing and affirming more life.

You talked about evolving and that seems to be an overall theme with everyone I interviewed for this book. When did you start to feel you were becoming successful in what you were doing?

There are levels to this. I first started to see results early on, having a clinical practice, being a strength and conditioning coach. I started to see results in people and I knew I wasn't an anomaly in getting myself healthier. That was a big aha moment—that this works for other people too.

This is key: We decide our own value.

There's an idea the market will determine your value, but I don't believe that; I believe we determine our own value. I finally realized I could set my price points and what kind of packages I offer. I started to see people buying these packages, people purchasing different nutrition plans. Once I set the standard of my value, people stepped up to be a part of it. I had to determine what that was for me instead of letting things happen.

One of the ultimate success moments was when my book came out. I fell in love with writing in the eighth grade, thanks to a teacher who took an interest in me. I always knew I was going to write a book, although I had no idea it would be a health-related book.

It was incredible to see the book when it was released and the huge wave it created. And it's still happening; it's been two years since the book came out and it was number two in the country on Audible last month. It's been translated into 17 different languages. That makes me feel an incredible amount of success and a sense of accomplishment.

It's one of the top five books I read last year—I wear blue-light blockers at night, one of the many things that influenced my getting better sleep since reading *Sleep Smarter*. Speaking of sleeping, what motivates you in the morning to get out of bed? What's driving you?

Each day is an opportunity. But here's the thing: Each of us has a different approach in how we operate, even with getting out of bed. It's a lot easier to get out of bed when we feel good. It's a lot easier to get out of bed when we're well rested.

But we need to have a target that's top of mind, something that's more seductive, more inspiring and visceral than being cozy in the bed. This means having something to get after, some kind of goal for the day. That starts with the evening ritual the night before, determining the number one objective for the next day.

This is the eat-the-frog concept. Decide the big thing to get done, then set it to the side and let your subconscious operate on it. Just have that top of mind—be aware of it, but then go to sleep…let it all go. In the morning, bring that thing back to top of mind.

Michael Hyatt is my coach. I love his system because we have a workday shutdown and an evening shutdown. It really clears everything to set me up for the next day. The day's morning routine starts the night before. It was an epiphany when I started doing that.

Michael is doing things at another level. He sets up activation triggers. He's just like a lot of us, especially if you're an entrepreneur and you're your own boss. We can be pretty crappy bosses for ourselves and let the time get away from us because there's no limit to how much we can work. His lights in his office are literally on a timer; they turn off at 5:00PM—he'd better be done with whatever he's writing because the power's going to be shut down. That's the trigger for him to let things go and do the thing he values the most, which is being a husband and father.

Last night, I was working until 8:30PM after having started the day at 7:30AM. I was bouncing around doing a variety of tasks. I wasn't working the entire day, but I don't want that to be my rule; that's more of the exception. Most of the time, I'm great at shutting down by 5:00PM, hanging out with my kids, having dinner, all that good stuff. But it's not about being perfect. It's about progress.

What are some sacrifices you've made to get to where you are?

I haven't sacrificed much—I know that might sound crazy. It's just my perspective, the way I look at things. Even the word "sacrifice" to me means "to make sacred." The things I've missed—not going to clubs, to this dinner or that event—I "sacrificed" those things, but it was for something greater. I knew what I was doing was truly a sacred act. In taking care of myself, my family, my craft, writing, speaking, my show, helping patients—all of those were sacred to me.

By "sacrificing," you get to a position where you can do those things whenever you want. But now that I can do anything I want anytime I want, it's not that attractive anymore.

What we're looking for is *the feeling;* it's not the thing. There's a feeling involved in knowing I can do things versus the feeling of needing something to complete me.

We should all enjoy the process. Consciously think about the journey you're on, those positive moments, those good things that happen along the way. Even think about the not-so-good things and the value they bring to your perspective. Those are the things that will bring you the most joy and fulfillment.

It's not the end goal. It's not the mission to sell books or become number one in something. That's fleeting, here today, gone today. It's not going to fill your cup. The process and who you become, that's what really does it. But you don't want to miss it. Pay attention to those small moments.

You mentioned some of those not-so-great times and the value they bring to your perspective. How do you get through when things aren't going so great?

I've talked to some of the most successful people and here's the truth: Everybody has a pity party. When something we don't like happens, everybody feels that way. We don't have an initial reaction of, "This is great. I'm going to learn so much from this." Nobody does that. But the quicker you can get yourself to that way of thinking, the better. That's a muscle we can strengthen.

I'm very aware when something challenging comes up, something that could entail potential suffering. We're all going to go through tough times; we all have challenges, but suffering is optional. It's really about perspective.

How I got into this field was through my own health crisis, the so-called incurable spinal condition I had…that I no longer have today. That was the worst thing that ever happened to me. It almost destroyed my life, as in literally not being around today. But in a way, it was also the best thing that happened to me. I'm so grateful it happened, because without that time, I wouldn't be talking to you right now. It took me nearly three years to get better and it took me years—probably half a decade—before I realized how valuable it was to go through that.

When challenges come, it's important to cultivate how quickly you can look for the good and ask questions because our brains operate on questions. That's how they work. We've got a reticular activating system, a reticular cortex. It's always seeking solutions to the things we're focusing on. When a negative event occurs, ask, "What is this trying to teach me?" Or, "What capacity wants to emerge in my character through this situation?"

There's always something to learn. It might be practicing more patience. It might be being able to see something from another person's point of view. It might be exercising the right to say no. There's a lesson and all we have to do is honestly ask ourselves. Ask and listen.

Shawn, let's talk a little bit about you personally. What are some habits that helped you get here? If you look back to advise a young Shawn, what would you tell him?

I don't want to mess up my timeline. I wouldn't go back and tell the young Shawn anything. I've seen *The Flash.* I've seen *Back to the Future.* Marty McFly almost messed everything up. But what I would say is this: Keep moving forward—that's the best advice. Take one step at a time; keep moving forward. If you're on a hike that's a significant ordeal, you get to that place where your brain starts talking to you. It's the same for people who do endurance events, thinking, "Maybe you should just turn back—everybody will understand." You start producing that internal talk.

The solution is simple. Just take the next step…just take the next step…just take the next step. It boils down to that in all areas of life. It's not a sprint; it's a marathon. Continue to take the next step. Do your best not to go backward. That's the big issue.

Life is about movement. Life is about growth. Life is moving forward. When you stop, you're not just staying still, you're going backward. Keep taking that next step.

Maybe things didn't work out with one particular plan, but get up the next day and make some progress. Make a couple phone calls, maybe write a few pages of something. Go get a workout—do something to get better. Just keep taking a step forward and eventually you'll arrive.

There's a lot of talk about making goals out of your comfort zone. But when you take that first step, make it in your comfort zone. Make that first step something easy. Take small steps and you'll see growth.

You wrote a book on sleep. Can you tell us your morning routine?

The first thing I do when I get up in the morning is to get super hydrated—the term I use for it is taking an inner bath. That's something I've been pushing. We take an external shower to get ourselves prepared for the rest of the world, but isn't your inside more important? We hydrate our cells, our organs, our tissues. There are benefits from water-induced thermogenesis, even just kick starting the metabolism.

These are little things people overlook.

After sleep is one of the most significant times of dehydration because the body goes through all of these processes during the night. There are a lot of metabolic waste products accumulated during sleep that need to get processed and flushed. If you're going right to the coffee pot, not having water or eating food, you're creating more dehydration, and then you wonder why you don't feel good. It's so simple, but yet, until they become aware, a lot of people aren't doing it.

Let's talk about your goal-setting process. Is it a formal process?

I'm a huge advocate of writing down goals. Michael Hyatt is a super hero with this and has written one of the best books on goal setting; he really spoke to my man brain and my science acumen. He looked at studies that showed more than a 30-percent greater chance of achieving goals simply by writing them down.

We're talking about well-done studies: When people wrote out their goals, they had over a 30-percent greater chance of achieving the goal, versus people who didn't write, who just had the goal rattling around in their heads. And for some people, the gain was over 50 percent.

Why does it matter? The writing is taking the first step toward achieving the goal. It's an action step. It also creates a sense of clarity. As you get a goal out of your head and on the paper, it's an important step in articulating what you want your goal to be. You can even get into details.

I'm in an incredible mastermind with some other friends of Michael's whose names you might recognize: Pat Flynn and Jamie Tardy. We share our goals to start the year. There's accountability and I feel obligated to accomplish my goals.

There's also another key when I write goals—I highly recommend people write three action steps associated with that goal. These aren't be-all action steps. But say if the goal is to write a book, write "Within the next six months, I'm going to finish the manuscript."

One of the steps may be to write 10 pages a week or two pages a day. Another might be to schedule a time to do the writing. Maybe you'd hire a coach or find an accountability partner. Write tangible steps toward the goal.

Accountability is so important. I just got back from a group and a couple people gave me a kick in the butt. I've got some work to do. It really does help.

Shawn, with so much travel and a busy schedule, how do you recharge?

There are micro-charges or recharges on macro level. On the micro level—and this might be controversial—but I think it's a bit of a tragedy that we get so pumped for a vacation. If we have to get a vacation from our lives, we need to change that.

I know this intimately, because there was a time when all I wanted was vacation time. Today, a vacation is just a bonus—it's an opportunity for completely unplugging. I love what I do and I love helping people.

That's what I want people to be aware of and move toward if possible. If you're not in the career you want, look for an out, and 99 percent of the time, there will be one. But in the meantime, start to embrace the opportunity you have now and be grateful because other people might give their lives for the job you have. Just look for how you can add value where you are now.

I did a show recently with Chris Ducker talking about job burnout and unhappiness in the workplace. We were talking about scientific facts about how workplace unhappiness impacts health. Most likely, your job in some way affects other people—think about the difference you can make in other people's lives.

I take care of me, every day—mainly taking the time for meditation, exercise, read and to do what I want. On a macro scale, I'm introverted. That has become a big term today—people are aware of being introverted; introverts are hot right now. Introversion doesn't mean you're shy or you don't like people or you can't be the life of the party. It's more about how your energy is derived.

I'm definitely more of a situational extrovert; I can get on stage and bring value. But in my day-to-day life, I need time to be alone. I'm much more at peace and recharge when I'm by myself. Other people are charged by being around other people. That's how my wife is—she loves it; she gets energized being around other people. That's beautiful, but that's just not me.

Personally, I recharge by being aware. After being on the road, I take a day or two to have minimal interaction with people. I'm still working; I'm still moving forward, but recharging in peace.

Shawn, I know this is going to be especially hard for you because you've had your show for a long time. You've had really interesting people on the show and have a lot of interesting friends. You've got to give us three people to follow we can all learn from.

For a general life check, to check in with yourself, get your head on straight, get your mind right, get focused, I'd definitely follow Eric Thomas. "ET" is the name he goes by; he's on all social media with a million subscribers on YouTube. He's the top motivational speaker in the world. I don't need a lot of motivation. That's not my thing, but I'm telling you, when he speaks, it talks to my spirit.

I was on stage the other day and had people raise their hands for a particular question, "Raise your hands as high as you can." And everybody raised their hands. I said, "Raise it higher." Everybody had another foot they could reach—we're never reaching as high as we think we can, especially if we're not triggered to or somebody brings to our awareness the fact that we can reach higher. That's what ET does. Definitely, Eric Thomas is somebody to follow.

For anything related to growing your business, Bedros Keuilian is the man and a half, I'm telling you—a superhero.

For fitness-related material, I would say follow Luka Hocevar. There's nobody better in the world with human movement. Definitely follow him.

You've made such great impact in this world and it's an inspiration to have you be part of this series. Thanks so much for doing this.

BE LIKE SHAWN

SLEEP SMARTER

There are exceptions, but the most successful people in the world make it a priority to get a good night's sleep.

Shawn's book, *Sleep Smarter,* was a game changer for me. Although we didn't talk a lot about it in the interview, here are some key takeaways from his book to getting better sleep.

A good night's sleep starts in the morning—Part One: Drink water as soon as you wake up. *"Sleeping is one of the most significant times of dehydration."* Shawn's idea of an "inner bath" is brilliant. A good standard I first heard from nutritionist Robert Yang is to consume half your bodyweight in ounces…and have 25 percent of that be first thing in morning. Before the coffee!

A good night's sleep starts in the morning—Part Two: Get some kind of exercise in the morning, even if it's just five or ten minutes, will help *"Reset something called the cortisol rhythm."*

A good night's sleep starts in the morning—Part Three: Go outside and get in the sun. Melatonin, which regulates the circadian rhythm and which will help with sleep, is influenced heavily by exposure to sunlight.

Caffeine cutoff: Caffeine stays in the body for up to 10 hours. Try to make your last cup of joe around 1:00 or 2:00PM. This is hard for trainers!

Training: Try not to train too late if you can avoid it. Your body might not have enough time to reduce core temperature. A lower core temp will help you sleep better.

Limit the booze: It might seem like it helps you sleep, but it completely messes with your sleep pattern.

In the bedroom

Keep the devices out of the bedroom—that means the phone, clocks with blue light and the TV. If you think you can't live without them, get blue-light blocker glasses. Blue light can suppress the secretion of melatonin. Exposure to blue light alerts the brain that it's daytime, messing with that circadian rhythm.

Get blackout curtains to keep the room as dark as possible. I also use eyeshades, which are especially good for naps.

Keep the room temperature cool. Sleep in lighter clothes and be comfortable.

"The bedroom should be used for only two things, 1) sleep and 2) that other thing."

Get and study Shawn's book *Sleep Smarter.*

Dave is the High-Performance Director for the Orlando Magic of the NBA, where he manages the strength and conditioning, medical and sports science department. Prior to his time with Orlando, Dave served in a similar capacity in MLS with the Seattle Sounders and the Kansas City Wizards. As a student athlete, Dave played and studied at Virginia Tech, and went on to play professionally in the minor leagues of Germany and indoor soccer. He would later complete a bachelors in Coaching Science from George Mason, and a masters in exercise science from Cal U of Pennsylvania. The best place to get in touch with Dave is via twitter.com/davetenney.

People are always interested in people who have been successful as both a player and coach. You played professionally and transitioned to high-level coaching. How do you personally define success?

I still sometimes wake up in the morning and wonder if I've actually been a success. I define success by the way my group—the people I'm coordinating with every day—continue to evolve and get better. If we're doing that, no matter what happens on the field, I consider what we're doing a success.

When did you consider yourself a success? People are always pushing, trying to get better, trying to serve people like you did with your educational conference, the Seattle Sports Science Conference. You don't always consider yourself a success, but when did you start to feel at least like you were becoming successful?

After I left the Sounders, the team made the playoffs again and got into the conference finals. The team I worked with over 11 years made the playoffs every single year. Once you get to the playoffs, so many different factors go into wins and losses. I knew there was consistency in what we were doing—helping our teams perform at a high level, stay healthy and develop good habits. I took pride in the fact that our teams were good enough to make the playoffs every year.

If I look back and ask how I'd define success for myself, the things I'm most proud of would be the people who have been with me who then went off and did other things, taken director jobs other places. I've had a series of people intern through me, guys like Garrison Draper with Philadelphia Union; Jared Philips is with Minnesota United; Jordan Webb is now at Notre Dame. One of my early interns was recently hired to be a Head of Research for the English FA.

When you're creating something where people are coming into your environment and striving to get better and then moving on to greater positions, you know what you're doing has been successful.

Sometimes it's hard to see the impact. You've had a big impact on so many coaches, whether it's from a podcast or through your conference. And the team record speaks for itself, with the 11 times they've made the playoffs. You keep getting promoted and were recruited by Orlando to be their High-Performance Director. You're doing something right. What is it that motivates you in the morning? What gets you out of bed in the morning?

I try to work on that intersection of physical performance and scale and tactics and the medical side. If you had a Venn diagram with physical performance, technical ability, tactical understanding and lifestyle—where they all connect is what gets me up in the morning. It's to live in that space where you can manage everyone in your organization to help optimize that little space where they all connect.

The latest thing we're working with is a study of complex systems theory. Systems theory is about how all these things interact. We know the person who's the best athlete often isn't the best player. You get players who, as they age, might become better players. They learn how to take care of themselves and we see improved performance on the field. We learn more about each of these areas of an athlete. It's not just about understanding one area and thinking, "If I improve this, I improve the whole athlete." It's more about looking at the interactions.

A good example I often use is a conversation I had with a coach about a player from Barcelona. The player hadn't lifted weights in a traditional American culture. He'd been here a few years and was very skillful. After a year, he said to his coach, "If I would've lifted like this, I'd be playing at a really high level in Europe right now." The coach was proud of that, but I reminded him, "Be careful, because if you take him out of what he was doing and put 20 percent of his time in the weight room, you've totally changed him. He's not the same player."

We can't take a reductionist view that just adding 20 percent more time in the weight room will make the athlete faster and everything else will stay the same. You change the whole athlete. That's what I've learned working on the field, on the court, in the weight room, on a track and in film. How all of those things interact and impact each other is not a linear process. That's where the really interesting learning is taking place for me.

Do you think being a player at a high level had a big impact on the way you coach?

We have a lot of coaches who were decent athletes; they got in the weight room and became a bit better athletes. They thought the weight room really helped them and decided they wanted to be strength coaches. What's their answer usually going to be? Weight room.

This is like the football or basketball coach who might have come into coaching through video. This person sees athletes making all the wrong decisions…and might not care about what's done in the weight room. What's the focus on? Showing athletes the right video.

At least having experienced the sport—and by no means do I consider myself having been a fantastic athlete; I was lucky to play to age 29, but I didn't have a stellar career by any means. However, the role of video, the weight room, off-season conditioning, daily coaching, the effect of travel—having lived through all those things, I got a better feel of what's truly impactful.

Also, it's crucial to speak the same language. Most coaches see things a certain way and use a specific language. Most players see things a certain way and use a specific language. Most strength coaches have their own way of saying things; most sports scientists have their own way of saying things. Language barrier is an issue. People don't know what other people mean because they're not speaking the same language.

This year was your first year with Orlando Magic. You have to be really organized in structure. Do you have something special to share about that?

I carve out couple hours in the evening to focus on things I'm questioning or that have been lingering in my head. As a coach, you need daily time to reflect on what's happened.

If I send out a daily report to the coaching staff, I don't do it from the office. I see the athletes during the day. I interact with the coaches after practice and I might see the training report once our staff has delivered that.

I just let the report sit and that process helps me work through things. And I have a couple hours at night where I synthesize. Where do we go from here? I lay out the report to the coaches and reflect on what I learned for the day.

You're probably more ready to answer questions and to get a better evaluation.

We live in a culture where we're reactive: Something happens and we react. But there's something powerful when you see something happen; you know you have to make a decision, and you just sit with it a bit.

If you've been involved in pro or collegiate sports, inevitably you'll be in the situation where the team will play a bad game. The coaching staff goes in a room to talk about why the team played an awful game and why this or that player was bad. I've been through hundreds of those discussions and inevitably I wake up the next morning with a totally different opinion. I wonder if we could just decide, "Let's not talk about this anymore tonight. Let's just sit with it and wake up tomorrow and reflect." Maybe we would see things a lot more clearly.

But there's something about our nature. We want to be reactive when things happen.

What are some other habits you think contribute to success?

Definitely patience. Humility. Probably echoed a lot in this book is never feeling like you know everything. Humility is feeling there's so much more for you to learn.

The power of reflection. This pursuit of constant evolution.

That's something that I see in the most successful people; they're lifelong learners. What about goals? What's that process?

Every season I make a goal for the season. In most of our positions, it's important those are more process-driven goals. By the end of the year we'd like to have the athletes do "X." Maybe it's a new athlete-monitoring tool. We want to attempt "Y" in terms of introducing a new methodology.

I find the introduction and evaluation of new processes more essential than the achievements. There's something strong about this, like the 80/20 rule, where it's something important. You might keep 80 percent from year to year and move on 20 percent even if sometimes that 20 percent in years past was something successful for you. There's something healthy about this constant rejuvenation and throwing out 20 percent of what you're doing every year.

Speaking of the long term, when I talk to young coaches, they might set a goal of "I want to be coaching in this league or at that level or with these types of athletes." From the Eastern religion and philosophy concepts, I always feel like you can't see that far down the path. You just know when it's the right time to do something different.

In my case, when I stopped playing I was a youth soccer coach and I was pretty sure I was going to be a director of an academy for young soccer players for the rest of my life. I'm now a performance director for the NBA and I never, ever thought I'd be where I am now when I started doing this. Ten years from now I could be doing something totally different. We can think of ourselves as evolving as practitioners and that next job helps fill some of the interests that had been stimulated by whatever we'd been doing.

You're certainly living proof of allowing that to happen in being in major league soccer and then unexpectedly turning things around to become the High-Performance Director of the Orlando Magic.

It's not something I expected or thought was going to happen or was even searching for. It's a reminder that sometimes the goal is also to work with the right people. I worked with great people in Seattle, and then I met up with Jeff Weltman and John Hammond, who are the president and the general manager for Orlando. I thought, "Possibly working in a few years with these guys will make me better. These are the right people. I need to align myself career-wise with them right now."

It's not always levels. Sometimes it's being in the right environment with the right people that helps you improve as a practitioner.

What are some sacrifices you've made to be in your position?

The sacrifice people don't always see working in pro sports or the upper-collegiate level of sports is the time away from family during the vacation periods. Being on the NBA schedule now, this will be my first year away from my family on Thanksgiving and Christmas, which is the cost of working in the league. On the other hand, for the first time, I'll be able to have a summer vacation with my family. Being in MLS for 11 years, I was not able to have a summer vacation with my family.

Clearly, working at an elite level, whether as an athlete or as a coach, you must make huge sacrifices in terms of the time you can spend with your family. This makes it most important to be fully present when you have time with them. That's the most challenging part.

Are there any apps you just can't live without that helped you be more productive?

I'm far more productive when I'm using the Headspace app. For anyone interested in anything regarding meditation, Headspace is fantastic—it's simple and easy to use.

Another app I've been toying around with is Inner Balance by Heart Math. It combines breathing and HRV and syncs your breathing with your heart rate. You get in a slow, diaphragmatic breathing and relaxed state. I've been alternating between that and Headspace because I find myself sleeping better, being a little more productive, less reactive and finding myself in a better frame of mind.

Dave, give us three non fitness–related books everybody should read.

One I continue to recommend is the book *The Undoing Project*. It's funny now that I'm in Orlando with new management and am conducting job interviews for the different departments. I ask every candidate, "Have you read *Undoing Project*?" I think it's literally that important.

The Undoing Project is about how we're wired to make decisions. As we go through each day, we're thinking about things, trying to decide what's right or wrong. There are so many decisions we have to make over the course of a day. *The Undoing Project* made me realize how much bias we carry with us. With every decision we make, we're making decisions purely out of experiential things that might have happened in the past. Most coaches are highly biased; we should try to bring that bias out in the light and make ourselves aware of it. Everyone is biased in certain ways that have worked for them. But it's still bias.

All of the books by Daniel Kahneman are good. You could probably include *Thinking, Fast and Slow* and then something like *The Checklist Manifesto* as well. As I consider *Thinking, Fast and Slow* by Kahneman, *The Undoing Project* was actually about Kahneman as well. *The Checklist Manifesto* is about setting up simple processes so we don't let little things slip through the cracks because of our bias. These books are about the way we organize our thoughts and make decisions.

Dave, success leaves clues. Give me three people you think we can all learn from.

When I open up my Twitter feed, I read everything Patrick Ward posts. If Patrick says read a book or read this research paper, I will. One hundred percent.

I love the ideas and thoughts of Mladen Jovanovi. I would also add Dan Pfaff, who's so experienced in track and field, but was also doing this performance director job probably 20 years before anyone called it that. I follow his career and I follow him.

Dave, thanks for being such a great leader and someone who has helped so many other coaches in their development. We really appreciate you sharing your journey.

BE LIKE DAVE

"I find that I'm far more productive when I'm using the Headspace app."

MEDITATION

Dave is about as busy as anyone can be. He is the High-Performance Director of the Orlando Magic with a big staff and he also has a family. He has so much going on that it's important to take some time out of the day to sit with your thoughts and not be reactive. Follow his suggestion to help settle your mind.

Download the Headspace app or another free meditation app.

Set aside 10 minutes a day when you won't be disturbed. It's probably best early, but it doesn't have to be; do whatever works for you. Try to make it part of your morning routine if you can (see Allistair McCaw's Be Like).

Challenge yourself to do it every day for 30 days.

Diane is the owner of Vives Training Systems and Fit4Austin in Austin, Texas. She presents globally on her progressive approach and functional training application to strength and conditioning for the complete fitness athlete. Scientifically based methods drive her practice and program design. Currently, she serves on the education team at Functional Movement Systems. She has served on the Board of Directors of the NSCA and has been featured in many magazine articles and publications such as Speed, Agility and Quickness, as well as Developing Sports Speed, both published by Human Kinetics. You can reach Diane via her website at dianevives.com.

You've had a great career with many successes. Though it's probably changed over time, how do you define success?

Like most young strength coaches, I started my career thinking that it would be the defining moment when I got to work with my first pro athlete. I was fortunate to be involved in a facility with our business partner, Juan Carlos Santana, that provided that experience with off-season athletes.

But as I've gotten further into my career, things have definitely changed. My definition now is geared toward trying to create more waves and having a bigger impact within the profession. I discovered I love to teach and that opened a lot of doors.

I have this idea in the back of my head: I want to be able to train one million people—but I can't do that by myself. I focus on being able to get in front of other trainers and coaches and working on my ability to teach them something to impact the practical aspects. What can I do that will help make them better coaches and trainers?

This is an exponential idea of bringing more to the table with my presentations. That's a definition of success, at least professionally.

And personally, I'm able to align with my values and have a good support system at home. I'm very fortunate to have that as well. That's a big part of my success. I've learned, through a lot of trial and error, how to bring balance. I've had to make some difficult life choices around that. You have to follow your head, heart and gut along the way.

In some ways, it's almost easier to look at what success "isn't." I don't want to wake up with regrets. I don't want to have a feeling I missed something the day before or wasn't in integrity with myself. Success is being able to wake up and know you've stayed in alignment with yourself and your environment.

Is "impact" what motivates you to get out of bed? Is that what excites you professionally when you're working?

What can I bring to the table professionally to increase my impact? How am I making myself better able to offer something of value? This profession is an exciting place; we have so many different areas of education and people with a variety of styles delivering those pieces. But it all comes back to, can you provide something people can take home and use?

At Perform Better, we have people who are great thought leaders—philosophically, we can be blown away. I love that. I get to put some of my attention on how to focus on the practical pieces. Let's bring some of the ideas from those thought leaders into material where trainers say, "I need this on Monday. These are the tools I need to help me do that."

The "it" that wakes me up is what I can work on today to drive that forward. And that's exciting, because I get to learn and keep an open mind toward things to make myself better.

I've been thinking something similar for a long time. Take people like Greg Rose, Gray Cook, Sue Falsone and Lee Burton—all these brilliant minds. We see them speak or hear a podcast and sometimes can end up feeling depressed, thinking we're never going to be that good. I used to call it the Gray Cook Effect. I'd listen to Gray and get that feeling every time. But eventually I started to understand I have value and can bring something to the mix. It takes time to find some aspect you know you're good at and where you can make an impact.

And that's what I'm currently thinking about, especially from the hands-on segments—really drilling down regressions and progressions, figuring out how to apply some of the principles of people like Gray and Greg and other great thinkers I was able to learn from and be inspired by. We've got to package and break things down into chunks to make it realistic so people can use it when they go home from the conferences. That's what I've been focusing on.

You've been a pioneer in this field. I never thought of you like that, to be honest, because I didn't realize there weren't enough women on some of the lecture circuits. We're seeing more women, which is a good thing. But you were doing this when there'd be maybe you and Sue Falsone on the tour—or just you at times. You pioneered being a female strength coach in this male-dominated industry.

I've always had a naive way of looking at it; it was naive ignorance. I was looking for coaches and trainers to learn from—I just wanted to be a better coach and to discover how I was going to stand apart as a professional. I'm always driven toward what's going to make me better.

It happened to be that it was men who were the speakers. All the mentors at the time were men. They were leading me to different aspects of training I didn't know existed. Getting excited about the work drove me toward taking that route and speaking and sharing more information. And I had the honor of speaking at Perform Better, NSCA and other events. But it didn't dawn on me it was a male versus female thing.

You've written books on speed—again, we don't see a lot of women involved in speed education. And you were on the board of directors at NSCA. If you can play Monday morning quarterback, what are some of the hurdles you had to go over to get to where you are now?

I'll be brutally honest—there's an experience when I was at an NSCA conference as a young certified strength and conditioning coach. Right after my first presentation, somebody told me a group of female strength coaches were having a get-together and they'd love for me to go. One of the coaches later found out I wasn't a university-based strength coach, which was their definition of a strength coach, and uninvited me on the spot.

It crushed me as a young strength coach passionate about being part of a community and helping each other move forward. There were a couple of incidents later when people did something hurtful—one was another woman who put a hurdle in front of me. In those moments early on I decided I'm not going to be that woman.

It drove me to want to run for the board of directors and get involved in NSCA. I was passionate about the organization and what it stood for. I wanted to make sure there were more examples that weren't female versus male; we're all trying to move forward and make each other better. It's not a competition where we're trying to knock each other down. That's driven me as I got into my career. I want to make sure women are standing up, showing integrity and not being the person who makes somebody else feel small.

You're definitely doing that. It's one of those things where because of your success—we were seeing you in books and videos and on the tour—more women were inspired to go in that direction. Were there any barriers to get into any of the speaking tours or when you were trying to advance your career?

The only barriers I had were of my own making: Do I submit this application to be a speaker? Is this a subject that will be accepted? Am I making the right decisions regarding which projects I'm getting involved in and who I'm involved with?

The only barriers are those I put in front of myself due to hesitation. It took gaining confidence, experience and continuing to take those steps forward to allow me not to focus on that as much. Just keep moving.

We're always our own worst enemies. Were there sacrifices you've had to make to push along and become successful?

It's very hard to balance the personal and professional sides, especially when travel is involved. The biggest thing is having a good support system at home. But even there, I've had to learn the hard way. There are people who are no longer in my life because I didn't know how to balance things. I was accused of being a workaholic, and I probably was. I needed to figure out how to bring that with me on the road and involve the people in my life more when I had the opportunities.

This means putting more quality into the time when you have windows with the people in your life—versus just going through the days and not realizing those are the times that mean the most. Don't forget to spend time with friends, family and your loved ones at home. It seems cliché, but it's so true. Often, they're not as concerned about how much—they're measuring the quality of the time you're spending with them. That's what I've learned over the last few years.

When did you start feeling like you were starting to get this stuff right, that you were becoming successful?

That's the elusive feeling that always feels right in front of us, isn't it? There was one point when a lot of things started coming together. I was invited to speak at Perform Better. I was speaking at NSCA. I got an opportunity to be on the Under Armour Performance Training Council—all within a very short window.

Those events started validating the hard work I was putting in and what I was trying to share, coach and teach. That was a time I felt I was becoming successful. But I still feel it's in front of me. I need to keep reaching.

The underlying message throughout this book is that people are still struggling to find it. Although we don't want success to be based on external factors, at the same time when we start to feel our impact and the validation develops, it can help to

drives us even more. Sometimes that's the balance we need to have; there needs to be an external piece to it.

I call it my "positive impact score." You're getting some of that energy back. You get email from people after an event—you've made enough of an impact, people take the time to write an email to say thanks or mention something specific. They're giving good feedback, and they give that energy back. That energy coming back really helps validate or at least supports the energy you're giving out. For all the energy you're pouring into things, it's really important to get some of that back.

What are some habits or personality traits you feel are needed to be successful?

There are two goals I always keep in mind. One is making sure I have a system in my training programs. If the mentors and colleagues I respect and whose opinions I value walked through my door at any moment, could they pick up my chart or iPad and know exactly why I was doing what I was doing? Could I explain it—here's the client or athlete in front of me—and it would make sense? Could I support why I was doing what I was doing; did I have a plan and a system?

That's an underlying theme to how I run my training and programs. That's been brilliant in a lot of ways because it's kept me accountable. And it's always in the back of my head to have that quality every day.

The other element is making sure I have enough tools to train anybody who walks through my door. That's always been important to me, that functional training background I was fortunate to learn early. Do I have enough tools if an athlete comes in versus a fitness client versus a Parkinson's patient?

Another trait that comes to mind is building our integrity muscles. Build a habit around doing the right thing when nobody's looking. The more you do that on your own and with your habits, it builds the integrity muscles that make it easier when you're faced with hard decisions. Focus on that.

That's the true test of character: Would you do it if nobody was looking? Let's go into some of the things you systematically do. Do you journal?

I do some journaling and some of what I call "results work." Results work is the Wilbert Alix program; it's a series of exercises that lead you to 10 results. It's personal to the individual, but it's basically writing 10 things down in the present tense, as if you already have them. You have to make sure you select the correct 10 things for you. It puts a more present mind focus on the results.

The participant journals on one of the results at a time to stay focused. Alix has different exercises to draw you through having the right 10 things on the sheet. I focus on that work and it's worked well for me. When you achieve one of those results, you mark it off the list and go back to work and fill that list up again. It's got a combination of professional goals, personal ideas, even income-based plans. I make sure my exercises are well-rounded. The goal setting keeps me in line.

We talk about recovery and rest with our clients. How do you recharge on a daily, weekly and yearly basis?

I sit on a warm beach two or three times a year because for me, the ocean is that peaceful place to recharge. The ocean always reminds you there's something bigger than yourself. And here in Austin, we recharge with live music. Live music is amazing.

Seeing live music is an escape for me too.

Diane, let's finish up with a couple suggestions. What are three non fitness–related books people should read for their development?

Pivot is a book by Jenny Blake that hits on practical points. She put together a lot of great information, not just her own—she also does a wonderful job pulling people together. It's important when it comes to a point where you need to pivot in your career when you're considering how to change your position for something better. There are steps you need to take during that pivot to know you're not just bumping off the wall, the Roomba effect: You come up against a hurdle and decide to change directions without a strategy. She does a good job laying that out.

A More Beautiful Question is another great book, by Warren Berger. It's useful when you're trying to create a thought process—it helps broaden your way of thinking. *A More Beautiful Question* helps reframe how to be more inquisitive, how to ask a better question. Instead of just eating up all this flow of information so we feel we're drinking water out of a fire hose, it teaches us to build the right question first.

This is something I love about Greg Rose. When you get into conversation with Greg, he'll just keep coming at you until he knows he's asked the right question. That's such a powerful tool when you're communicating with others or trying to dig deeper into a project. Keep asking questions.

For a third suggestion, it's a tie between *Ego is the Enemy* and *Extreme Ownership*. *Ego is the Enemy* by Ryan Holiday is not just about extreme egos or negative aspects of ego. It also teaches how to understand more about the ego within yourself and the egos you're encountering. The author describes specific traits that help us communicate and have a better perspective on reality. He reminds us to recognize when we're around egos that aren't serving us, and what to do about that.

Extreme Ownership by Jocko Willink and Leif Babin is great. In leadership and when dealing with a team, one of my favorite aspects is that I'm able to trust my team. I come from a big family and I don't like to be out on my own; I like to feel a team is working on things together.

I'm always involved in a team atmosphere. I love *Extreme Ownership* because within a team, having those leadership skills is important. It really helps you understand if you're a leader. Are you somebody who needs to be working on leadership skills?

Listening to that book is the way to go. I listened to that and couldn't stop.

Audio is how I get most of my books completed; *audible.com* is one of my best friends. When training or running, I work through books on Audible.

Success leaves clues. Who are three people we can follow? The topic doesn't have to be fitness; it can be anyone you feel we can learn from.

These days, I tend to think more in terms of groups—think of Athletes Acceleration and who they're pulling together for their events. From a practical standpoint in training, especially with speed and power, some coaches and trainers need good progressions and a better understanding of them. Athletes Acceleration is calling on people like Robert dos Remedios, Lee Taft, Wil Fleming, Mike Boyle and Dan John. They've got a great team and are talented people to watch.

As to thought leaders, of course we think of Gray Cook, Pavel Tsatsouline with Strong First…Greg Rose. I know I'm giving you more than three, but I can't stop. Brandon Marcello is an authentic presenter who pulls together terrific evidence-based information and makes it easy to understand. That's what a lot of these people do well.

Nick Winkelman is driven not only to teach about different aspects of coaching, but he also loves the science and he's a great presenter. We're going to see much more from him.

For inspiration, I love Todd Durkin. With him, I think about success and the qualities we take outside of training, too. He pushes us personally and his energy is incredible. You can't go wrong with Todd—he's definitely worth checking out.

Many of those people are interviewed in this book; those are great choices.

Thank you so much for sharing your journey and describing some of the struggles to success, Diane.

BE LIKE DIANE

"The only barriers I had were of my own making: Do I submit this application to be a speaker, and is this a subject that will be accepted? The only barriers are those I put in front of myself based on hesitation. It took getting some confidence, experience and just continuing to take those steps forward to allow me not to focus on that as much."

SELF-LIMITING BELIEFS

Like Diane, for many of us, our own self-limiting beliefs are part of the biggest barriers to moving forward. Bad self-talk can prevent us from taking action on or being part of things that would help our growth and success.

I always loved the saying, "You would never let anyone talk to you the way you talk to yourself."

Let's put an end to that right now.

In my coaching group, I do an exercise I call "The Turnaround." For this exercise, you'll identify and list some of the negative things you say to yourself that might be holding you back.

For example: I'm not good at sales.

I'm not as smart as (insert smart person here).

I can't start a (podcast, book, blog) because no one wants to hear what I have to say.

Now, The Turnaround: Turn that into a positive phase with a growth mindset.

Turn "I'm not good at sales" into "I provide value with my services and it would be doing a disservice to people if I wasn't offering it to them. I believe in my product and its value."

Turn "I'm not as smart as (insert anyone here)" into "I am smart and a voracious learner who can achieve anything I put my mind to."

Turn "I can't start a (podcast, book, blog) because no one wants to hear what I have to say" into "I have so much training, educational and life experiences that can help others. People respond when I am coaching and they want to hear what I have to say."

Put these in a document to read in the morning every day as part of your morning routine. Read these turnarounds over and over until they get into your head.

Try to identify when you start negative self-talk during the day and turn it around on the spot.

The more you do this, the more you'll stay away from limiting self-beliefs.

DANA SANTAS

Dana Santas, AKA "Mobility Maker," is a breathing, mobility and mind-body coach in professional sports, a bestselling author, on-air fitness expert and an international speaker on ways to help people breathe, move and feel better and be happier and healthier in their lives. Learn more about Dana at mobilitymaker.com.

Dana, you've achieved success in two completely different careers and your definition of success has certainly evolved. How do you define success now?

I've had an Emerson quote about success on my desk for at least 15 years:

"To laugh often and much; To win the respect of intelligent people and the affection of children; To earn the appreciation of honest critics and endure the betrayal of false friends; To appreciate beauty, to find the best in others; To leave the world a bit better, whether by a healthy child, a garden patch or a redeemed social condition; To know even one life has breathed easier because you have lived. This is to have succeeded."

I like the "breathe part" because I work with breathing. Hopefully, I've made some people breathe easier. That's success; it wasn't always my definition of success, but has been for the past 15 years. But success can't be summed up with a pithy short quote. It's so rich and all-encompassing. If I had to make it one word, it's truly happiness.

When did you start to feel you were becoming successful?

I realized my prior definition of success was false 15 to 18 years ago. I'd been in an entirely different career; I was the North American director of marketing and PR for an international corporate real estate firm. I lived in a million-dollar house and drove fancy cars. I traveled all over, played golf on the best courses. I had the life everyone thought was ideal.

I worked so hard to get all of that because I grew up poor. When you compare that to where I am now, my life was extraordinarily different. Back then, I didn't know where I was going to get money for the next meal. I was a teenage mother—there was a period of time when I lived in my car with my child. I worked multiple jobs.

I barely made it through high school and I didn't know if I was going to be able to make it to college. It wasn't because I wasn't smart enough—it's hard to be in high school, have a baby, pay for an apartment…have a job. I haven't lived in someone else's house since I was 15. I was just trying to survive and eventually get away from that life. I was running away from the stigma of being poor. I felt like I had the scarlet letter of a poor teenage mother.

I spent two weeks on food stamps, because when you're 15 years old, it's hard to have the means to support yourself and someone else. I had welfare, and then I thought, this is not the life I can live. That tied me into money as the be-all, end-all mentality. It was the answer to everything. And I hung onto that.

Ultimately, I got to that place where I had a giant house and I had what everyone thought was a perfect marriage. I picked everything according to what it looked like to the outside world…even my career. It's not that I'm not good at marketing and PR, but it wasn't something I chose because I loved it. I chose it because the opportunity presented itself; I was good at it and I knew I could make a ton of money.

That's how I got there.

Someone introduced me to a literary agent who said, "You have an amazing life and you're so successful and I want to help you write a book so other people can look at your path and learn from it. Your book should be a roadmap to success for other people."

When I was faced with that, I realized I didn't want anyone to go through my path thinking I was successful. When I was forced to look at the place I was in my life and hear someone say I was a role model for other people, I realized I didn't want anyone to be what I was: I was empty inside.

I hadn't spent any time figuring out what really mattered to me, and I was constantly reaching for the next thing. I was trying to layer accomplishments and material things and win after win after win for everybody to see because I didn't want anyone to look at who I might really be. It was a stressful, horrible way to live. Inside, I hated myself. I was just running from the stigma of being the poor teenage mother. I had never given myself the opportunity to know who I was or what I actually liked.

When faced with that, I kind of freaked out. I would say that was probably pretty much a breakdown.

From a book offer!

That's hilarious, right? I got a book offer at a meeting at The Four Seasons. A literary agent told me I was going to be on *Oprah* and I would change people's lives. It resonated with me when she said I'd be impacting people. Let's go back to that Emerson quote—making someone else's life better matters to me. And it wasn't until that conversation that I realized how much it mattered to me. I wasn't going to make someone's life better by telling them what I was doing. I was a stressed-out person who was all about material things; no one should be like that. That's when everything changed.

And talk about painful. I had to look at my marriage—I was married to someone not because I loved him, but because he fit an ideal. He was in sales and made lots of money. He liked to buy things as much as I did; he liked to go on vacations and spend money on things that didn't matter.

You know what I loved? I loved making dinner and being with my children, but I had a nanny watching them because I was traveling all the time. I was missing all the things that genuinely made me happy.

At that time, I started doing yoga—only because I was always at the Ritz-Carlton, The Four Seasons or other hotels that had spas. In one of these classes, the instructor had us quietly lie on a mat. I had been in a race against myself for pretty much my entire life. To just lie there and breathe and focus only on breathing was profound. Suddenly, I tuned into that person I had been hiding. And it wasn't so bad; it was okay to hang out there.

That's the same person who would enjoy time with her kids and making dinner and taking walks with the dogs. Those are the things that matter. It was the combination of starting to tap into that and having a book offer that changed everything for me.

I ended up getting divorced. The whole process was painful. To everyone else, it looked like I had a perfect life and I was losing my mind…destroying everything. Think about that: If you were on the outside looking in, wouldn't you think I was crazy?

I gave up everything when I got divorced. I didn't want any of the belongings—I completely started over. My attorney made me sign a document that basically said, "I've advised my client that everything she's doing doesn't make sense." I ended up claiming bankruptcy two years later because I had nothing. But that's what I wanted because I did it wrong the first time.

Talk about self-awareness! When you have that, it makes decisions more clear. You knew things were wrong and had to change. Those external forces weren't driving you. What is it that pushes you now?

Through all this process, gratitude has played an amazing role in my life, having the opportunity to live this life and to be able to redesign it. I've lived through a lot of what people around me didn't live through. In my life, I've been to more funerals for suicides than any other type of funeral, although I'm getting to the age where people I've known are dying at older ages.

When I was in high school, with the level of poverty and drug abuse around me, many people dropped out of school in the eighth grade. Even my guidance counselor wrote me off. I was a teenage mother. I didn't live with my family. I didn't even know what the SATs were, although I ended up graduating with honors on a full scholarship from Tufts University. But a lot of people got written off in my hometown town, which is why when I was in college, I studied sociology. I was trying to figure out how that happens. Culturally and as a society, how do we end up writing off other human beings, deciding they're poor and therefore unable to succeed?

I don't know where I got the strength. I was fighting with myself and running from all of that and that saved me in a way. I was miserable, just fighting for survival. When I wake up in the morning now—every morning I wake up—it's an opportunity to happily live my life. Selfishly, there's this, "Holy shit, I'm happy; this is wonderful." That's what motivates me.

But it's also incredible to have the opportunity to help other people. That's why I'm so jazzed when I get to speak at Perform Better. I'm so excited to be in front of people and know what I'm sharing is genuine; it works and it helps people, and I can personally attest to it. My motivating factor is just that I'm alive.

Let me ask you about some of your past. Was there a mistake you made? Would you go back and do something differently?

I wouldn't change any of it because I needed everything in order to become the person I am today. I had to go through it all. There was a time when I was trying to change everything—everything was so painful, breaking away from everything I had worked so hard for—it was difficult to get over that feeling of, "poor me, this is so unfair." I know a lot of people have felt that way, and maybe they feel that way right now. But when you come out the other side, you're grateful for all of it because that's what you needed to learn.

My husband and I will soon have been married 10 years. He's the most amazing human being. We're similar in terms of our priorities and values; he's motivated by the same things. But he had an awesome life and his family is tremendous. I'm so lucky to have them be my family now. He didn't have to go through any of the stuff I went through.

Some of us need to be dragged through the mud to understand what it feels like and to appreciate what it feels like to wash that mud off. Others don't have to; people aren't successful because they lived through hardship. I want to make that clear because when I tell my story, people might be thinking, "But I didn't go through that." You don't have to.

A lot of people almost have a guilt that they don't have a failure story and have to redo everything. But everyone has challenges. Let's talk more about you personally and your habits. Do you do anything specific in the morning that sets up your day?

One of the things that impacts my morning is what I set up at night. My husband and I do this together. We have a gratitude whiteboard—gratitude plays a huge part in my life.

The whiteboard is on the back of our master bathroom door, where on the top, I wrote "Gratitude Rocks." Every night before we go to bed, we write three things we're grateful for happening that day. I write three; he writes three. What's the first thing we do in the morning? We start in that bathroom, close the door and stare at this whiteboard. We're reminded every morning of what we're grateful for from the day before. Is there a better way to start your day than being reminded of what was great about yesterday?

And you know you're going to have to come up with three things every day. I don't even know how we ended up doing that, but it's been a habit that has become a lifestyle. There's so much research on gratitude, the latest from the University of North Carolina, where they studied couples who expressed gratitude to one another on a daily basis. They noted the strength of their relationships and what they reported in terms of happiness in their relationships, then compared that to people who didn't and found a big difference.

We take so many things for granted. My wife and I went to a doctor's appointment yesterday. She was complaining, but when we got there, there were people using walkers. She looked at me, "I'm complaining, and then I look around. We're lucky." Suddenly, you realize you're in a better mood because you can't be sad when you're showing gratitude.

Sometimes you have to work to figure out something to be grateful for because every day isn't rainbows and unicorns. The day one of my dogs died, I wrote on the whiteboard, "Nothing." I was pissed because he'd died. Then I started to go to bed, but my husband saw what I'd written and pulled me over to the whiteboard. He said, "No, you're not going to go to bed with this written on the board. You had the opportunity to have the dog in your life."

He forced me to think. I wouldn't have been that upset if I hadn't had the opportunity to have this relationship with this dog. He gave me perspective.

Some days we feel terrible. I have my health; I have a family. I don't have to worry about money, which was something I've had to worry about in my life. Even if that's all I can come up with for the day, those are huge.

You can always find something to be grateful for. In just looking for the best part of the bad things, you'll come up with something. Talk about goals and your process for them. Do you have a formal process?

For quite a few years during my rebuilding process, I had what I called "birthday goals." Every year at my birthday, I'd write some crazy goals I wanted to achieve…outrageously crazy goals. I'd review them the next year when I wrote new ones and year after year, I was achieving these outrageous goals. I was going for it, because when you recognize the sky's the limit, you just go for it.

I'll give the example of when I decided I was going to work with professional athletes. Living in Boston, I wrote, "I'm going to work with the Red Sox this year," but I was just starting this business. I ended up working with the Red Sox, the Bruins, the Patriots and the Celtics that year. There were crazy goals and they just kept happening. There were even crazier things and it got to the point where I recognized it wasn't that I was writing out these goals; it was living this life that was about just being happy and going for it.

Another quote to think about, "The answer to every un-asked question is no." You're already at no. What are you afraid of? Just ask; what are you going to lose? If you stop being afraid of being rejected, you're going to accomplish a lot more. So, I reached out to every team I wanted to work with—I put some time and effort into it…in fact, a lot of time and effort. It's one thing to write a goal. It's another to take all the steps to make it happen. It was less the process of writing goals and more the process of making things happen and not being afraid of failure.

That's the other thing. You can't be so attached to an outcome or a destination; the journey is fun. It's fun to be badass and willing to put yourself out there. If you're excited about trying, you're not going to be as disappointed about the outcome if it's not a full success.

Meditation is a big part of your life, but what do you do to recharge?

Breathing is my recharge. I don't want to call these breathing exercises because it's more of a breathing reset. Breathing is part of our autonomic nervous system. However, just because you're on autopilot doesn't mean it's working well.

Before I get out of bed in the morning, I take five long, deep breaths where I'm getting my rib cage moving. If your rib cage is moving, your diaphragm's moving. I'm a big proponent of not saying "belly breathing." I understand what people are trying to accomplish with those words, but in the actual biomechanics of breathing, anatomically, we don't breathe into our bellies. If you're just pushing your belly out, it doesn't mean your diaphragm is functioning properly or that you're filling your lungs completely.

It's more effective to focus on rib kinematics—if you focus on your ribs, externally rotating as you inhale and getting that expansion as much as possible. As you exhale, drive your ribs in, back and down, so your whole rib cage drops down into a better position. Then your diaphragm gets the opportunity to relax. I take five really good breaths like that. The money's in the exhale; take really long exhales and you'll reset the diaphragm and leave the rib cage in a better position.

From a movement standpoint and with posture and alignment, at that point I'm in a good place. It only takes 90 seconds to give your body a relaxation response. It inhibits the stress hormone production; you lower your blood pressure and decrease your heart rate. You can do all of that with five long, deep breaths. And it's like boom—there you go. You're ready.

I do that before I get out of bed—and do it a couple of times a day, especially if I'm at my desk. I do that after workouts and before training sessions.

Breathing is a super power.

What is it you do when you want to give up; how do you push through bad times?

There was a book I read that had a huge impact on my life: *Man's Search for Meaning* by Viktor Frankl. Victor survived living in a concentration camp and essentially losing everyone in his family. He survived and eventually thrived by having hope and being grateful. He found things to be grateful for…and he was in a concentration camp! It was bleak, but he was able to find peace by being grateful. If he can live through that, I can certainly live through eating government cheese. It's a matter of perspective.

We all have things going on in our lives. We all have family members going through hardships. We personally go through hardships; things happen that are not always easy. This is life.

I recommend reading that book. And if you can't relate to it, read it again.

This whole interview has had a theme of gratitude. It makes sense you recommended that book. No matter what you're going through, there's always hope. Could you give us two more books?

I read constantly as a child because it was an escape. I was in the third grade when I first read *Jonathan Livingston Seagull* by Richard Bach. You don't have to be a child to read it—I don't even think it's meant for children. *Jonathan Livingston Seagull* inspired a passion in me for more in life.

It doesn't matter whether you came from, sometimes you need an inspiration to encourage you to want more out of life, more than just the rat race. I'm thinking of people just trying to get through their weekday jobs, living for the weekend or the two weeks a year they go on vacation. That's a tough life. I have trouble relating to that, but can see how people get stuck in it. If you work in our profession where you have this opportunity to positively impact people's lives, you'd better not be just trying to get through your work week. You should love what you do—you should absolutely love it.

That spark of looking for something I love was still with me and helped me change my life, and it started with *Jonathan Livingston Seagull*.

It's a really quick read. He was a seagull. The seagull life is pretty much finding food and flying as a means to an end. For seagulls in the book, it was a means to an end. But for Jonathan Livingston Seagull, flying is so freaking cool. What if I could do tricks? And he'd work on perfecting his flying; he was getting more out of life because he realized there could be more if he made his life into more. He got up excited every morning to try this new flying trick. He inspired other seagulls to enjoy flying. He was finding enjoyment in life, instead of this means-to-an-end idea.

The next book I recommend is an Emerson biography called *The Mind on Fire*, and it's just super.

On that note, give us three people we can follow.

Jason Glass is doing life right. I could give you names of the people everyone already knows to follow, like Mike Boyle and Gray Cook. And of course, follow them; they're awesome. But Jason Glass is cool in the things he shares about his life.

His sense of humor isn't for everybody, but in terms of living life out loud, he's doing it right. He's a neat guy.

Maya Angelou is not alive anymore, but her foundation still puts out good work. She was inspiring and we need that in the world today.

You're not going to find Ralph Waldo Emerson or Thoreau on Instagram because they are long gone, but look up some of their work.

The Heath brothers also put out some cool ideas.

As strength and conditioning professionals in particular, we can always do the workshops; we can always go to the Perform Better events. And we should do those kinds of things to learn more tools for our trade. That's awesome. But we have to keep enriching our lives so we can be better people for the people we serve. It's not just about the tools we can give them. The better we become as human beings, the better the world's going to be. And we can constantly keep learning how to do that.

I didn't expect to go down that road of how everything started in my life, but I hope it helps people. I want to reinforce that you don't have to go through that kind of trouble to be successful.

Just recognize your blessings and stay focused on being grateful. That's the game changer.

It's been interesting hear about to your journey through your two different lives and how you became successful on your own terms. Thanks for sharing your journey.

BE LIKE DANA

"We have a whiteboard on the back of our master bathroom door—this little white board, and on the top, I wrote "Gratitude Rocks." Every night before we go to bed during the nighttime routine, we write three things we're grateful for that happened that day."

30-DAY GRATITUDE CHALLENGE

We have heard from many people how they incorporate a gratitude practice in their lives. It's not just fitness professionals—you'll see it in a majority of successful people.

Dana has by far the most unique practice I've come across. Try to replicate this as much as possible.

Before you go to bed, write down three things you're grateful for.

It doesn't have to be in the bathroom; you can put it somewhere that you know when you wake up and go through your morning routine, you'll see it.

It could be on a mirror or on the shower door (get the erasable markers), the refrigerator door or the door leaving your home (get one of those small white boards or corkboards).

I keep my keys and wallet on my kitchen island; you could put it there if you have one or put it on your kitchen table.

You can use post-it notes or just a piece of paper, it doesn't matter.

If you live with someone, try to get them to do it with you. It will help with accountability as well.

Try it for 30 days and see how you feel.

You can't be sad when you are feeling gratitude.

Mike is one of the worlds' foremost educators in the areas of performance training, personal training and athletic rehabilitation. He has been involved in training and rehabilitation with a wide range of athletes, including stars in every major professional sport. Mike has also served as a consultant to some of the top teams in the NFL, NHL and MLB, as well as numerous Division One athletic programs. In addition, he has been involved in Olympic Gold Medal efforts in women's soccer, women's ice hockey, gymnastics and judo. He's an author and video seminar producer and recently released The New Functional Training for Sports, his fourth book. You can keep track of him via strengthcoach.com.

You've been very successful in what you've done across different sports at the pro level, the collegiate level and in the private sector. From a general perspective, how you define success?

Before I had kids, I would have defined it with a typical fame-and-fortune answer: I'd like to be famous; I'd like people to know my name, to read my books, to hear me lecture. I'd like to make a lot of money.

Then I had kids and my whole thought process changed. I want to be a good husband; I want to be a good dad; I want to raise successful kids. I view everything differently now.

You're famous for talking about the lenses through which we view things and obviously that lens changed when the kids were born.

I began to see people who are materially successful and would think, "They're total losers. They've got all kinds of money, but their kids are screwed up. Their lives are a mess. They hate their wives." That's not the success I want. I'd rather give the money back.

It would be nice to have it all. That's the ideal situation, but I'd much rather have less and have those parts of my life be really good than have more and have those parts of my life be really bad.

From the business perspective and from what you've been doing as a coach, when did you consider yourself a success? When did that start happening?

In my 40s when I started to lecture often, I noticed people actually cared about what I thought. I started in this business in the pre-internet world and was limited in the number of people I could reach—the athletes at Boston University and the athletes on the Bruins.

Suddenly, I was working in professional sports and people wanted me to write books. People asked me to lecture and I thought, "I'm actually making it here. I'm succeeding." I was getting the recognition I sought at that time.

From a material standpoint, that's what everybody at that stage is looking for. This dates me, but it's like Sally Field at the Oscars, "They like me; they really like me."

I'm still fascinated when people ask if they can take a picture with me. Absolutely, you can take a picture! The fact that anyone would give a shit about a picture with me is great.

I started to feel successful when those things started to happen. It's been the last 15–18 years when I started to think I was getting somewhere.

You were a 10-year overnight success story.

I've used that joke all the time. I tell people I'm a 20-year overnight success. And that's why I always encourage people to write, because I believe my success coincided directly with writing and speaking. When you write and lecture, you're putting yourself out there for people to have the opportunity to hear you. If there's nobody there and you're not affecting people, people won't know you exist.

Many people have a career moment when they may be really good at something, but it takes a while for people to realize they're there. Suddenly, things start happening.

In the beginning when I was starting the *Strength Coach Podcast,* listeners had to load it into an iPod. It was much more of a process to listen to it. I really didn't care how many people were listening. We just wanted to get the information out and talk about what was happening on *StrengthCoach.com.*

The podcast evolved into a monster, but I had no idea it was happening at the time. I realized what a great thing it was when I'd ask a question at a Perform Better workshop and people would recognize my voice and come up to me afterward and ask, "Are you the guy from the podcast?" They'd tell me how much they'd learned from the show.

It was making an impact and that made me want to make an even bigger impact.

No question—I completely agree with you. It's amazing. But I also have the recurring dream of people finding out I'm a total fraud. There are only two dreams I have: that one and the one where I haven't finished school, where I never went to class and then had to take a final. I still have those two dreams in my late 50s.

The impostor syndrome—yes, I know that one too. From the business, fitness and coaching perspective, with all the things you're doing, what is it that gets you out of bed in the morning?

I'm not sure what gets me out of bed in the morning because lately it's been getting harder. Some of it, in all honesty—I hate to say this; it so sounds terrible—it's obligation. I owe it to the people coming in to train. I owe it to the kids who are interning. I owe it to the people who work for me. I owe it to Bobby Hanson, my partner…I have to show up. I used to get up eagerly, "Oh my God, another day! I can't wait." For the first time in my life, now, it's not like that anymore. But a lot of people count on me to do my job.

Sometimes I think I'm not as involved in as much of the day to day as I need to be. But other people are surprised to see how much I'm there. I hear, "I can't believe you're there this much," while I feel guilty I'm not there eight hours a day.

I can think of a couple of your habits that have contributed to your success. What do you think are some of the habits that are why you've been able to get to this place in your life?

I read a lot about fear of failure. When we started the business, we were thinking, "This is not going to not work." You need to have some of that fear. Some of that can come off as false confidence and that was probably what I presented outwardly, but looking inward, it was a fear of failure. I didn't want it not to work—I didn't want to have to look back and know I started a business that didn't work.

That's more of an attribute—not really a habit—but it's one of the things people need to consider. People have to be willing to do whatever it takes to succeed.

I worked a lot of hours—I was all over the place. I basically said yes to everything. And I felt like I just outworked people. I cared more; I coached more; I read more; I worked more hours. That's the way it was going to be because I didn't want to fail. And that's the mindset people need if they plan to succeed. The hard part about that is you have to be able to turn it off, which I wasn't as good at. I'm getting better.

Fear can sometimes hold people back from trying things.

That's absolutely true. That's why I always loved the "ready, fire, aim" idea. Just *do things.* There are people who fear failure so much, they don't even try. They don't attempt anything, and that's wrong.

When you start something, a healthy fear of failure is a good thing unless it prevents you from trying. I don't want to spend my life on the sidelines—I want to be in the game. Sometimes the game is a little dangerous. You play and things can go bad. There are a lot of things that could have gone bad for us, but we were determined to outwork the people we were competing against.

The first time I heard the quote, "Nobody cares how much you know until they know how much you care" was from you. That genuine care drives a lot of what you do. People understand that when they meet you—even something as simple as returning an email or getting back to everyone quickly displays that care.

You said earlier, you don't say "no" enough. In a lot of ways, you personify the opposite of what everybody writes about that makes people or gyms successful. We always kid around about how fitness business consultant Thomas Plummer almost had a heart attack when he walked into one of the most successful strength and conditioning facilities in the world—Mike Boyle Strength and Conditioning—with all those black shirts, the dark walls, the unshaven boss.

But business doesn't always have to be the same as everyone else's.

When the economy was bad in 2008–09, my accountant said, "I don't understand. Yours is the only business we work with that's up. What's the secret?" I looked at him and said, "The secret might be caring about your employees, caring about your customers and charging a fair price. And if that's a secret, a lot of people suck at business because that should be common sense."

I want the people who come to our gym to feel better. I want the people who work for us to succeed in their definition of success. And I want people to be able to afford to train with us. I don't want to be one of the places where we're charging such a premium that we're only working with the super rich. I don't consider any of that particularly brilliant, but it seemed to have worked better than I expected.

I know you set goals. Do you have a formal process you do every year?

I haven't done that the last couple of years. It's funny because the years when things really took off were the years I did that. In all honesty, I've slacked a little the last couple of years.

Maybe it's because my goals have changed—they used to be much more financial and business-related and now they're not.

In some ways, gratitude writing has taken over the goal-setting space. I recommend it to everyone. I use Craig Ballantyne's *Perfect Day Formula* journal. I always write about what I'm thankful for. I've gotten into a rote situation of writing the same things about my family and my life. Every day, I want to remind myself I'm thankful for my family and I'm thankful for the great life I have.

Go to *earlytorise.com* and get a gratitude journal. It works. The research is clear that it improves your outlook and improves the way you think. I know from personal experience that it absolutely does.

When you understand what season you're in, it helps determine what's important. What are some things you sacrificed to be where you are?

In some ways, I nearly sacrificed everything. Cindy wanted to leave me at one point because all I did was work. It's a funny story now, but we once decided to go to a marriage counselor. I remember thinking, "It's going to be open-and-shut. The therapist is going to explain to Cindy how great I am and how lucky she is and in a day this will be over."

I remember the therapist looking at me as we laid out why we were there. Then she said, "Tell me a little about yourself." I went on, almost proudly, telling her how I get up at 6:00 o'clock in the morning and we have winter workouts; then I open the weight room and I work for the Bruins and then I go to games at night. She said, "You work from 6:00 in the morning until 11:00 at night. Sometimes you don't see your wife awake for a couple of days at a time?"

I said something to the effect of, "I'm grinding it out." I was proud of the fact that I was working all those hours and doing everything and how successful I was becoming. The therapist gave me a look that said, "There's something wrong with you!" I remember sitting there with the most defeated feeling, thinking, "This is not going to be nearly as open and shut as I projected coming in."

It ended up being the best thing we ever did. When you ask what I sacrificed in trying to be successful, I almost sacrificed everything that's now the most valuable to me.

For some people, there's a process of realizing that you have to find some balance, particularly when you get into a relationship or when you have a spouse or kids. It's amazing how many people say they do things for their family or for the kids, but the reality is, they don't. They do it for themselves and they do it for their own ego and they do it for the money.

When Mark was little, people would ask what I did, and he would say, "He's a coacher." I used to think, "He doesn't know what I do; he doesn't even know the word yet." The truth was he didn't care. What he cared about was would I play catch when I came home.

What I did made no difference to him. We'd go to a Boston University hockey game and I'd point out guys who would be playing in the NHL. He answered, "What's the NHL?"

You can get a false sense of importance that children can strip away from you.

With him, it was, "Can we play catch?" or "Can we shoot pucks?" That was what mattered to him. The other things didn't matter. I hope at some point he'll realize that was really cool. But the flipside of that is realizing we've got to be present at that time for each person, giving them what they need.

It's been great for me. It's made me a better person, a better speaker, a better writer... better at everything.

One of the things I learned from you was that these come from a conscious effort. You can't just say the words. Ten years ago you said, "I'm going to be a better dad, a better husband, a better person."

Ten years later, it still has to be a conscious effort.

I think it's in *The 7 Habits of Highly Effective People* by Stephen Covey, where he said about relationships: "Love is a verb." Before reading that, I never thought about it that way. There's a section in the book where he talks about one of his coaching clients. The guy said, "I don't love my wife anymore."

And Stephen Covey says, "You need to love her." The guy said, "You know I don't love her anymore." Covey said, "Then you need to."

At this point, the guy is getting confused and said, "You're not getting it." Covey says, "No, you're not getting it. Love is a verb; it's something you do. It's not a feeling."

It's something we have to practice on a daily basis. That's tough for a lot of people. There are people who are emotionally undeveloped but financially successful who are hiding in their work.

I want nothing more than for my kids to be good adult human beings. If that happens, I'll be as successful as I've ever dreamed about being. If my kids are not good human beings, I didn't get the job done.

Speaking of Stephen Covey, why don't you give us three non fitness–related books everybody should read?

Obviously, *The 7 Habits of Highly Effective People* is near the top of the list—that would be in the number-two spot. *How to Win Friends and Influence People* would be number one. It was written in the 1930s, but every person in every field should read it.

I really liked *First Break All the Rules* by Marcus Buckingham. From a business standpoint, that book helped me become a better boss. It provides a good understanding of what people value in a job. It's much like what we've talked about through this conversation—it's not the things most people think.

The first two book choices are more about becoming a better person and the third is about becoming a better boss.

Success leaves clues. Give me three people we should follow to learn from.

The two people who first came to mind are John and Josh Feinman, the guys who run Inner City Weightlifting. I love what they do. It's incredible that they can dedicate themselves to a cause day in and day out.

I don't know the right word in terms of being jealous or envious, but there are days when I look at them and feel selfish because I help athletes.

They have literally made it their mission in life to reduce or end gang violence in the United States. And they're doing it! Everybody should check out their website at *innercity-weightlifting.org*. If you can, donate money. Try to help them because they're two of the most amazingly selfless people I've ever encountered.

I'd love to think we're helping the world to be a little better place, a healthier place. But we're certainly not working at the level of the guys at Inner City.

Mike, you've had one of the most impactful careers, not only on athletes, but on trainers and coaches worldwide. You set the bar for so many of us on a personal and professional level. Thanks for all you do and for sharing your journey with us.

BE LIKE MIKE

"I believe my success coincided directly with writing and speaking. When you write and lecture, you're putting yourself out there for people to have the opportunity to hear you."

WRITING AND SPEAKING—YOUR GATEWAY TO SUCCESS

Start writing. It doesn't matter where—get a journal, start a blog, use Facebook. Come up with a plan to be consistent. You only get better with practice.

It's helpful to have themes for different days so you can plan your writing ahead of time. For example, "Motivation Monday," "Workout Wednesday" and "Nutrition Fridays." Ask people what they want to learn.

Ask peers for feedback on your writing style (see Don Saladino's Be Like)

Look for places to get published and submit your work. Some ideas include *StrengthCoach.com. Men's Health,* other trainer's blogs, *T-Nation* and *Simplifaster.*

Start to shape some of your writing into a presentation and try to speak everywhere that's available: where you work and train, workshops, local clubs, country clubs or corporations.

Make it simple: "Three Things Everyone Can Do to _____"…fill in the blank—lose weight, become a better runner, hit the ball farther.

Do it as often as you can and aim higher and higher.

Steal the Show by Michael Port and *Talk Like Ted* by Carmine Gallo are great books on the subject.

Watch as many TED talks as you can; they put an emphasis on speaking style.

Toastmasters or an acting class are great places to start if you're nervous about speaking.

JIM KIELBASO

Jim is the president of the International Youth Conditioning Association (IYCA) and the director of the Total Performance Training Center in Michigan. He has written three books, produced multiple training products and has spoken at events all over the country. Jim is a former college strength and conditioning coach who has worked with high-profile sports programs as well as many high schools and thousands of young athletes. You can get more information from Jim at IYCA.org or follow him at facebook.com/jimmy.kielbaso.

Jim, you've been serving the fitness professionals and have been successful for a long time. Let's start from a general perspective. How do you define success for yourself?

Success is something that's difficult for me to hold onto, accept and enjoy. Success is when I know I've made a significant difference in somebody's life or made an impact. I've been successful in something when I've made a difference without creating a massive imbalance or a wake of destruction behind me.

I've interviewed with many ultra-successful people, specifically elite athletes and coaches. There are massive imbalances in their lives, and they'll readily admit it. Making a difference without creating other problems is something I've always wanted.

When did you start to feel successful at what you do?

I still don't feel as successful as I want to be, but it hit me when I started recognizing I was changing lives. Some of the people who worked for or interned with me are now big-time strength and conditioning coaches and I've helped many athletes get into the NFL. When those people started referring others, it began to sink in that I was making a difference.

Mike Boyle said that strength coaches know they're successful when they see an athlete they haven't seen in years and that person stops and talks rather than walking in the other direction. A few months ago at the airport, I saw a kid I'd trained years ago and he yelled my name across the terminal. It was a pleasant surprise and made me feel great. It's happened many times over the years where I've run into students I trained years before; they always yell for me and we take a few minutes to catch up.

Having relationships with former athletes, employees or interns makes me realize I must be doing something right—it's a transformational relationship rather than a transactional one. When I started seeing that, I felt successful.

You talk about the idea of transformation and helping people. Is that what gets you out of bed in the morning?

Making a difference and an impact on other people is what gets me out of bed in the morning. I'm on a constant search for the next right thing to do to make a difference. But this also wears on me; it's my burden and sometimes I don't want to do this coaching thing anymore. It's one of those good and bad things. It gets me out of bed and it gets me excited when it's working. At other times when I don't have absolute clarity, it feels like a cross to bear.

It's so important when setting goals to write down why you want to achieve a goal. When you connect that "why" to what you're doing, it's a lot easier—it has meaning. It's especially important for trainers and coaches who are trying to serve the masses.

Being the president and CEO of the IYCA, working with youth athletes and being a dad, you've obviously had to teach others about life skills and habits. What are some of the habits that helped you get to where you are?

Butt in the chair! Honestly, it's often just taking the time to sit and knock something out.

You have to be proactive, taking initiative and trying not procrastinate things that need to be done—just get them done. It's difficult for a lot of people, but I enjoy it. I like getting things started and taking action. Creating and taking advantage of opportunities has really helped me.

You need to be able to recognize when there's an opportunity in front of you to work with or connect with somebody. Developing relationships has been a huge part of my life and my career. If I have an hour-long training session with somebody, I don't mind spending another half an hour if there's something we need to discuss. This gets a little deeper into the relationship side of things. I'm always thinking about how I'm going to make a difference. One way is by understanding people and caring about them even though I may not always do that right.

It's not so much daily habits; it's the bigger picture things that helped me.

Certainly, the books *How to Win Friends and Influence People* and *Never Eat Alone* would agree with you; it's a conscious effort. Those are things we need to make sure we're doing to connect with people. What about goals? Is there a formal process for you?

I used to do a goal-setting process Anthony Robbins taught back in the early '90s and it was fantastic. I taught the process when I was teaching college classes and I used it for a long time. Today, I don't use a goal-setting process as much as I make plans. Now I'm more into the process.

I obviously have goals; otherwise I'd have no plans to make. But it's morphed into more of a planning process, which is interesting because I am not good at that from an organizational standpoint.

What about recharging? How do you recharge?

My recharging is mostly about having alone time. I need to be in the right state of mind to think and write. In the summer, one of my favorite things to do when we're up at our cottage on a lake is to wake up and make coffee, then take a pontoon boat out into the middle of the lake, turn off the engine…and just sit there. I do that every chance I get and that helps a lot. Sometimes I have trouble with it—I'm distracted and not settled, and I have to change my outlook or go back out later.

If I don't have some big-picture thinking time somewhat frequently, I start to feel myself go downward. If I get stuck in task-oriented days for too long, it drains me. I need that time to sit and make bigger picture plans.

There's a lot of science behind the creativity that comes with alone time. Taking time in nature or unplugging to think about the bigger picture activates the part of the brain that's not working on specific problems. As one part shuts down, the other turns on.

What sacrifices do you feel like you've made to get to where you are?

The main sacrifices I made was saying no to things and not jumping on opportunities where I could have made more money or done something different. I say no to those things because I want balance in my life. I don't want to be someone who works 18 hours a day and looks back later and realizes I missed my life.

If you go back to my definition of success, it was making a difference without creating a massive imbalance in my life. It's the way I make decisions and it's sometimes hard because I miss opportunities. There are things I could take advantage of, but that would require too much time away from my family. It's not worth it to me. There would have to be a massive payoff.

I remember talking to an older strength coach about the schedules we kept in college. He started shaking his head saying, "I'm going to puke thinking about all the time I missed with my kids, sitting in a weight room waiting for stuff to happen." That hit home because my kids were fairly young at the time. I don't want to do that; I don't want to look back and have those regrets.

Balance is so important and almost everybody struggles with it. What about during the tough times? Was there a time when you wanted to give up, and if so, how did you get through it?

I've felt like that several times. I remember specifically one point maybe eight years ago, when I was working every night and wasn't able to get home. I was making "okay" money, but it wasn't enough to offset not being home. My wife hinted that something had to change, and when I suggested quitting, she stopped me. She said, "You can't do that. This is who you are. You won't be happy doing something else. You're just going to have to figure out how to make some changes."

I was able to make some changes in my schedule where I began doing more in the mornings, and it changed everything. She put things into perspective.

Social media really messes with people's heads. You look at what people are doing online and equate that with someone "crushing it." In reality, you could be looking at somebody sitting at home without a job and making all those posts with all that extra time. Somebody reminded me not to compare the outside of other people to the inside of ourselves. People aren't going to talk on social media about the bad things they're dealing with; they're just going to publish the awesome things. Everybody has to do laundry and dishes. It's what you're doing on top of that that makes a difference.

We've talked before about reading, not just in the fitness field. What are three non fitness–related books people should read?

There are so many non-fitness books people should read. In fact, people who are in the fitness profession should make sure they spend at least half of their reading time reading books not about fitness. That's where the magic is.

One book that really helped me is *The On-Purpose Person,* a book Gary Gray suggested that was written by Kevin McCarthy. It really helped narrow things down for where I wanted to spend my time. Gary Vaynerchuk's book *Crush It* was great; it came at a perfect time and really spoke to me.

Ari Weinzweig and Paul Saginaw own a deli called Zingerman's in Ann Arbor. It's an unbelievable business—they've expanded into multiple businesses. They even have training programs where you can learn their systems. Ari has written books on business. One of them is called *Building a Great Business*. That's a fantastic book.

Back when I was doing a lot of martial arts training, part of the process was reading books. I read a book by Chuck Norris called *The Secret Power Within*. I also read a Bruce Lee book called *Words of the Dragon*. Those books, at the right time, hit home and connected things for me.

What about three people we can all learn from?

I'm not prepared for that question; there are so many awesome people. Ron McKeefery and Brett Bartholomew are two coaches who really make a difference in the coaching space. In the fitness business space, Ryan Ketchum and Nick Berry are fantastic. They own and run Fitness Revolution. There are so many of my friends I should suggest here, but those are people I definitely watch.

I love this idea of balance. Trying to strive for it as much as we can is important. We really appreciate your talking about your journey, Jim.

BE LIKE JIM

"If you go back to my definition of success, it was making a difference without creating massive imbalance in my life."

BALANCE

This is the Golden Egg so many are searching for: Work–Life Balance. I love Craig Ballantyne's idea that there's no such thing, only Work–Life Mastery.

Here are a few things to help you get yourself as balanced as possible.

Know what you're good at—Don't try to do everything. You're a great trainer, but probably horrible at doing the bookkeeping. Outsource your weaknesses and things that you're not good at or don't like doing.

Block out your time (see Nick Winkelman's Be Like)—The more in control you are of your schedule, the less stressed you will be. Block out your schedule so you're not drifting all day. You'll be much more productive.

Schedule downtime during the day—This means walks, naps, coffee with friends and time for exercise and meditation.

Have cutoff times (see Janet Alexander's Be Like)—Set boundaries for work, computer time, phone and TV time. This will allow you to be more present with friends and family.

The evening shutdown (see Alwyn Cosgrove's Be Like) and freedom session (see Vince Gabriele's Be Like)—are practices that will help give you closure on the workday and workweek. You don't want to be thinking about what you need to do on Monday when you are relaxing over the weekend. Both of these practices are like brain dumps.

Schedule your continuing education and vacations (see Kevin Carr's Be Like)—Prioritizing things you want to do will ensure they get done. You don't want to leave these things until the last minute; they'll never happen.

Visit other trainers (see Derek Hansen's Be Like)—Keep your network alive. A lot of us work alone. Make it a habit to visit other coaches and trainers. Have coffee, talk shop and build those relationships (see Patrick Ward and Jay Ferruggia's Be Likes).

Meditation (see Dave Tenney's Be Like)—This does not have to be a long drawn-out, hour-long practice. Get the Headspace app and do 10-minute sessions when it's convenient. Just be consistent.

ERIC CRESSEY

Eric Cressey, MA, CSCS, is the president and co-founder of Cressey Sports Performance (CSP), which has facilities in Massachusetts and Florida. While CSP works with a wide variety of athletes and general fitness clients, they are best known for their extensive work with baseball players. Eric has been a widely published author and presenter in the fitness profession for over 15 years. He maintains a popular blog at ericcressey.com.

You've had success in several areas—your athletic endeavors, as an author and a co-creator of videos…with CSP, which has blown up. How do you define success?

It's a moving target. If you ask me now, as a father and a husband, compared to 10 or 15 years ago, it has changed substantially. There was an interview with Cheryl Sandberg of Facebook where she said there are five things to consider and you have to pick three: family, friends, fitness, sleep and work. You can have only three of those, so how are you going to allocate them?

For me, it was family, work and fitness. Friends came about because there were people we knew through the gym and they were rolled in under the work umbrella. I'm not a good sleeper, so I figured maybe I'd get my three-and-a-half out of the five if I was lucky.

Success is living up to my potential and to whatever discipline I'm devoted to at the time. I struggle with being 100 percent present in what I'm doing. I do a very good job of that at work, but I need to do a better job with my family life—like turning off the cell phone when I walk in the house, not answering email when I'm playing with the girls, not letting my training time be interrupted by phone calls…things like that.

I do really well when I put my life in different silos. I struggle I let things blend together. Success for me is working hard and working smart in each one of those disciplines.

You were certainly successful before your daughters were born. Was that an advantage in terms of already working the hardest and making those mistakes earlier?

That would have been a massive difference. I was talking with one of our interns and through the course of our conversation, I realized I've been writing blog articles for 17 years, consistently writing content year after year.

It's like that Jerry Seinfeld line, where he wrote comedy every single day. He didn't want to break the chain, so he drew a daily big X on the calendar. When I look back, a lot of the success I'm having at 36 has to do with putting legwork in my mid- to late 20s. I put systems in place to work hard, to establish a sustainable brand and to go through some big life lessons during the pre-30s era. It certainly made work easier now.

I've been willing to give a little on some of those things in my 30s—things don't bother me as much. If I don't produce as many videos or if I write only twice a week instead of five, I'm okay, in part because my focus has shifted.

I'm also questioning, "Do I worry about money at night? No, I'd rather have the extra two hours with my kids," instead of quarantining myself on a Sunday afternoon to work. My priorities have changed over time, but certainly, many things I did when I was young and single helped the cause.

People often don't understand the concept of making sacrifices in their 20s.

I didn't go on vacations. I didn't spend money on alcohol. I didn't drop $5 a day at Starbucks. I didn't do those things in my 20s because I had a very clear idea of wanting to do bigger things longer-term. Every penny you spend in something—often basically setting dollars on fire—takes away an opportunity to be in a fiscally sound position.

I recently read *Dollars and Cents* by Dan Ariely, which was outstanding. He had some intriguing quotes; one was that something like 46 percent of financial planners have no retirement savings. People who are 100 percent invested in that idea don't have retirement savings. That's outrageous, but also intriguing. Food for thought: If we do the right things at a young age, we put ourselves in fiscally sound positions.

I had an IRA when I was 27 only because I have accountants in my family who taught me to do that. If you can get that 10-year head start in saving for retirement, there's a good chance you can retire 10 years earlier if you need or want to.

Tony Robbins wrote the book *Unshakeable* with that in mind, advising millennials, "You don't realize what a small investment you make now and how huge that will be later in life."

You talk about sacrifices; you're in a great position now. Do you have any regrets?

I don't think about it in that context. I still had great experiences; I just had them professionally. I was able to do more internships and that was profound for me. There were times when I hopped in the car with a buddy and drove to a powerlifting training weekend.

I still went to UConn basketball games—I wasn't deprived of fun. But it's interesting how much of my fun in one way or another led back to my occupation, whether it was strength and conditioning or being involved in the baseball world.

My wife and I joke that I'm really lucky she likes baseball because of how many of my birthdays have been spent at a baseball game. It also helps that she's intimately involved in the business. She knows all the athletes and she's friends with players' wives; our kids play together. It becomes a big casserole that works.

A lot of marketers talk about going an inch wide and a mile deep. Everybody knows you for your work in baseball. There was an article about your work with the Minnesota Twins calling it Cressey University. When you're mentoring young business owners, do you feel that focusing on this kind of a niche was a key to your success?

Yes, absolutely, but I didn't know that in 2006; I stumbled onto it by accident. The important lesson is that you have to be a good generalist before you're a good specialist. You need to be able to check different boxes of proficiency before you decide, "This is something I'm very good at. This is something I should continue to develop and then I can command a higher level of attention and compensation in that avenue."

The mistakes we often see are when people think they need to force a niche, like, "I'm just going to train soccer players." You're in the middle of North Dakota; you're not going to train just soccer players—there aren't enough of them. People sometimes don't understand that they actually have to be good in the niche and explore that really well.

Following your passion is the single worst idea you could possibly have. There was a good book called *The Four*. The author, Scott Galloway, talked about Amazon, Google and

Apple—large corporations. The point was that "Follow your passion" is the advice rich people give, but it isn't smart for most of us. You're better off following your marketable skill sets. You're better off building career capital. Ultimately, with marketable skills, you'll be in positions of both leverage and authority, where you can build autonomy.

You can effectively work with the clients you want to work with and you'll become more passionate because you'll get very good at it. I don't think Lebron James rolls out of bed angry. He plays professional basketball and feels darn good about it. He's passionate because he knows he's one of the best in the world. When you become really good at what you do, the niche happens over the course of time if you pursue it.

It takes a long time to do that because you have to build a network. People think it's this work involves being good at training specific athletes. That's certainly a big part, but there's a lot more to it. It's also important to speak the language and to establish a strong network of people with whom you collaborate. I have strong relationships with teams and agents. Many of our referrals come from word of mouth because of those relationships.

That's an excellent point: Follow your marketable skill set. I worked with golfers at Five Iron Fitness, not because I'm passionate about golf, but because I caddied growing up—in the U.S. Open and for a local pro for a few years. I live in one of the wealthiest counties in the country with one of the largest concentrations of golf courses. It was a good demographic.

Once you've figured out your marketable skill, by all means, do fewer things, but obsess about them and be meticulous. I'm not a great foot-and-ankle guy; I go to other professionals for that. My business partner, Shane Rye, is a lower-extremity nerd. He loves feet and ankles and knees. He does that incredibly well, partly because he's had six knee surgeries. It fits very well.

You have to experience different things before you realize what's working for you. It's easier for me to write a program for Max Scherzer, Noah Syndergaard or Corey Kluber than it is for me to work with a 37-year-old powerlifter with hip pain. It's so different from my typical day. I can still do it, but if you look at the time it takes, it's markedly less efficient. I need to rewire my brain to write that program.

You're a mentor to many people and you help people in their businesses. You have CSP and you're working with baseball players. Besides family, what is it that motivates you to get out of bed?

I don't know that it's a single "it." I'm very competitive. We trained Jacoby Bressett, the quarterback for the Colts. His mentor throughout his entire career has been Bill Parcells, who lives here in Jupiter. I had a chance to chat with Coach Parcells for a while, when he made a comment: "Don't ever confuse routines with commitment."

In sports, everybody talks about the importance of routine. Pitchers talk about their starting rotations—what they do four days between starts. Some people are just trying to go through the motions and that's different from being committed to working really hard.

I asked Bill what he's up to these days. He still plays golf. He's really involved in horse racing. He notes that he had a competitive outlet every Sunday at 1:00PM when he was an NFL coach. Now he has to find a different avenue to satisfy that competitive drive.

There's a lot of the competitive athlete in me that needed an outlet after I retired from powerlifting. You look at other ways you can satisfy that competitive outlet, whether it's in more quantifiable things like revenue, sessions or writing a book. If you're an objectively driven person, you need ways to challenge yourself. It's an itch you have to constantly scratch. That sounds like a good thing, but it can also be a very bad thing.

My business partner, Pete Dupuis, and I rarely stop to smell the roses. If we have our best month ever, we might give each other a fist bump in the office. Then we're right back to the grind. That part of entrepreneurship sometimes can be unfulfilling. We have to take a step back and celebrate some of those achievements. We're 11 years in business. Over 80 percent of small businesses don't make it to a decade, so that alone puts us in approximately the 20 percentile. I need to do a better job in celebrating.

I'm a competitive guy and I'm always going to try to find ways to satisfy that itch—that continues to motivate me.

I often talk about a Dan Sullivan phrase: "The gap and the gain." We get to 80 percent of a goal, but all we focus on is the 20 percent gap we didn't achieve. My coach reminds me to note what the celebration will be when I attain a goal. It puts it in your head that you're going to reward yourself upon completion.

We lament our losses way more than we celebrate our successes. You see it over and over again. Nobody talks about what an amazing season the Seattle Seahawks had when they lost the Super Bowl. They talk about the final loss, the goal line play.

Most successful businesses are run by pessimists. They're people who are always looking for ways to make things better—that's a challenging dynamic to manage. You have to make sure you're pessimistic in a way where you look at your business and say, "This is something we can do better." At the same time, if your colleagues perceive you as an unyielding pessimist who's always mad about something instead of focusing on the 99 great things that went right, you're perceived the wrong way.

You have to be more introverted in your pessimism and more extroverted in celebrating the successes. It's something I struggle with; I need to do a better job of continuously pursuing that.

As much as entrepreneurship throws challenges, it's fun. It's a big puzzle you're always trying to solve. You're trying to find different ways to approach things, reinvent your business, to continue the successes and shore off the failures.

How do you push through the hard times?

To be honest, I don't know that we've had a time when I felt we were screwed. That never seems to happen. We were opening up our Florida facility and were behind schedule and racing to get open. Then our contractor informed us we were $100 grand over budget. How does that happen—to get taken to the cleaners like that? That was a pretty awful day.

My wife was seven months pregnant and emotional, bawling her eyes out. I slept okay that night and I'm not somebody who normally sleeps well. I remember thinking, "This is a problem. We've got to solve it. It's all part of the process. We're going to have a business we want to be around for 50 years. We have time to sort this out and get where we need to go."

Look at it as marathon and not a sprint. It's cliché, but it's so important.

Eric, let's talk about some of your habits. Do you journal or mediate in the mornings?

For me, 20 years down the road, yes, meditation and journaling and other valuable habits might be exactly what I need, but in the meantime, I've got to get stuff done in the mornings before the family gets going.

John Berardi's work routine starts after the kids are gone to school. It still works.

John has been a huge mentor to me. I remember distinctly: We knew we were pregnant with the girls and JB and I were both speaking at the Chicago Perform Better Summit. We went out to lunch—honestly, he gave me some of the best insights on time management and how he structures his day.

What John does so incredibly well is deep work, as we read about in the Cal Newport book, *Deep Work*. John understands how to batch his time. When he's with his family, he's all in. When he's writing, he's all in. When he's with his staff, he's all in—and that's a hard thing to do, especially working from home as he does.

Being able to separate those portions of your day is challenging. I have a bad habit of letting things blend together.

I was writing a program the other day for one of our guys. There's a knock at the door; the door opens; there's Rage Against the Machine playing in the background, and one of our minor league guys asks, "Hey, do you have a band-aid?" There's no reason I should be handling that request at that moment. I had literally gone to the farthest corner of the gym and closed my door looking for silence so I could work. It's my fault for not establishing better systems, for not empowering our front desk person to let everybody know she can meet their needs.

It was an insight moment for me.

It's very hard to batch our time. John is a guy who does a very good job of that, and maybe if I was better at it, I'd have more time for more mindfulness routines.

As part of my coaching program, we learn strategies of how to say no, how to automate it. It's not easy.

There's a great book called *Bored and Brilliant* by Manoush Zomorodi. She made some enlightening statements about how we don't get bored anymore. We stare at our phones. We always have to go, go, go—we don't know how not to work. Yet boredom is sometimes when things happen.

Looking back, some of my most productive times were when I was still able to get bored, to have a drive from Connecticut during grad school to my parents in Maine—to have those three hours with music playing and my mind wandering. We shouldn't always be trying to listen to audio books or podcasts. We need to do a better job of finding ways of not thinking about work.

You're trying to balance things, trying to be proactive and always learning and trying to be a better version of yourself—at the same time not realizing you probably need to let your brain rest just like we rest muscles.

Eric, how do you set goals? Do you have a formal process?

If you look at our income statement, you'll see our business is cyclical. We do about 40 percent of our revenue between November, December and January. It's baseball off-season and is a crucial time for us. What does that mean from an objective standpoint? I'm not taking seminars in November. I can't leave the facility. That's why goal setting is so valuable. You realize where the holes were in previous years where you fell short, where you came in on top or you misjudged.

The hard part is the most important to your family. How do you quantify being a good dad, being a good husband? Your personal and your professional lives are approached a little differently. We're always robbing Peter to pay Paul.

The thing I've learned over years of building a business and a family is that for every time you give in one place, you're going to have to take from somewhere else. You have to be cautious about not always taking from the adoring three-year-olds you have at home who want to spend every last minute with you, and giving it to the guy who wants free advice over email or the baseball player who wants to schedule an evaluation at the last minute. Those are hard to reconcile.

Eric, let's finish up with three non fitness–related books people can read to help in their professional development.

I think Dan Coyle's book *The Culture Code* is outstanding. I've known Dan for a couple of years and got an advance copy. I blew through it because it's so good. It has a bit of a *How to Win Friends and Influence People* dynamic. There are some bolded sections highlighting things you can do to markedly improve your culture.

I think *Legacy* by James Kerr is still one of the best books I've ever read. We gave copies to our college development program guides who came to the training last summer. It talks about life lessons from all blocks. It talks about being a good teammate and never making your problem someone else's. There are valuable lessons there.

Another book I like is *Decisive* by Chip and Dan Heath. They're brothers, both psychologists—one's at Duke and the other at Stanford. *Decisive* was a book I've given out as a gift to some of our athletes over the years and to interns.

The biggest takeaway from that is that the answer is very rarely either/or; most of the time the answer lies somewhere in the middle. It goes through some great historical perspectives of decision-making, how things went well or didn't based on how they approached things.

I'd say *Decisive*, *Legacy* and *The Culture Code* are three books people would like.

Success leaves clues. Do you have three people we can learn from?

I'd say if there's anybody you need to follow, it's your local physical therapist. When I consider fitness professionals, I've never gone wrong going to hang out with PTs.

There's a high standard of care. In physical therapy, there's licensure as opposed to certification; there's a longer education process and more professional credibility. There's a higher level of professionalism across the board in the physical therapy community as compared to the fitness profession.

I spend time around people like Eric Schoenberg and Mike Mile and Bill Hartman and Michael Hope. All of those people were impactful in making sure I positioned myself as a professional, both education-wise and how I carried myself. Those are good folks.

Pat Rigsby is a guy I've looked to and who's helped me a lot. I really like Pat, and not just because he's an awesome guy. He's a former baseball coach too—we a have baseball in common. Pat really helped me in terms of taking a step back, understanding that you run your business; your business doesn't run you. You need to set guardrails to make sure you don't go off the tracks. It's very easy to let your life as an entrepreneur consume you.

If we're still talking about business success in the fitness field, it's hard to have that conversation without mentioning Alwyn Cosgrove. Alwyn was one of my first mentors and someone who helped me understand the dynamics of running a semi-private business, learning to charge what I'm worth and things like that.

You can't go wrong following any of those people.

It's a great point about the professionalism in the physical therapy profession the occasional lack thereof in our field.

The way the field is unfolding, if you take time to hold yourself to a higher standard, it's definitely going to open more opportunities than you thought.

Eric, thank you for sharing your journey not only of success, but in pushing through some of the struggles you've had.

BE LIKE ERIC

"Many young aspiring entrepreneurs don't realize that what they do at 25 markedly impacts the position they'll be in by the time they're 35 or 40.

"If you can get that 10-year head start in saving for retirement, there's a good chance you can retire 10 years earlier if you need or want to."

YOUR FUTURE

If you don't have a retirement plan set up, it's time to start. It doesn't matter what your age, you're never too young or too old to get things going.

Start by figuring out all of your expenses. Track what you're spending your money on.

Can you make your own coffee instead of buying it from a coffee shop? Can you make your own meals more often instead of eating out all the time?

Are you spending excessive money on clothes or things you don't need?

Are there expenses you can cut to start thinking about putting that toward a savings plan?

Once you get a handle on your expenses and decide where you can cut back, do some research on financial planning. Dan Riley's book *Dollars and Cents* or Tony Robbins book *Unshakeable* are great places to start.

Ideally, you could seek the help of a professional. Ask your clients and friends whom they trust and make an appointment to see the person who sounds like the best fit.

You don't have to start big; as with fitness, you just need to be consistent with your savings.

Nikki is the owner of BODI, a high-intensity strength and conditioning gym in Scottsdale, Arizona. She's a Nike Trainer, Mike Boyle Certified Functional Strength Coach, Certified Personal Trainer, fitness nutrition specialist and the 2015 Women's Health magazine's Next Fitness Star. Keep up with Nikki at scottsdalebodi.com.

You've had success on several levels. You have BODI, your gym in Arizona; you won the *Women's Health* Next Fitness Star and you're also a Nike master trainer. How do you define success?

All of those are great on my resume. Money is what defines success for some people, and obviously that's great. But I'm not a money-motivated person. I feel successful because I love my job and I get to be a positive change in people's lives. That's success to me.

What in this business motivates you? What's your "it?"

I'm grateful for all I've been blessed with. I'm living out my dream. When I wake up, I try to make the most of that day. I want to make sure I give my best to my family, employees and gym members so we can all continue to grow together.

People tell me that going to my class and going to BODI is the best part of their day. That's my reason to jump out of bed in the morning. That really keeps me driving to get better in a lot of different ways.

When did you start feeling successful with what you were doing?

I could answer that a few different ways. Going back to when I taught my first fitness class—I'm sure that class was horrible, but right then, I knew this was what I'm supposed to do with my life.

From there, other things started falling into place: becoming a lead trainer and a manager at the gym where I was working, being noticed by Nike, becoming a Nike master trainer, opening up my own gym, winning *Women's Health* Next Fitness Star. Those fell in line and reminded me I was on the right track. I started to see a broader impact and that also motivated me to keep pushing to get better.

There's something about opening your own gym and seeing that grow that really boosts your confidence. That made me feel successful at my career.

You're a super positive person, somebody who's bouncing around, happy and easy to be around. But things aren't always easy. How do you push through the tough times?

Sometimes people look at us as trainers and we do a great job of putting on a mask. I always try to leave the challenging things in my life where they belong; I know part of my job is to be a positive influence.

We have to understand that everything happens for a reason. Even when things don't make sense or don't seem fair, all events—good, bad or indifferent—take place for our own good. It's up to us to be resourceful and turn those events into opportunities.

I really try to make sure I keep all the good things in my life top of mind, and that keeps me positive and gets me through most of my bad times.

Was there a time you felt you had to go back to working for somebody else or maybe push out some content and travel for Nike?

I definitely thought that, but I try to remember all the good things that are going at my gym. I love seeing the gym members. I love knowing the impact I can have on them.

There are things about working for someone else that can be appealing. It would be easier—less anxiety, stress and worry. But at the end of the day, I wouldn't change what I'm doing, not for anything.

I know you've made sacrifices. Can you give us an example?

It's definitely freedom. Don't get me wrong; as the owner, I gain a lot of freedom that most people don't get to enjoy—like spending time with my baby and my husband, and I can go out to lunch whenever I want. Those are all positive.

But you give up a lot too. I haven't taken a single personal vacation where I'm completely shut off from the gym. My weekdays and weekends are the same and I can't turn everything off. But if you love and have a passion for what you're doing, every day feels like a vacation; you get that bonus.

The biggest sacrifice would be overall freedom and that ability to shut off and leave the job at work.

We talk to our clients a lot about recovery, about recharging. How are you able to recharge on a daily, weekly or yearly basis?

I'm such a go, go, go person. I have an ADD personality. For me, recovery is planning a day of nothing: Today we're going to sit on the couch and watch movies. And we are not going to work until later. Or we're going to get this job done and then we're going to have a nothing moment.

That's been the best thing because we're always running around and working. Shutting down means we set that time of—no matter what—today we're doing nothing. We're going to be at home. We're only going to be checking email and doing work from this time to this time.

That's how I feel the most recharged, when there's some structured downtime.

When I had my facility, one of the mistakes I made was not setting it up so it would run without me. Have you made any mistakes in the work aspect?

One of our mistakes was that we started in a smaller facility, although at the same time, this is kind of awesome. We noticed the membership was getting bigger and classes were getting too packed, so we pulled back our marketing campaign once we started to grow. Then, even after we expanded, we started to see a downturn in new customers.

Once we moved into our new spot and it was time to expand, we made sure to continue with what we were doing and even pick up our efforts so we were not falling off track. That's a good problem to have, having a lot of customers. But at the same time, it was something we quickly learned: Even though you're growing too much, don't stop the marketing. That was the biggest mistake.

It's definitely important to set up the structure early. I was the only employee for six months, teaching seven days a week—teaching every class, doing everything. This was before my husband was helping; he was working another job at that time.

Asking for help when you need it and being okay delegating tasks are really important skills. Starting off with an office assistant and a part-time trainer would have really helped, and could have kept me from burning out.

What are some habits or personality traits you would attribute to your success?

Being intentional with my goals and what I want in life have been important, as well as surrounding myself with others who push and inspire me to be that person.

I'm not sure I have many habits that have contributed to my success, but I've always had a chip on my shoulder that made me want to prove everyone wrong. I've always had high standards and goals for my life. And I've had that drive to do everything it took to get myself in a position to achieve those goals. It might be part of the reason why I didn't get any help for a while: I was trying to prove I could do it on my own.

It's sometimes hard to distinguish between habits and personality traits, and we discount some of the things we do because they come automatically. When you do it for so long and it becomes ingrained, we forget that's not something everybody does. You mentioned goals. Do you have a formal goal-setting process?

I create a vision board. I started doing it after my husband did—and then, seriously, everything on his vision board came true. I needed to create a magic mission board like his. Goals change and get updated, so I update it as often as I need to. And it's something I look at every morning. Putting it in a place that you will see it every day is key. I'm really intentional about my goals and having that vision board keeps them top of mind.

I've read different books on goal setting where goals are categorized into different domains: physical, emotional, spiritual, financial, career, vocational. Talk about how you come up with the things on the vision board.

My main categories are my family, friends and personal life. The board is a mixture of pictures and words. I think, "What's going to make me happy? What am I envisioning for each area of my life?" and I find pictures and words that represent those things to add to the board.

I have my business, but I also have a section that's personal, which could be anything from personal growth to things I want to work on in life. It's important to balance things; everything can't just be about business and career, even though that obviously effects you personally. Now that I have a child, my goals have changed and the board reflects that.

You're looking at that every day as a reminder, but having them in writing is really important too. For example, in my planner, I write my quarterly goals every morning—I actually write them down every single time so they're top of mind. Let's finish up with three non fitness–related books you feel have been influential in your life.

Right as I was opening the business, I read Richard Branson's book, *Like a Virgin*. If you're an entrepreneur or want to be one, that's such an inspirational book.

And I love Phil Knight's *Shoe Dog*; again, it's in the entrepreneurial mindset.

I also think we should read mindless fiction from time to time, even if it's not fitness-related, not career-oriented, not personal growth. I love a cheesy romance novel. And sometimes, it's just good that you're reading something unrelated to work and not about growth—just read for fun.

My goal for last year was to read or listen to 36 books; this year, it's 48. And one of the things I'm trying to do is make one book a month have nothing to do with fitness or business. It's important to not always be "on." It's hard to do that when you want to push and try to be the best you can.

Who are some people you feel have been instrumental in your development?

There are so many people I follow for different reasons. Like now, there are a lot of moms I follow. I've always loved following everyone in my Nike community because we all have a common goal. But we're all still so different. There are always so many things we can learn from each and every person.

It's too hard for me to even narrow it down to three. But if I just had to pick one person I love following, it's Brian Nunez at *briannunez.com*. Everything about him is so positive and inspirational; there's so much to learn from him, from being a family man to being a business owner, to being a trainer. All around, he nails it.

Nikki, you've been an inspiration yourself, not only as a trainer but as a female business owner. There should be more women following your lead, understanding that all of this is possible.

BE LIKE NIKKI

"I create a vision board. I started doing it after my husband did—seriously, everything on his vision board came true. I needed to create this magic mission board. I update it as often as I need to. And it's something I look at every single morning."

CREATE A VISION BOARD

Vision boards are a great way to keep your mission, vision and goals top of mind.

Jack Canfield is a great resource for creating one; check out his website to go deeper: *jackcanfield.com/blog/how-to-create-an-empowering-vision-book.*

Use the "Be Likes" from Todd Durkin, Christa Doran, Mark Fisher, Dan John and Gray Cook to make a list of goals and achievements you want to accomplish and the life you want to lead.

Find pictures that represent those goals, achievements and vision.

Put those pictures on a bulletin board or a wall you will see every day.

Have fun with it, and think BIG (see Charlie Weingroff's Be Like).

"It's something that I look at every single morning."

Try to put it in a place where it will get maximum exposure. You want to intentionally look at it and review it EVERY DAY, so it reminds you to take action on the things you are trying to achieve.

Brian is an expert in the fields of posture, chronic pain and functional performance. His mission is to use The Egoscue Method to educate, motivate and build working strategies for people living in pain. For the last three decades, Brian has been speaking, consulting and conducting high-level training in The Method all over the world to crowds ranging from 100 to 15,000. In his presentations, he takes people through his P3 mindset to create a compelling future and these professional and amateur athletes and business game changers come back to dig deep into Egoscue for next-level results. You'll find Brian and his teaching at egoscue.com.

You've had success in different areas as a trainer, speaker and educator. How do you define success these days?

There are people displaying key performance indicators who say we have to base success on metrics. There's value in that, but the one thing I learned from Pete Egoscue a long time ago is there's nothing like what people are saying about you.

One of my major indicators in business and in life is when people talk about you, is it in a good way? Are you adding value? For me, there are probably negative whisperings because my sense of humor gets a little out of control. I'm trying to get people to a place where they can make a two-meter shift, break their state and move into a belief mechanism so they believe in themselves. Once people can leap from hope to belief in the body, mind and spirit, they tell you about it. That's my overall performance indicator as it relates to being effective.

You've had success early in your career, especially with the Egoscue Company. When did you start to feel like you were starting to become successful?

In 1991 when I hooked up with Egoscue, we were on a mission to completely shift the paradigm of health care. Pete sat across the table from the American Medical Association, where they told him that chronic pain was not his forte. He was looking at the cause of chronic pain, not the pain itself—looking at the actual *reason* for the symptoms versus the symptoms; there was no treatment. His idea was to correct joint positions and help the person feel better, which he wrote about in his book, *Pain Free*. It was that simple.

My university training would say, go deeper, look at it from the micro level. But once I finally adopted the mentality and backed out to the macro level, everything changed. If you asked how I gauge success, it was when I finally shut up, started listening and really opened my mind to what was truly there. The body's organic nature was something I was interested in, versus thinking if the shin hurts, it's got to be this or look at that nerve, rather than why it hurts—the mechanical structure.

We're almost 30 years into this and can see the paradigm shift where people are now using the word "function." Back in the early '90s, that didn't exist unless saw it in Vladimir Janda's work or somebody from the Czech Republic. People didn't think alignment was that big of a deal; in fact, people used to tell me, "Posture doesn't sell."

My success was based the natural human organic mechanism that has a way to heal itself if we just provide the right environment. We can talk money; we can talk businesses; we can talk how many clinics we have. Those are measures of success, but the big success was when we started hearing people enter the stage sounding like us.

Our goal in the early '90s was to shift the paradigm of health care to a point where people quit talking "symptom" and started talking "problem." That's our success.

Is that motivated you?

I've always been motivated by the idea of taking care of other people. I had to question myself a couple of times, "Is this about you, Brian?" If it is, that's a dangerous place to be. I asked that of myself about a bazillion times and came to the conclusion it wasn't about me. This isn't a significance thing for me.

I know that sounds esoteric and foo-foo, but that's what I ingrained into my teenager's head too. You have two choices in the morning: Get up, change the world for the better or worse, and the second one doesn't exist for my family. I get up in the morning and say these little incantations and get up on the positive and no matter what happened the day before, it's a new day. I don't want to sound like a Tony Robbins guy, but it really is a mindset, and more importantly, it's an instinct/gut/heart set too.

If you trust your instinct and go with your heart, you can get up in the morning and have that drive. Until chronic pain is eradicated or at least controlled in an easy way that's non-invasive, that wakes me up in the morning.

I joke that ego stands for "Edging God Out," whatever God you believe in. Remember, this isn't about you. You may have amazing skills, but you have this because you have a belief system that your body was given to you. It's your job now to utilize it for what it's worth…mind, heart, everything.

What's your morning routine?

I'm going to assume this is being read by hundreds of thousands of people—close to a million. I want everybody to sit back, close their eyes and enter my world. Here we go. I get up in the morning; I get that big, white, comfortable cotton robe and throw that on. Get your eyes around that; it's not the Hugh Hefner look. I walk downstairs and I have a 15-minute routine where I start prepping my coffee in the morning.

With me, it's always been about the Bulletproof Coffee. I'm not here to sell it. I'm not here to promote it, other than telling you it's completely changed my life, from a nutritional standpoint coming out of university with a nutrition degree too. Before everybody else gets up, I'm hanging out downstairs, start the blender, pour it into the coffee and start sipping it for the next hour or two.

Bill Clinton had a statement at a Tony Robbins Platinum Partner event when I was teaching there. He's made some great strides later in life in personal growth, and he's had some negatives thrown at him. Somebody asked him, "What do you do with all the negatives?" He answered, "I absolutely don't take them personally anymore. I take them seriously, but not personally, and I assume they're right."

Let's say you say something negative about me. I can take that personally and start to fight back, or I can take it seriously and wonder, "Did I do something to give him that reaction? What can I do to change his perception?"

Now it's an inner-self look, and I believe that's the answer.

What are some of the habits that helped you achieve success?

You used the word "habits." Habits can be looked at as "not being present." Habits are things you do because they're just what you normally do. But when you're really present, habits don't work.

For example, my morning routine is not a habit, it's a need. A habit is something you can tune out. You get in your car and drive to work—that's a habit. Often, you don't even remember the drive to work because the habit took over.

But if you're present in that moment, a habit can't take over. It becomes who you are; it becomes a need. You have to be willing to learn and change your habits to get things done. I like to use habit not as a negative; I like to take it out because it sometimes means I'm not being present.

When you're truly motivated to make a change in your life and in the people around you, habits just don't work. Routines become part of your belief system. I know it's just a play on words, but when people start looking at getting caught up in a habit, their training can take a different turn. Get out of the habit; ask your heart, "What do you want to do now?"

The main difference in what you are saying is about mindset and how you approach it. Let's move on to goals. Do you have a formal process for goal setting?

When I look at goals, I know this: They continually reset. When you have a list of goals on a whiteboard and there are 10 of them, a week into it, numbers six, seven and nine might be gone. Then three weeks into it, nine might come back because it didn't meet the need earlier but does now. By the end of 90 days, you want to give yourself a winning percentage. Maybe of those 10 goals, I hit three because seven of them weren't true to my belief. They were things I wrote down because in a fleeting moment, that's what I was thinking.

They're ever-changing; they're upping the bar; they're not setting the bar back. It's move forward, move forward, make it higher, make it better. At 50, the things I should be able to do physiologically, mentally, emotionally should be 10 times what I was able to do at 25.

As long as you're moving onward and upward, it's all good.

You have a lot going on between education, traveling with your lectures, Tony Robbins Company and being the vice president of Brand Development of Strategic Programs at Egoscue. Expand on the sacrifices you've made to be successful. When you add something, sometimes you have to take something away. Talk to us about that.

We suffer on the family end. Do I wish I could've been at every one of my kid's academy soccer games? Yes, of course. Do I wish I could've been home more? Yes, but I try to balance things. I've learned listening to some high-end billionaires and the Tony Robbinses of the world. A lot of them screwed up the first part of their lives, only to realize: "Could you imagine what it was like being married to me 30 years ago?"

Their first and second wives were put on backburners. They'll flat-out tell you they learned from every mistake, and they've apologized to themselves and to other people. But it was all part of their lives. I've learned by watching and listening and decided I have to get better at not needing to be everywhere at all times.

Delegate—that's a big lesson. When you don't delegate, everything is about you, your ego. When I delegate, I never look at it as me in control. Why don't we give more responsibility and authority to another person to help them grow? That feeds my ego too, in that I'm helping other people learn.

It's not all fun and games. How do you push through the worst times?

Self-talk is number one because it can be very destructive. Your inner talk in your head can crush you. I try to meditate—I'm not talking about "ohm," just sitting there with my legs crossed. I put myself in an Egoscue tower that'll give me a good 45 to 90 minutes on my back, allowing my hip to adjust. I know I'm multitasking, but at the same time, I'm clear in my head.

Get out of your head and into your heart. What did that person say to you that got under your skin, and why are you allowing someone to control your thought process and emotions? Why are your feelings hurt?

I was in a belief system that I had the answers. It all ties back into ego and significance, why you need to be right. How about being a little more open to somebody else's beliefs? Once you can be open to other people's belief systems, you might learn a thing or two.

We can learn a lot from everyone and it's by asking the right questions.

Let's move into some recommendations. First, what are three non-fitness books for everyone to read?

Absolutely: *The Four Agreements, Man's Search for Meaning* and *Unshakeable.*

Man's Search for Meaning by Viktor Frankl is an unbelievable book about how he survived Auschwitz and what kept him going. This should be required reading 10 times for every person who's diagnosed with cancer, because their belief system is what's going to keep them going.

Why do certain people die? Why do certain people live? People tell you it's mindset—it's emotion. There's a disease side to this, but there are people who beat it.

I read *The Four Agreements* probably three times this year—that was the book Bill Clinton was reading too and it absolutely shaped his entire mindset. When you make those four agreements with yourself, be impeccable—it's to speak the truth, no matter what.

You need to bookend it nicely, but it's a way to use neuro-linguistic programming to get people to understand they're going to hear the truth from you. It may hurt; it may be amazing, but at least you're not there to hurt their feelings.

Unshakeable from Tony Robbins is a game changer from an investment standpoint. That importance of that book is on the low-cost index funds and the examples he gives from investing from 19 to 28 years old. You need to be investing a $100, $200, $300 a month into low-cost funds, and even if you stopped at that point and just let the compounding interest ride, they're amazing.

I'll reread all three of those books over the rest of my life.

Let's finish up with some people.

I have an idea who you're going to name, but give three people we should follow.

I'm a little biased here, but Pete Egoscue, no question. That dude has been given a gift like no other. Gray Cook said it perfectly when we were on a ride back to the airport after teaching and he said, "It took someone like Pete Egoscue—outside the sphere of influence of fitness, who didn't come from our world in rehab or fitness—to see things and let us know what we weren't seeing."

Pete's psychological, emotional tie to that is his real genius. Anybody can make you sweat; anybody can make you puke. Here's a dirty little secret about Egoscue: We're great listeners. We really want to find the need of that customer, not just take away the knee pain.

Knee pain can be taken away by a pill—and sooner or later, we're going to be taking a genetically modified pill that takes away all pain. If pain's my focus, I'm out of business at that point. But connection is big. That's why we did a rebrand on the company to "connect and correct." That's what it's all about and Pete Egoscue just oozes that.

Another person, of course, is Tony Robbins. Everybody thinks he's a motivational speaker. I promise you, he's not: He's a strategist and if you can adopt one two-millimeter shift from this dude, it's an absolute game changer. I learned from him the power of proximity, putting myself closer to influencers in order to spread the word of Egoscue.

The third person to follow is Pete and Tony's friend, Paul Tudor Jones. Just look what he's done with the Robin Hood Foundation; he's forever changed poverty in the world. He's one of the only people who can raise $70,000,000 in a four-hour session. He puts himself in the power of proximity and gets people to match it.

These aren't people who are just making hand-over-fist money; they're people who are giving back. If there's one thing I'm going to teach my kid, it's that it's not how much money you make; it's how you influence the world. Did you leave it a better place?

We have to leave this world a better place.

As you said about the power of proximity, surrounding myself with people like you is my direction and how I'm trying to make people better. You're certainly one who's doing it. We really appreciate your telling us about your journey to success.

BE LIKE BRIAN

BRIAN BRADLEY'S TOP KEYS

I credit my success to multiple things, but here are the top three.

ACTIVE LISTENING is critical to learning and meeting the needs of anyone I'm coaching. Always.

OVER-DELIVER on my promises.

KILL MY AGENDA to meet their agenda.

ACTIVE LISTENING—ACTION STEPS

1) When you're in a conversation with anyone—whether on stage or on the phone—shut up! This is your chance to really understand your client or crowd. Listen with your ears and eyes (visual cues). Remember, "The one in charge of the conversation is the one listening," so ask questions.

2) Over-promising and under-delivering is never a good thing. Help your customer base get to the next level and how to do this is simple. Know your product or service at the highest level, speak about it at the simplest level, and meet their wants and needs. Talk about raving fans!

3) Remember, it's about them...not you. They are coming for help, guidance and hope. Make it about their agenda 110 percent and your job just got easier.

Just start listening! That's right, I said "start" because we may think we listen, but I bet that "our" agenda has muffled our listening abilities and the result is a client who may feel better, but never really buys into what we do.

Jay is a high-performance coach with over 25 years of professional experience. Sometimes known as "The Career Extender," he has worked with thousands of athletes from MLB, NFL, NHL and WWE. His work has been featured in Men's Fitness, Men's Health, Muscle & Fitness, MMA Sport Mag, Details, ESPN and CBS Sports. You can find out more about Jay at jay.fit.

In your bio on your website, you're very transparent about your struggles. It says, "I have struggled with all of the issues I discuss on this site. Over the course of my life, I've been physically and mentally weak, skinny, fat, sad, depressed, insecure, painfully shy, socially awkward, crippled with anxiety and indecision, struggled with addiction, and have gone broke on more than one occasion. Overcoming those obstacles took many years and a lot of hard work."

You've had an up-and-down road and you've learned from it. You're trying to help other people learn from your mistakes. How do you define success?

I initially made the mistake of measuring success in dollars. People might measure it in followers or notoriety or fame, but those are fleeting. To me, success is doing what you love—and I don't just mean that from a business perspective. If we can get up and put food on the table by doing what we love, that's great. But what are we working so hard for? It's to be able to do what you love with people you love.

I prioritize relationships. I love adventure sports, surfing, hiking, rock climbing. I love stand-up comedy. I love live music. If I can do those things—if I make enough money to do those things with amazing people and friends I love, that's success to me. I don't measure it in dollars anymore.

I need a certain amount of money to be able to do what I want to do. But I've figured out what's meaningful to me.

You were leading the field for a long time, but you'll say, "I was doing stupid shit and I went down." When did you begin feeling you were starting to get toward what you define as success?

It was only the last few years as I looked around the circle of really close friendships I'd built. I went into my early 30s when it was all about me, me, me. I was selfish. I was insecure. I was unhappy with who I was. I had almost no meaningful relationships in my life. Over the last several years, I've become known as a guy who gets everyone together, who creates relationships and epic experiences and great connections for others. I'm now a catalyst.

I'm a strong believer in not only auditing yourself, but maybe once a year when you're planning, asking a handful of your closest friends and your most trusted advisors, "What's my greatest strength?" I want to know my weaknesses too, but what's my greatest strength?

It's not always going to be what you want it to be; you might want it to be that you're the best leader, but maybe you're not. You're the person who produces work and you want to get feedback from other people, from another set of eyes. People told me, "You're the guy who brings people together and creates relationships, bonds and experiences better than anyone else. That's your thing."

Even just 10 years ago, I wouldn't have said that. Who would say that's their thing? You don't grow up saying, "I want to be the person who connects people."

But that's what everyone said about me, and I decided to embrace that and continue to work on that as my strength. People waste too much time trying to bring up their weaknesses. If your weakness is communication skills, spend all day on that, but often, your other weaknesses aren't worth worrying about. Just play to your strengths and be the best at those.

It's only been the last handful of years I would say, "This is success to me."

You've tried to leverage that through your business. You're changing some of the things you're doing.

Everything I do now is all about building relationships and making connections and connecting other people; I'm being a super connector. I never do it with the intention that it's going to come back to me. There are people who try to do that. They try connect people while they're counting favors and hoping it's going to come back to them in some way.

You can't do this for the return; you have to do it because you enjoy it. It makes you happy and you want good people to come together and either be friends, do business together, help each other in some way, help with some kind of suffering…whatever it might be. Do you have the right intentions? It does help me business-wise, but in a roundabout esoteric way. I don't do it with business intentions.

While I'm sure this has evolved, what it is that gets you out of bed every morning?

It's making people feel better. For 20 years, all I did was fitness. In retrospect, back then I was doing what I do now. Parents of high school athletes were saying, "Pat's a better kid, a better person, a more confident person; he's just better all around after training with you and from your influence."

I was giving them more than fitness. It was always the Mr. Miyagi approach, where I was there to help get a scholarship or a rushing record, whatever. But I made sure they were better people and their approach to life was different when they finished with me. I didn't make that my main focus until more recently.

When I get up, I'm excited to talk to people, to be able to perform. I love performing. When I say "perform," that could be onstage. I take stand-up and improv classes; I do more speaking. I run a lot of events; I do a podcast and I'm always around large groups of people.

People think of me as the guy who entertains and brings people together. I look at life as a performance because if you're going to be successful, you should be performing. You should never let people see you in a negative light. Sure, we're all going to be down and we're all going to get sad. We're all going to get tired, but I don't believe in letting people see you that way all the time.

Leave the house and perform; be your best self. People buy into energy, clarity, passion and excitement. You can do anything in life if you have passion, energy and excitement—people will get on board with that; they'll help you…they'll invest in you.

People tell me being around me energizes them because of an energy that's infectious and they love it. It's almost surreal to see people of whom I'm a huge fan in the entertainment industry, people I've watched on TV say, "I love being around you. I feel I've known you for years."

Believe me, no one would have said that about me 10 years ago. I worked really hard to get to that in my life. Now relationships are pretty much everything I do. I always have coffee and lunch and dinner scheduled with people. I'm always out socializing and looking to help, looking to make people laugh and smile and feel better, have more energy and reframe the way they look at things, and get them saying yes instead of no.

That excites me all day long.

While we're on this, you were talking about some of your strengths. What are some other habits or personality traits you can attribute to your success?

It comes down to prioritizing people and relationships. No one in life will get by a hundred percent on their skills. If you're an elite-level athlete, you might not need people skills. Usually, for the rest of us, it's not technical skills or business acumen that works—it's really your people skills, and often, people skills will supersede talent.

We don't work enough on people skills. We read a million business books and try to get better at our craft, but we don't work on our people skills. I work on my people skills 24/7 because I know it's the most essential skill in life.

When I'm booking lunch with friends, it's not just to connect and unwind and have fun. That's part of it, but it's also because I can get better. Even Arnold, The Rock, Bill Clinton and Oprah constantly get better at the way they communicate and the way they build their relationships.

What's your body language? What are your eyes doing? Are you pausing enough? Are you asking the right questions? How's your pitch, pace, tone, melody, volume?

These are all things I think about all day long…and I practice them. I make mental notes of, "I screwed that up. I shouldn't have done that. Let's get better next time. I like how that guy does that. I'm going to add that to my repertoire."

Those are the game changers for anyone.

I recently read *Steal the Show* by Michael Port. That was an eye opener and got me thinking—it doesn't have to be only on stage. It could be in conversations when you start to think about where you're looking, your posture and body language. It helped me a lot.

Talk to us about your goal-setting process.

I like the idea of habits over goals—forcing yourself to adopt certain habits, like training every day or meditating for five minutes or eating a healthy breakfast. Those small things add up over time; if you do something like that, you're more likely to lose weight than just saying, "My goal is to lose 30 pounds." Great, but super vague. How are you going to get there? How you're going to get there is by getting up to go for a walk for a half hour. The most important thing is to create daily success habits.

But I always have work-related goals too. I don't look at what doesn't work, what didn't work or what's not working. Instead, it's, "Here's what's working. Let's make it work 10 times better." I have a certain dream, a list of guests I want to get on the podcast. I'm getting closer to getting all of them on and will continue to do that.

It's funny about gym goals. Just saying that out loud makes me realize why I haven't been quite as into training in the last few months: I haven't had a goal. That's important, especially if you're new at training or want to lose a bunch of weight.

I've been comfortable where I am—the reason I haven't had a goal in the gym lately is that I put so much into that for so many years that my life was too unbalanced. It caused a lot of problems for me. I neglected important stuff. But lately, I haven't been that into training. I never miss a workout; I still go, I clang and bang…I'm into it, but I can't say I had the most fun training these recent months. Part of that is probably because I haven't had goals.

Just us having this conversation caused me to I write in my journal in huge letters, "Set some training goals."

How do you recharge?

I've been using the sauna at least three days a week for a half hour. Some weeks I'll get it in four or five days. I do cryotherapy four or five days a week, and I feel better when I do both on a regular basis: better energy, mood, sleep, less anxiety and I deal with stress better.

When I'm out with friends, no one ever sees my phone; my phone's off. I'm there…I'm present. I'm having fun. That's always what I do; that's how I recharge on a regular basis.

Tonight we're going out bowling with friends and then I have brunch tomorrow. Sunday brunch is always at least six to eight people deep, and it's always me drawing them together. I always make sure the ball's in my court when it comes to planning social things. That's one thing I don't outsource. I never let anyone else say, "I'll get back to you" or "I'll make the plans." I'm always making the plans and I know how important that is for everybody. Everybody is too busy. No one's going to do it, so I make sure I do it. That recharges and energizes me.

Are there any sacrifices you've had to make along the way to get to where you are?

I don't want to be cliché, but it doesn't occur to me that much stands out. I made many mistakes along the way and I certainly sacrificed relationships and friendships earlier. I also sacrificed the health of my spine and knees when I was obsessed with powerlifting. But nothing stands out as a tremendously huge sacrifice.

What about when things have been tough? When you're at the bottom of that roller-coaster, what pushes you through those times?

I was about 12 years into running a six-figure business; I was completely broke at 31 and I had to move into my mom's a basement with tears in my eyes—I had to ask her if I could do that and that sucked.

If you stay down too long, it tends to snowball, and you're on an even worse downward spiral. One thing I've always been able to do is recognize, "I'm in a bad place. I have to turn this around immediately." Don't sulk too long, not spending time being down too long, just doing anything—inactivity is the worst. I would do anything I could do, train, be around positive people, around that energy. I'd see live music or simple things like that.

Keep moving and have a positive mindset.

Awareness is a big piece of the puzzle, as well as knowing you'll get out of it. Jay, let's wrap it up with three non fitness–related books you think people can read that would help their development.

I love the books *Essentialism* and *The One Thing*—they're like the same book. It's a two-for-one answer; they're similar—I love those two books.

I think everyone should read the *Tao Te Ching*. My favorite interpretation is by Steven Mitchell. I highly recommend it.

I really like the book *Tribe* by Sebastian Junger; it's a great book.

Name a few people we should follow.

The trick with social media is, if you end up following a million people and are focusing on what they're doing, you're going to be comparing yourself to them.

When I first got on Instagram, I only followed three of my friends and The Rock because I was interested in what The Rock was doing; I've followed The Rock since 1996. I like his career path. I appreciate that he, like Arnold, has been able to transcend and do so many different things. That's what I'm trying to do; that's what I'll continue to do.

When people ask me this question, I usually go to The Rock and Joe Rogan because they're doing things I like. Joe has a podcast and is as successful as possible. I want to do that. He's a stand-up comedian. Awesome, I want to do that. He's maybe 10 years older than I, in great shape. I love that. He's all about fitness; he's in a fight sport. Joe does a few things at a very high level. I've really only paid attention to what those two guys are doing.

There are some close friends of mine who are also really successful and inspirational—like Bedros Keuilian and Craig Ballantyne, certainly good to follow for getting shit done and staying focused.

Jay, you've had such an interesting journey and are helping so many people with everything you're doing. Thanks for being such a great leader and for sharing your successes and struggles.

BE LIKE JAY

"Everything I do is about building relationships and making connections and connecting other people. I always have coffee and lunch and dinner scheduled with people."

BUILDING RELATIONSHIPS

Within the next week: Arrange breakfast, lunch or coffee with someone you haven't seen in a while.

Within the next two weeks: Arrange a lunch or coffee with someone you don't yet know.

Within the next month: Arrange a lunch, brunch or dinner with a group of friends.

Take the lead and make the plans.

Rinse and repeat.

Try to make these actions habits you do weekly, bi-weekly and monthly.

DEREK HANSEN

Derek is an international sport performance consultant who has worked with athletes of all ages and abilities in speed, strength and power sports since 1988. Early in his career, he worked with some of the top performers in the world as a coach, including Olympic medalists, world record holders, Canadian National team athletes and professional athletes from numerous sports. He currently serves as a performance consultant to numerous professional teams in the NFL, NBA, MLS and NHL, as well as major NCAA Division One programs, specializing in speed development, strategic performance planning, return-to-play protocols and neuromuscular electrical stimulation programming. Find out more at his site, sprintcoach.com.

Derek, you've excelled on many levels, in the private sector as well as the collegiate setting and have mentored some of the biggest names in the fitness profession. How do you define success?

Success is a case-by-case assessment. If I'm asked to work with a person or team, as we move along, we want to see some improvement. If I work with people and they improve or if someone gets better in a rehabilitation case, that's a success.

From there, you look at your body of work and ask, "How many successes have I had?" I don't assess success based on how much money I make or on fame or notoriety. In my practice, I look at every case and every person with and I ask, "Am I in helping?" That allows me to go out and present them as a case study of my successes. Hopefully, other people will acknowledge that success and help me reach more people.

I could write a book or I could do an interview or give a presentation, but that's not part of my assessment. Personally, success is based on what I'm doing on the ground.

When did you start feeling you were getting it right and that you had more successes than failures?

Early on, I discovered I was good at coaching and at the hands-on skills. I started to string together a consistent bunch of successes, but I didn't think I was good at this until I was in my late 30s or early 40s. It wasn't until then that I thought, "I have a good understanding of what I'm doing, why I'm making the decisions I'm making and I see consistent success based on that approach." My approach is based on my experiences and from my mentors, but I didn't think I had it put together until then.

How much have your goals have changed over the last 10 years?

When you're in the performance field, your goal is to work with the best athlete or team. You want to have their successes somewhat attributed to you, and I've had a chance to do some of that. I'm not saying it's not important to me anymore, but people should know that the higher you go up the performance chain, the easier it is to train the athletes because they're so good, you only have to make small adjustments. The difficult part becomes more of personalities and politics.

When you start working with the general population, it's a challenge because they don't have the same gifts. You have to work harder to pull more out of them. That interests me: how to take what I've learned working with superstars and apply those concepts to others.

I've gone full circle; I began working with kids when I was younger, then moved to working in the NFL with elite athletes. Now that I've had that experience, I'm back to "How do I help general population in fitness?" That interests me and that's my goal now, to help more people rather than just a few.

What motivates you to get out of bed in the morning?

There are people who want to get better and want gain knowledge. I want to simplify things because everything can be so complex. Everybody is trying to give the impression they have a new idea. I'm trying to use science and my experience to explain that things don't need to be that complicated. We can simplify things and make the outcomes better by not getting too crazy by being pseudo-innovative. Those are the things that interest me; how to keep things simple and still get people to reach their goals.

What are some things you've done to get to where you are? What are some of those habits you attribute to success?

You have to spend time with people you want to learn with and from. At a young age, I traveled to spend time with people to watch them work, and then talking to them about it.

I don't know if people do that as much anymore because there are internships and mentorship programs. However, the old-school way of spending time with people and learning from them was important to me. I learned from them—you spend time figuring out why things work, and that's different than school learning.

In school, you'll learn theories, read the textbooks and get the notes. Then you go to work. Learning by doing is the best way to work…and making mistakes is part of that. In fact, I'd reverse the whole thing: Start working first and do follow-up classroom sessions to discover why we're doing what we're doing. Working backward has worked well for me. I'm not against school; I just think it takes us too far away from practical things.

Another part of what I want to do is to work with people to help them get a start in the field. We'll debrief and discuss why we did what we did and why something worked, or didn't. That sort of reverse learning process interests me; that's what helped me and maybe other people can learn from that.

We talk to our clients a lot about recovery, nutrition and sleep. How do you recharge?

I've spent a lot of time in the last few years working with Fatigue Science. They have a valid, wearable device called ReadiBand. It's about 94-percent valid compared with taking an actual lab-based sleep test, whereas many of the consumer-based products are below 50-percent accurate. I've been using that, even for my red-eye flights; I see how little I slept on the flight and I have to make up for that. I use it to figure out where I lost sleep and decide if I need to take a nap.

They have an effectiveness score based on your amount of sleep or lack of sleep. It rates you on a 0-to-100 scale. It's really good if you're in the 80s or above, but if you dip into the 70s or below, it starts to equate to a blood alcohol level. You're at .05 if you're in the 70s, essentially drunk. That hit home for me.

Last night, I had a red-eye flight and during the day I tried to get some things done, but I was essentially impaired. I use that app with their technology to balance myself, and I'll take a nap when needed.

That's a good example using the digital techniques to monitor my physiological state and try to fill in the gaps. It has helped with my personal sleep issues.

What are some of the sacrifices you've made to be successful?

If you work at a facility or a school or a pro team, you're away a lot. It may not be large blocks of time where you're traveling, but throughout the day, you may not be engaged with your kids. I did that for a long time and now I'm at the point where I see the value in being away for a period, then I can super-saturate the kids with my time when I'm home. I can help with their teams, volunteer coach, help with their schoolwork and drive them to music. My kids are between the ages of five and 13, and there are a lot of activities I want to be involved in.

You make the sacrifice on one end; it's short-term pain so you can have a long-term gain on the other end.

People get into this profession to help others and make an impact, but the grind can get hard. How do you push through those times?

That goes back to what brought me into this field: I want to help people. Sometimes you do something, and keep hammering away at it because it works. After awhile, it isn't as exciting, and it may not work as well for some reason. When I've had failures or when I'm not making as much of a difference, I can feel it's affecting me physically and mentally. Sometimes you have to change lanes. That's very hard for some people.

I have friends who work in pro sports, and that's what they feel they must do. They coach in the NFL or the NBA and think they can't do anything other than that. There are a lot of options, but it's difficult to make a change. It may be stressful to make a decision to do something else. However, in the long run, it may be the best thing for a person's health and development.

Many people think that sticking with something makes them more virtuous and mentally tougher. Even though you're not very enthusiastic and aren't achieving your goals, you may still feel good about sticking to something. I've learned the hard way that it may be better to do something else. Free yourself up, try something different, face a new challenge that gets you more excited. Don't waste your precious years.

I don't want to get to the end of your life having stuck to doing the same thing for 40 years. People do that, and they get value out of it. I'm not that guy, and most of our peers aren't either. We have to push into different areas and try other things; it's important to figure out where you fit along that spectrum.

Making a change is often the best possible thing you can do. There will be fear and apprehension, but once you do it, you fall into it—you're enthusiastic and things will improve.

You have to be open to allowing things to happen. Fifteen years ago I was in the bar business, then I became a trainer and opened my own gym. From there, I would have never have thought I'd be hosting a podcast.

I'm in a coaching group with people who are writing books. I thought I didn't have an interest in writing a book, yet here I am. You have to be open for opportunities.

As I'm sure you discovered, being in the bar business helped you in other ways as you've moved into different areas. It's not like you wasted time. Those are qualities you've moved on with into your future life.

They're all related, where you're using your skill set to project yourself into a new endeavor.

Give us three non fitness–related books people should read for their development.

I'll give you a list of what I've read recently and explain how they've helped me. There's one book I read not long ago called *The Content Trap* by Bharat Anand. It isn't about the fitness profession—more toward information technology. I liked that he kept saying, "Don't worry so much about your content."

Everybody thinks your content has to be good, like "This interview has to be the best possible interview and I have to have all the answers." What he's saying is that the connections are more important; in the future and over the long term, what's important are the connections you make and the quality of those connections.

The content can't be bad, but even if the content is mediocre, those connections are more important for your future. If I could take one thing out of that, it was that I was worried too much about the Skype connection when I did an interview or worried if I asked the right questions. Now I don't worry about that as much, although there's a certain level of quality control that's important.

I've been doing more exploration into the brain and how it affects performance and even injury and pain. *The Brain's Way of Healing* by Norman Doidge is a book I recommend. We're involved in a physical field, and sometimes it's important to look at the way the brain perceives things, how it functions and how it controls and regulates a lot of what we do.

A book I recently finished is called *Runaway Species* by Anthony Brandt and David Eagleman. It's about how humans are guided by, "How do we improve things?"·and "How do we innovate and continue to innovate?" Some things we try to keep innovating, like the bicycle. The bicycle hasn't changed; it has two wheels, and it steers and has gears, but people are still trying to make a new bicycle. That's our human condition.

We try to make things different and better, and there's a part of our brain that down-regulates. If we repeatedly do the same thing, the stimulation is not as great; that's the human part that propels us to progress. We see that often in the fitness profession: Things keep changing—is it for the better or is it just for the sake of change?

Success leaves clues. Give us three people to follow you think we can all learn from.

You look at people like Elon Musk and wonder, "What does this guy think; how does this guy operate?" He's always trying to push the ; people are saying, "We just need to figure out what's going on here on earth," and this guy thinks we've got to get to Mars. I wonder why there are people like that. He's interesting.

I try to diversify my sources of information; I'm always looking outside the profession at what other people are doing. My motivation is to find people in different areas and try to learn from them and see what they're thinking.

When you break things down, it's not much different than what you or I do; it's just a different environment. That's the best thing I can offer to people.

I listened to Richard Branson's podcast when he told the story of how when he got into the airline industry. He wanted to bring his knowledge of entertainment and make it an experience for people on Virgin Atlantic.

It makes a lot of sense to take something you've done in the past, something you have expertise in, and apply it to a new area. We're often insecure and think, "I haven't done that; I don't know anything about the airline industry." Just bring what you know and then get other experts to help you where needed. That'll make people move into new areas more smoothly and give them the confidence to operate in a new arena.

Businesses are roughly the same. Everybody's has to do bookkeeping and everybody has to do marketing and advertising. When I worked in New York City, I worked at the hottest bars and there were always lines. The security would call in and say, "Ant, we have 20 people in line; what do you want to do?"

I'd walk around the bar to determine if it was comfortable to move around. Yes, there's room to walk around. I'd look at the bartenders to see if they were too busy. No, the bartenders weren't too busy and the waitresses are standing around. Then I'd call security and say, "Give us five people."

How I relate that to fitness is, we're always worried about getting more new people into our gyms. But what about the current members? You have gold right in front of you. I don't care about who's outside my bar—I'm worried about who's inside.

It's the same in the fitness business. Why are you worried about getting more people in for your promotions? You're spending time on that when you could be nurturing all the people who have already said, "I want to give you money every month." If you stop paying attention to them and are just worried about the line outside, the people inside are going to stop giving you money. You can take those concepts from the other businesses and relate them to what you're doing.

There are always people who have moved into the fitness profession and have extreme enthusiasm for it. They may not have all the content yet on how to train people, but they bring a lot to the table regarding their other knowledge just like you did. I like learning from people within our field, but it's more interesting to talk to you about the bar business.

It's been really interesting speaking with you, Derek. You have such a unique perspective that so many in the profession continue to learn from. Thanks for sharing your journey.

BE LIKE DEREK

"At a young age, I traveled to spend time with people to watch them work, and then talking to them about it."

ROAD TRIP—VISITING OTHER COACHES

One of the best things you can do to get out of the "bubble" you're in is to visit other trainers and strength coaches.

Ideally, it's someone who's successful and has a business similar to that which you'd like to have some day, but it doesn't have to be. You can learn from anyone, even from someone who you don't think is doing great work. You can learn what not to do!

Connect with a coach or trainer you would like to visit. Ask if you could come to observe what they're doing during one of their sessions. Offer to buy lunch, dinner or coffee before or after.

Or come bearing gifts. Bring something that tells them you're appreciative of their time.

If it's someone you really want to connect with, offer to pay for the hour.

Be respectful when you're there. Take notes and write down questions for later. Be quiet unless they're engaging you. Save questions for after the session or in a follow-up email.

Send a hand written thank you card after the visit.

Try to get to another facility at least once a month.

Luka is a former professional basketball player turned coach and entrepreneur who is the founder of Vigor Ground Fitness and Performance in Slovenia (Ljubljana) and the U.S. (Seattle). Luka helps clients create better bodies so they can write better stories of their lives. He helps coaches create better fitness businesses so they can write better stories for themselves, their families, clients and communities. Luka and Vigor Ground have been featured in Men's Health, Stack Magazine, Onnit Magazine, Entrepreneur Magazine, Precision Nutrition, as well as CBS, FOX and KING5 as Seattle's top fitness expert. He also runs a business consulting company that has worked with hundreds of gyms as well as companies such as Onnit, Box n' Burn, Training for Warriors and Boeing. Look him up at VigorGroundFitness.com.

You've had some amazing success, especially coming from Slovenia to Seattle, where you had to start over. Talk about how you define success.

The idea of success has changed over the years. People often look at success as financial freedom and security for their family. Certainly, one of the things I believe about success was that it's doing something you're truly purposeful and passionate about. Purpose is not found—it's forged. You have to bust your ass to forge your purpose. We want to make a good living doing something we're purposeful about and enjoy. But I would add that it happens while going through a lot of ups and downs and challenging life situations.

Success is a separate parallel from happiness. Once you figure that out, you can work on both, to be successful and also happy. One doesn't necessarily drive the other.

I got to the point where I was making the money I wanted to make. Meanwhile, part of my life was in ruins. The success I was striving for—being born under communism and then making good money—was thought of as "making it." But when that happened, I burned things down around me. I wasn't happy. Success without fulfillment is the ultimate failure, as Tony Robbins points out.

Intrinsic motivation and confidence are such a big part of what drives us. We're continuously working to get better at our craft. But at the same time, we learn how to enjoy life and not attaching our wellbeing and happiness to those things. Thinking, "When I'm the best," "When I make XYZ," "When I'm respected in the field," is a slippery slope. Attaching success to external factors is dangerous.

There's the idea of going to school, get good at what you're doing and work your ass off to create security in your life. That's a picture of what many people think of as success, but that's not true. You can do something purposeful, be great at what you do and also have amazing experiences, treat people well, learn ways to be happier and be more in the moment. You can live in two parallels, but they're different.

People get discouraged because they think passion is going to fall in their laps and it doesn't. They're not consciously seeking that out. Can you elaborate on how people can forge their purpose?

I love Cal Newport's book *So Good They Can't Ignore You*, which talks about deliberate practice and about the passion hypotheses. There's still a belief that you bump into something and decide, "I really like this; I'm going to go do this."

But, let's take a look at my basketball career. I was a scrawny kid. I never got picked. When we'd play five on five or three on three street ball and kids would pick a team, it would come to my turn and I'd hear, "I guess I'll pick that kid." That was painful. I was angry and I used that anger and frustration to practice because it was a chip on my shoulder—I'll show them.

The reality is, I busted my ass; I trained and trained and trained, and I got better. The better I got, the more passionate I got. The hard work stemmed from a painful experience. That led me to doing more deliberate practice and building career capital. It made me more passionate. That's what I mean by forging your purpose.

People might think, "I was there for six months and I just didn't feel passionate about it. I didn't feel like I was making an impact." That's crazy. If you put in your all, even into something that may not be your purpose, you're building deliberate practice and skill sets that will transfer to another field.

For example, say you were doing insurance sales. You might not be passionate about it. But what if you did that for two years—you gave it your all and became great at sales. Then, you end up in coaching. Get this: Being great at sales while owning a fitness business is insanely powerful. Businesses live and die by sales. If you don't sell it, your revenue dies.

As you work your ass off and become better, that's you forging your purpose. Whereas, what if you quit regularly? You're practicing quitting—if we understand neurology, the patterns of the brain and engraining habits—that's exactly what you're doing. You're practicing to get better at quitting.

You're also stepping to the side versus stepping up. Maybe you're going to go through several things before you find something purposeful. You're going to have to bust your ass or you'll never find it.

Anders Erikson, who coined the term "deliberate practice" in his book *Peak,* talks about the idea that eventually for elite performers the skill they've developed becomes the reward. Over time, you don't know where it's going to lead. But if you keep developing that skill, sometimes that becomes the reward. And that becomes what you can be passionate about, which can lead to other things. Talk to us about your specific passion. What gets you out of bed in the morning?

This is going to be a long answer. In my heart, at my core, I'm a coach and a leader. Now "coach" can be a few things because I coach fitness and business. But the heart of everything for me still is Vigor Ground Fitness and Performance, which is my gym. What gets me up in the morning is to make this the greatest gym on the planet.

We have to be great at coaching, but also the best communicators, the greatest at storytelling, culture and experience. Customer service has to be high. Our business has to be on point. We're constantly drilling this. I'm obsessed with finding better ways to do things and also checking myself and having the self-awareness that I might be the bottleneck. What do I have to do to get myself out of the way?

Building a business, being an entrepreneur and coaching is an art. This is also the reason I chose not to have multiple gyms. My thought process was if there were four *Mona Lisas,* there wouldn't be THE *Mona Lisa.*

If you want to build something into the best in the world, it's a lot more difficult when you have 10 gyms, 10 managers and 50 coaches to oversee.

Kudos to anybody who's doing that; we need more quality gyms to help more people. But for me, I want to go deeper.

Actually, the deeper version of this is that I'm working on something called Vigorville. I bought the Vigor Ground building—12,000 square feet that we ripped apart and now have other tenants. I started other companies and have a team to start buying more real estate and putting in businesses essentially in line with what we believe about health and changing people's lives. The 10-year working vision is a brunch spot, a spa, a co-wellness working space and the like.

Environments trigger behaviors. I want to create an environment that triggers positive behavior. It will be one that helps people change their health and fitness, and also how they treat people, their wellbeing, understanding of happiness, being more present, giving more—virtues and attributes that are proven by science to make people's lives better.

I started asking myself what else we can do to create a mini city. It's somewhat utopian thinking, but it drives me. It's such a big dream; it gets me out of bed in the morning because I know there are people I need to meet, things to read, coaches to hire…all to become the person who can help put this together.

The big dream is this: If we do it here, we can show people how to do it anywhere—my little snippet of changing the world. It sounds very foo-foo-ish, but I get fired up about it. It's all connected.

I studied marketing. I studied sales. I've studied storytelling, communication, leadership and social skills. It all comes back to building the best of the best—not only the gym—but this "mini city" as an environment that triggers all the behaviors to start moving America in a different direction.

I've been listening to Grant Cardone, who talks about the 10X rule. He says we don't dream big enough. And it's sad, because there is a lot of potential in all of us. Thomas Plummer talks about striving to be the best in the world. At first, it can sound overwhelming. But what he was saying was be the best in YOUR world first. Your world might consume a one-mile radius; work on that first. You've got to take those initial steps, but if you don't dream big, you're never going to get there.

There's a line I love from Gary V: "It's clouds and dirt." There are two places you look, up or down. You look up in the sky and your cloud is your big dream because there has to be something guiding you. It can be big and overwhelming, but there's a skill of breaking things down into daily practices.

But you need something that pulls you. Without that, it's like a life of quiet desperation; people don't even know what's missing, but they know it's something. People should dream bigger—and the truth is, they have it inside, but they're afraid to say big dreams out loud.

What happens if you declare to the world that you're going to do something huge? It's a responsibility. People have big dreams inside of them, but never want to make them public or make a decision to move toward them because it's scary.

When I started the Vigor Life building project, I had months of push and pull inside. It was millions of dollars of commitment. And not just that, but the time, the energy—the problems and the resistance become bigger…and you wrestle with it.

There's something pulling you to a safe place. It's not the place you want to be, but it's safe. There's not as much threat. That's a life of quiet desperation.

Part of my calling is to trigger people to say, "Screw it. Let's go. I've got one life. Death is motivation. I've got to get this out of me." Even if they fail, people feel more content and happier when they go after something, and later they don't have to think about the what-ifs. What-ifs are a disease.

I want to go into your habits and behaviors to get as much done as you do, to have such big goals. Let's start with, do you have a morning ritual?

I have a bed of nails—not real nails; it's a product from Finland. I lie down on that and meditate anywhere from five to 15 minutes, depending how much I have to do that day. I'll either do the Calm app, or sometimes I do binaural beats and breathing drills. Sometimes I do mantras. I switch that up a bit, but I almost always meditate on my bed of nails.

Do you have a formal process of setting goals?

What works for me is something called Tomorrowland for the big visionary work. A while back, AJ Roberts came to my old gym to visit. We were in the office and he asked, "What's that behind you on that whiteboard? It says Tomorrowland." There was a list of bullet points on the Tomorrowland whiteboard. When he came back recently, he said, "This is insane. You are 95 percent in line with everything you wrote on that board!"

I always have a point of reference to reverse engineer. From there, I set goals for the year. I've become a long-game person. I set goals for the year, but every Sunday I also do something called "Key Four."

Let's say we have a 90-day goal of getting 45 new members. That means every 30 days, we should see 15 new members. That's the goal. I broke it down into weeks; it would be a little less than four people. On Sundays, I break down four keys under one thing I want to achieve.

Key Four is the four most important action steps. If you had to scratch everything else, what would be the four action steps to reach that one thing for the week? Then I write why that matters. After that, how am I going to get it done? I'm going to build a full-strategy map with things to execute. When will you get this done? I tick it off which day I'm going complete it.

What are your four keys? What do you need to do? When do you need to do it? Why do you need to do it? That model has been very effective. I also teach this to my business coaching clients. When we're in a small business or entrepreneur venture, there are a million things to do. It's just insanity.

If we did only three things a day related to our goals and looked back a year later, we'd be amazed at how much we'd have achieved. You're super busy. Talk to us about how you recharge on a daily, weekly or yearly basis.

I'm a huge fan of mobility flows, partly because once you start doing them, the flows become playful. I feel childlike and lose track of time.

And I'm focused on engaging in the moment.

I'm a huge fan of float tanks. I go to a Russian bathhouse at least once a week. It's a super hot sauna, a cold plunge pool, a salt water pool. And I read a chapter or two of a book—reading is a big part of how I recharge. I also try to get a massage throughout the week.

I travel a lot for work, and I'll add a couple of days on the front or back at the event location to relax. When I'm here in Seattle, I'm as A-type of crazy as it gets, but when I go away, changing the environment allows me to shift.

I've found a balanced periodization of my life. I go super hard and on the back end, I'll spend three days unplugging and doing the important things I need to do. Then, I'm back at work and going like crazy. That's what's worked well for me. And throughout the day, pattern interrupts work incredibly well.

As has everyone, you've had struggles in your life. Talk to us about how you get through those times.

As my mindset changed, this changed too. I used to tell myself, "This too shall pass."

But that came to mean two things. When things are really hard, you know they're going to pass and that gives you hope. It also started to mean, this too shall pass as things are really good, so cherish them because they're going to go away too. It's a double whammy.

I started looking at the challenges as the only way I can become the greatest. If there are no challenges, I can't become better. If there's no challenge, it becomes a cul-de-sac—I'm spinning in circles. There's nothing making me better in life. This is the only way you can become great. I started getting curious about what's on the other side of this challenge. The bigger the challenge, I think of who I will become once I've overcome it…and anxiety turns to excitement.

Part of our wellbeing and happiness is attached to fulfillment and is constantly growing, an intrinsic motivation to get better. We're pulled by that. The people who don't answer that call never know they're living a life of quiet desperation because they're not playing at their highest level.

I recently read Ryan Holiday's *The Obstacle is the Way* that describes a similar thought process. While we're talking about books, give us three non fitness–related books people can read to help with their development.

Asking me for three is like putting a gun to my head. I'm going to break the rule; here are the books that pop into mind that everybody should read. My favorite book of the last couple years is a book called *Resilience* by Eric Greitens. It's phenomenal—resilience is one of the greatest virtues to have.

As old and as classic as this is, the next book is *How to Win Friends and Influence People*. People should just keep reading it over and over again. Most of us aren't good enough with communication. One of my favorite quotes came from it: "People forget what you said; people forget what you did, but people never forget how you made them feel." I'm constantly encouraging not only interns, but everybody around me to read that book… or reread it.

The third is *The Obstacle is the Way*, Ryan Holiday's great book. There are some similar messages about resilience, but the books go different directions. Another book that changed my life was *The Go Giver* by Bob Burg. It's a short read and insanely powerful. If you don't get fired up after that, you need a pulse.

There's a book I enjoyed by Robin Sharma called *The Leader Who Had No Title*. The point is, you don't need permission to be a leader. Leaders act, and that's how they become leaders. It gets people to move; it will for sure get you fired up about what you're doing. If you have a team or you're a part of a team, this book's an absolute must.

Who are three people we should be following to help us learn or move forward?

There are so many people who have made a difference in my life. I'm going be a little biased; this is one of my best friends in the world: Jay Ferruggia. If you follow him, you'll be fired up. His *Renegade Radio* podcast has every guest you can imagine and covers every aspect of everything.

On the training side of things, Eric Cressey is a great person to follow and is a close friend. He's obviously genius level when it comes to training and performance.

John Berardi has been a really good friend for a long time and I can definitely say I have journals written of wisdom from him, although not necessarily nutrition education—his life and business suggestions have influenced me massively.

Nate Green is another close friend who's under the radar. He's an incredible writer.

Adam Bornstein is a good friend who shares a lot of great stuff in the fitness space. He's incredibly good at business and marketing. I call him the ghost in the machine because most people don't know all of the things he does behind the scenes. He's helped some incredible companies—multibillionaire companies too. He's another great person to follow.

This is one of the toughest questions, because I'm sharing people I'm close to and think are amazing. Never stop building relationships. Go the extra mile; go the extra 10 miles. One of the best things I ever did was committing myself to building relationships and always investing in them: time, energy, even money. You could lose everything in your business, but if you have your tribe, a community, your people around you…you're still rich.

One of the best parts of this game is building the teams, relationships and tribes who make your life better. Then you can build incredible things together.

You have such a great message and you're so inspiring. There have been so many great nuggets out of this one, Luka. We wish you much more to come, especially with Vigorville.

BE LIKE LUKA

"I have this belief that environments trigger behaviors. I want to create an environment that triggers positive behavior, that helps people change their health and fitness, and also how they treat people, their wellbeing, understanding of happiness and being more present and giving more, and all of these different attributes that are proven by science to make people's lives better."

YOUR OWN VIGORVILLE

Many readers might be just starting out and the idea of Vigorville is a little out of your reach at the moment. It was for Luka at one time too, so you need to think bigger (see Charlie Weingroff's Be Like).

What can you do now to create your own virtual Vigorville? Building relationships and partnering with people is a great first step.

Write down the things you think are important for overall health and wellness, what some would call your "Big Rocks." If money was not an obstacle and you could have a building that would house all of the disciplines that are important to you, what would they be?

Just because you can't have those things in your gym right now—assuming you even have a gym—doesn't mean you can't partner with practitioners of those disciplines to bring those services to your clients.

Is there a café close by serves organic, healthy food? What about a food delivery service? Is there a smoothie or shake place near you?

Who are the best physical therapist, chiropractor, massage therapist and nutritionist in your area?

Contact them and ask to visit them. Make sure your philosophies are in line and start recommending your clients to them.

If you don't have a newsletter, start one and start educating your clients on all aspects of your Big Rocks. Ask your partners for contributions to help them establish themselves as experts for your clients as well.

If you have a website, add these experts to your "Partners" page. If you have a gym, make a bulletin board with their cards and info on it. Get your partners to come in and speak to your clients.

Let your clients know you care more about the time you're spending with them at the gym. Let them know you care about every aspect of their lives.

Build your network, partner with and surround yourself with the best people you can find and you will see the incredible impact you can have on your clients and in your community.

CASSANDRA FORSYTHE YORK

Cassandra is an Assistant Professor of Exercise Science at Central Connecticut State University. She has a PhD in Kinesiology from UConn and an MS in Nutrition and Metabolism from the University of Alberta, Canada. She is a Registered Dietitian and has a CSCS. Visit her site at cassandraforsythe.com.

Cassandra, you've had success as an entrepreneur, professor, author, trainer and in competition. Talk to us about how you define success.

Success is achieving goals you set out for yourself. People can be successful in many different areas and one person's success may not be another's.

I set the goal of wanting to be a household name. I remember specifically being on the StepMill at the University of Alberta Fitness Center in 2001 and reading an article—it might've been a *Women's Health* magazine—where the writer was quoting experts and I said to myself, "I want to be one of those experts." I remember going to *johnberardi.com* and thinking, "I'm going to be *cassandraforsythe.com*. Watch out, John Berardi." Not that I've come up to the heels of John Berardi, but I definitely made a name for myself in the fitness and nutrition arena.

I've always wanted to teach. When I was a little kid, I used to teach the neighborhood kids. I'm a teacher today; coaching is teaching. I remember being a gym rat, being there so much that people would ask, "Do you live here?" I said, "One day, I'll have my own gym." And I did.

These were goals I set for myself. That's what success is, accomplishing your goals. It doesn't matter what money is made. If it's something you've set out to achieve and you achieve it, that's my definition of success.

When did you start to feel like you were becoming a success?

I worked on the *New Rules of Lifting* with Lou Schuler and Alwyn Cosgrove and at the same time I did the *Women's Health Perfect Body Diet*. Rodale Publishing approached me to write a book when I was writing another book…while I was doing my PhD. I felt like things were coming together because leaders in the field were recognizing something in me and that made me feel successful. That's when I felt like I was starting to have success. I started being invited on podcasts and different interview shows. That's when things started to click.

Just this past week, I was with some amazing fellow faculty at a get-together at a local pub. I was telling them I've written four books and have no student debt and own my own home. They said, "Holy crap, that's not normal for academia." They're still digging themselves out of debt. They've never written a book that made money. That made me think, "I'm on a good path to success."

What is it about being a household name, teaching or owning a gym that made you want to do that? There's got to be something under that. What's the motivation?

I wasn't the most popular kid when I was younger, but I knew I was had a brain. Things made sense to me in ways that didn't make sense to other people. It's my drive to be able to share knowledge. That's the thing that gets me out of bed every morning. I just finished my courses at Central, and I've gotten numerous email messages from students saying they appreciated me as a professor; that keeps me going. Women say "You've helped me in the gym." Some of my female students have come to me and asked for advice in the gym or even life advice. The drive is to help and teach others.

The drive isn't to be a household name; it's not even to be someone who gets to brag about my accomplishments. It's just to help people. And that's what I do: I help people. I've always liked reaching out and supporting people. That's my drive.

You've gone from one goal to an even bigger goal…to an even bigger goal. Sometimes there are choices we have to make to move forward. Do you feel like you've sacrificed to get where you are?

I've sacrificed a ton. I currently live in Connecticut, nowhere near any family or the friends I grew up with. I grew up on the west coast of Canada, in British Columbia in the middle of nowhere. Now I live in the bustling Northeast. I'm around people who have family and friends they've known their whole lives. I've made great friends here, but it's different than being near people I went to elementary school with. I don't have family near me for when I'm having a hard day or just want to sit around at my parents' house and cuddle on the couch with my parents' cat. I've given up that extra support.

I married, divorced, married again. When I went through that divorce, I had to restart my life. When people go through divorce, there's often a choice between the spouse's friends or your friends. That was a new thing.

I've sacrificed 12 extra years for education. I graduated from high school and went straight through school for another 12 years, going through four different universities to get a doctorate and an RD.

There may be people who have more life experience than I do, so although I have this academic experience and I'm well suited to be in academia, there are things I missed out on. I've sacrificed a lot: money, time, friendships and family.

I had a goal—I wanted to be better, to do better, to do more…not at the expense of other people, but I had a goal. I didn't know I wanted to do a PhD until I was in my bachelors program. I was working with one of the nutrition professors at University of Alberta and got into research and realized I liked it. He sat me down and asked, "What do you see yourself doing in the future?"

I was going to school to become a registered dietitian, but I love teaching. I love my university professors; that's what I want to do as a career. He said, "You're going to do your PhD then. Apply for this grant. You're starting your masters, and you'll apply for more grants to do your PhD."

That's how it happened. It wasn't exactly planned, but I was destined for more than I originally planned.

Sometimes we can get really low wonder, "What am I doing here?" How do you push through those worst times?

When I first came to Connecticut, I drove across Canada by myself, with paper maps—before there was GPS in phones. I didn't even have a cell phone.

When I got here, I didn't have any money or resources. I wasn't allowed to work, being an international student.

I went out to buy a digital camera to take pictures to send back to my family. I bought the camera—it was $200. I didn't have enough money to pay my rent the following month, so I had to return the camera. I wasn't able to have everything I wanted, but I still pushed through because I knew I'd be able to afford that camera one day.

I've been fortunate, but it was because I kept working while I was in school. I used to be a study hall monitor for the UConn basketball team. I'd sit there with the UConn female basketball stars, monitoring them, making 15 bucks an hour to sit there and study—plus they had good food they brought in after their practices and always shared.

I think back to the crazy stuff, of not having any money, not going anywhere, not being able to afford anything. I'm fortunate I ended up where I am now. It was because I had a goal. There was a light at the end of the tunnel; for five years, I was seeking that light. When I got my PhD, I had to set a new light.

You knew your "why" and you reminded yourself, "This is where I am. I'm heading toward that light." That's why it's important to get clarity and recognize the "why."

Now my "why" is having a good family—my priorities have changed. After getting divorced, I realized I was focusing a lot on me, my goals and what was good for my life, not my husband and our life. I've backed off from pursuing professional success.

After work, if I'm not going to the gym that day, I want to be home with my family. That's more important than getting a workout or sitting at the computer and working on an article or interacting with people on forums. My priorities have changed.

I'm a Girl Scout troop leader. I have 14 girls in my troop and I adore them. I get to make a positive influence on their lives.

In terms of my current success plans, I want to get tenure at my university and to publish. I've got a research project in process and two more I'll start in the spring.

It's not a transparent success everyone sees on social media; it's a different success of my happiness and my home and success in my job and respect from my peers—a different success, but it's still success to me.

Success seems to start externally and ends up being internal as we start to mature and get clarity. Can you talk about your goal process?

My goal is tenure and promotion within three years. I know everything I need to do. Every day, I have a to-do list that helps me reach my goals. When I'm on winter break from school, I'll write a research proposal grant. When I send these applications for research, it adds to my research experience, to my promotion and tenure portfolio in order for me to get tenure. I need to have more peer-reviewed publications and to present at conferences. All these are on my to-do list. I know what needs to be completed in this promotion and tenure binder.

I'm in the department of education, so I'm going to take some classes on educational leadership philosophy and learning and teaching styles. I'm going to keep improving because one of my other goals is to be someone who deserves tenure and promotion, someone who's great at teaching.

Let's talk about some of the habits that made you successful. Do you have specific sleep habits?

I struggle with depression. I'm not the most stable mental health person—a lot of people struggle with mental illness. It helps me relate better, especially with this new generation who are struggling.

Adequate sleep is my most important factor. If I have to sleep in a little extra in the morning, I will. I don't make myself get up and feel tired all day long. I've found that getting the right amount of sleep helps me function better emotionally throughout the day.

What do you do to recharge?

During the winter break, I tend to relax more. That's my recharge—I relax on the school schedule. In the summer, I get four months off while still getting my salary, so it's nice.

Traveling is incredibly important to us. Last year we went to Punta Cana and to Canada to see my family. We did some local trips to New York City and to Rhode Island. I have to plan a vacation; I need something to look forward to.

You're pretty driven and fearless. To get in the car and have no money, move across the continent and to a new country—what are some of the habits you attribute to your success?

I wasn't the most popular kid growing up and I became a loner. I depended more on myself than anybody else. That's one thing that has allowed me to be successful: I don't usually depend on other people. Being an independent worker has been something that served me very well.

Give us three books people can read to help with their development, preferably not fitness related.

I'm the worst about reading books because after grad school, I just read research. My suggestion will be short stories of motivation—I love *Chicken Soup for the Soul*. That's a good one.

If you're in a relationship, look into *Seven Principles for Making Marriage Work*. After my divorce, I started learning how to work on relationships.

The *Illustrative Happiness Trap* is another great book and an easy read.

There's another book I like called the *Gifts of Imperfection*—it's saying that there's no such thing as being perfect. We're all imperfect and it's a gift.

There's a really good book called *What the Best College Teachers Do*. It talks about teaching and can apply to any kind of coaching as well.

Do you have mentors or other people we can follow and can learn from?

Rachel and Alwyn Cosgrove are great people to follow. They've overcome a lot. I remember the first time Rachel spoke publicly at a conference and now she's untouchable.

Brad Schoenfeld is such an inspiration.

Krista Scott Dixon is just an outstanding woman.

Erin Brown does some really cool stuff as well.

It's been great to follow your career and see how much you've done and how many people you've impacted. We really appreciate you sharing your journey to success.

BE LIKE CASSANDRA

"If it's something you set out to achieve and you achieve it, that's the definition of success. My "why" is having a good family—my priorities have changed. I've really backed off from pursuing professional success. I'll come home after work and even if I didn't go to the gym that day, I want to be home with my family."

THE EVOLUTION OF SUCCESS

Cassandra's definition of success has completely changed as she's evolved.

What's your definition of success? Have you really thought about it? How has that definition changed?

Write down your current definition of success.

Think back a few years. Was your definition different?

If you told your younger self what you're doing now, how would your younger self react?

Does your definition align with your mission or purpose statement? (See Christa Doran's Be Like)

Does it align with your values? (See Molly Galbraith's Be Like)

Do you consider yourself a success on any level?

Like your mission statement and values statement, your definition of success is part of your road map to where you want to go and how you'll get there.

Hopefully this book will help keep you on track.

Rick is the founder and CEO of Alloy Personal Training Center, established in 1992, Alloy Personal Training Solutions, Alloy for Women and the Secret Trainer Society. Alloy has licensed over 2,000 clubs worldwide and has consulted with many more. To learn about his training, visit him at teamalloy.com.

Rick, the work you've done is incredible—you're helping other gyms and trainers become the best they can be. You're fast tracking them to becoming more successful business owners. Talk about how you define success.

Having been in this field for 25 years, I define success by the number of people we can positively affect, whether that be business to business—going to another club or gym and helping them with their businesses—or the end user.

If I help a club become operational to sell and service more training, more of their clients get in better shape. They're getting the results of something I built from a tiny gym during college in 1992. Certainly there are financial metrics, but it's really about how many lives we're changing on those two fronts—the businesses and the individual members.

When you're helping somebody in Minnesota, Washington or Arizona, you might not be directly helping all of their clients, but you're helping them indirectly. You're making that facility owner or trainer better at what they do and they're affecting other people, who are in turn affecting more people.

We have 800 gyms running our plays worldwide. Some are making great profits. It's a life changer for them, especially some of the smaller gyms. But if each gym had a hundred personal training clients getting some level of coaching, think about how many people are now getting help based on the systems we created.

That's it; that's what we're trying to do.

Is that what drives you—how many people can you help; can you change what they're doing to get a bigger reach?

The great thing when you're coaching someone is that you get to see the fruits of your labor. Someone engages with you to do a certain job; people pay you well to do that job and once you've done what comes second nature, they thank you for that and pay you. It's such a self-satisfying and gratifying enterprise.

We moved into this licensing business and opened a couple other businesses, and I spent most of my days in business meetings, talking to attorneys and doing things that are not close to the end product. I was traveling 42 weeks out of the year and doing things I didn't do for 20 years when all I did was go to my gym every day.

I started to lose touch with why we were doing what we were doing because my daily work wasn't as enjoyable as it had been. My wife and I set this big, hairy, audacious goal to donate 50 percent of our income. We're not just helping the gyms, but parlaying the work to keep me motivated.

We try to do well financially because that's how adults keep score. That's the byproduct of helping people. If we do, let's give away as much as we can—let's make a game of that.

I like to chase those goals. We set this big, crazy goal, and we had a wacky year. We had kids who were coming of college age, so we didn't quite make the full goal. We got close, but didn't make it.

The next year I said, forget it; the only way we're going to make this happen is if we bake a giving structure into our business. The following year, we contracted with a local charity company that vets charities. We built it into a hard structure of our business. We give $10 to charity each month for every member of any of our gyms and we give away $10 for every licensee.

We do the same for the Secret Trainer's Society—which is our business coaching group. If you look at 800 licensees and 500-plus members doing training, we're able to give away tens of thousands of dollars a month. That allows me to reach my goal of giving enough away by year's end to feel good about what I'm doing.

I love what we do. The people are wacky and crazy; they have tons of passion and it's a fun field to be a part of. Having been in it for 25 years, the real key is, are we doing something purposeful and meaningful every day? And today, the answer is yes.

But are we doing something even bigger than that? It's given me so much. I've built my life around it. I owe it more than just the profession—there's more we can do. At this stage of my career, that's ultimately what gets me out of bed every morning.

When did you start to feel like you were becoming successful?

It wasn't until a few years ago, and I still feel I could be doing so much more. We could be better even locally at our gyms, and we could be training better. And I mean, literally, our kettlebell swings could be better; we laugh about that, but we can always be better.

The year we baked the giving structure into our business, I felt we did good work. We got a nice summary of what we gave to different charities. We looked at the gyms we brought out, and we put together a report of all the client successes—not in our local gyms, but from all the clients of the other gyms we work with.

That's probably the time I took a step back and took stock of where we were and felt really good about what we were doing.

It's a great lesson about the long haul. This is a marathon, not a sprint. You touched on your goals a bit. Do you have your formal goal-setting process?

This is the most basic, simple thing and is how I coach it. I'll shout it from the mountaintops because it made such a difference for me: It's the old "five things on an index card" trick. I try to do this the night before a business trip or on a plane on the way home. If you're leaving your gym or before you go to bed at night, grab an index card. Certainly, you can use tech to do it digitally, but I find it's more meaningful if it forces me to go old school and write.

On a 5x7 index card, I write down exactly five things I'm going to do the following day—five purposeful things—because we all know what happens when the whirlwind starts. When you're training in a gym, you're going to get through your morning, try to figure out a way to get lunch, sneak in a workout…or maybe you're half asleep. Go back in at 4:00PM, finish up until 8:00, and you're spent.

You absolutely have to write something down that will move you in the direction you want to go. The five things can be like, "I'm absolutely going to write that letter of gratitude to that person because I've been saying I'm going to do that. I'm going to do that tomorrow. I'm going to call this person. I'm going to start the process of….I'm going to finish this. I'm going to finish the last chapter in that book."

These can be simple things—in fact, they should be. They can't be too big or you can't get them done. They have to be attainable. But think about it: 365 days a year, five things every single day. Some of those are incredible, because it's about doing purposeful work every day.

Every time I get away from writing a daily card, I notice a drop in my overall performance. It sets up the discipline to do those five things every day. It's probably the simplest thing I could offer, but it's been the most impactful habit for me over 25 years.

You're talking about the discipline to do it and of course, that's a habit that's going to help people. What other habits have helped you achieve some of your success?

I try not to stay self-focused. That's a trend we see these days, but you can spend too much time worrying about what you need to do better. Instead, do your five things, get out of your head and look for ways to improve other people's lives.

I heard it described as being the end to your means—meaning everything you do in your life, it's all for the purpose of what it can do for you. You're the ultimate end to all the means; all the things you do circle back to yourself. I don't think that's the right way to live a good life.

Some metrics I use—you could say these would be goals—I try to spend about 15 percent of my total time on big ideas. These are the purposeful things moving me forward. The other 85 percent of our time, we have to work. That might mean training clients; that might mean running a business. But we have to spend at least 15 percent of our time working on things that are going to move us and our businesses forward.

How do you recharge?

This might sound surprising because of how much we hustle, but I take a month off every year. And more often than not, it's a straight month, not broken up.

One of my hobbies is riding motorcycles. I might take a month off and go to another country, rent a motorcycle and ride around. I just completely detach, which sounds impossible—I know that's a lofty, crazy goal for those readers who are in the weeds right now.

I started this practice 15 years ago when I was in the weeds too. It started out at one week and the business didn't blow up. Then it went to two weeks, and then three weeks. It proved over time that if I have the right systems in place, the business can run itself.

Taking a sabbatical is one of the recommendations found in the book *Rest*. If people take a month off annually, they'll be surprised what it does on so many levels. You did it right, taking baby steps and allowing it to grow over time.

Michael Hyatt takes a sabbatical every year and he talks about how he started thinking about it: What would it take to take that month off? Would you have to get

somebody to cover for you and what would need to be done? When you start doing that, it can become a reality because you can see the tangible things you're going to have to do.

I remember the first year, we'd had a rough patch where we almost didn't make it. When we scratched our way back from that, I remember thinking, I'm back to normal. I've now have business systems that almost anyone can run. I've got a good team in place. I'm going to take a week off.

I took a week off and I was nervous and kept checking in. I came back there were a few things that came up that people had questions about, but not as much as I expected.

The next year, I took two weeks…and same thing happened. Fast forward to the following year, and I decided to do a month. I told the team if the place isn't on fire and nothing horrible has happened, I don't want to hear from anyone—that's the rule.

I came back and was really excited. I'd been gone a month, and I had all these ideas and was completely recharged. I also wanted to feel valued, like they missed me. I distinctly remember sitting down with my team and asking how things had gone. I expected a flurry of issues and problems and I was ready to solve them all. And what answer did I get? "Business is up. We're doing great. How was your trip?"

I remember feeling strange. Everyone wants things to go smooth in their absence, but it's funny how I felt almost hurt that no one needed me. I could disappear and it wouldn't matter. I was the least important person in my business at that point in time, which was, looking back on it, the best feeling ever and I'll never forget it.

What happens now, unfortunately, is I go into the gym and have to introduce myself.

That's the dream, but when it happens, it can be an adjustment. Rick, let's go back to that rough patch, because every business has its ups and downs. Give us an idea about a rough patch you went through. Was it due to mistakes you'd made? And talk to us about how you pushed through that worst time you had.

We opened in 1992 at 1,500 square feet. Then, we moved to 3,000 feet—not big, but in 1998, we did a million bucks in training. Anybody who has a small business or tracks numbers knows that $83,000 a month in personal training out of 3,000 feet is amazing, especially back then. It was all high-level, one-on-one training.

I didn't have any real business systems in place and the people working for me were independent rock stars, which was great…until it wasn't. They looked at me and thought, "Rick's not that smart; I'll go and open my own business."

Looking back on it now, I don't disagree.

They left and when they did, it really hurt my business. I went from $83,000 a month down to $12,000 in a really short time because we were selling packages of sessions. Mind you, I was married with two kids and a mortgage. We lived within our means, but from $83,000 to $12,000 was a shock to my ego.

Maybe I wasn't as smart or as good as I thought I was.

It was a rough patch. I thought maybe I should do something else. This is too hard and certainly other things are easier. I remember sitting down with a friend who owned a business and having a discussion when he basically told me what I'd tell anyone else, which is, "If you like it, suck it up, buttercup."

This is the way it is: You have to have grit. This was the first stumble you had, and it had all been roses before. Pull up your bootstraps and learn some business systems and get with it. He had a completely different type of business, but he had grit and I admired that. So, that's what we did—we clawed our way back, which took two or three years.

What we built because of almost going out of business has now parlayed into an 800-gym licensing franchise. The worst thing that ever happened to me turned out to be the vehicle that's allowed me to help all those people, that wakes me up in the morning, that gets me rolling. It's just grit. There's really no other way to do it. What would you do? You either quit or you don't quit.

There's a difference; don't get me wrong. There's a time when you need some advice and it may not be the best idea to continue to throw money or energy at something; that's being smart. But if it's an honest assessment of something you could change about your behavior, leadership style or business structure, you need to suck it up and get it done.

Everyone has to do it. Everything looks rosy from the outside, but if you peek under the covers of anyone's business, everyone has their warts and they all have their hiccups. They all have to work their asses off to be successful.

This just proves two things: It really helps to have a coach and to also have some kind of accountability partner or a mentor. When you first started out, your numbers are going up, you're doing great, but were you getting coached?

Up until 1995, when the business was growing, I didn't. Geez, why would the smartest guy in the world need to get help? When reality slaps you the face, you realize you're not nearly as talented, smart, savvy or tough as you thought you were. You start to look for help.

For me, it was friends. Some of them had been clients, savvy businessmen who think training is cool. You probably have friends like that who are running big businesses and think fitness is neat. They like to hang out and have lunch with you every now and then.

But we never had those deeper conversations until we were up against a wall. When I reached out for help, they were there. Those people are in your life right now. You have to open up and ask, "I need some help. Can I buy you lunch and ask a few questions?"

There's not a person on earth who if they care about you wouldn't offer you a bit of time.

An accountability partner is incredibly valuable. You can find somebody to call every week: "These are three things I'm going to do by next week, and I want you to write them down so I can answer to you. And I'll do the same for you."

It doesn't have to be a costly coaching program. Once you start making some money, great. But there are ways to have an accountability partner or have people in your life you can answer to without spending money.

I'm paying it forward now because I had those people in my life. That's my favorite thing to do. If I get a call from a young coach who says, "I'm working at this gym; I've only been in the profession two years, and I'm thinking about opening my own gym. I'm going to be in Atlanta; can I swing by if you're in town?"

I will do everything I can—move mountains and appointments—to meet with that person because to me, that's a smart individual who's probably going places and has the guts to ask for help. People are so afraid someone will say no or they'll be exposed for not being smart enough, they don't even ask. If somebody has the guts to ask, I'll give as much time as I can.

You have a family and a crazy travel schedule. What are some sacrifices you've made to be successful?

The first thought is my health. I laugh when I think back to how I used to coach my clients who were traveling business people. They would say, "This travel schedule's tough." I'd say, "You need to suck it up." They'd ask about workouts and I'd say, "Just work out in your hotel room."

"What about client dinners?"

I said, "Don't drink. Just eat dry chicken and broccoli. It's easy."

And then when I started traveling, I thought, there is no possible way. The first time I ever worked out in my hotel room, I didn't bring workout clothes, so all I had on was my underwear. I was rolling around, doing burpees and bodyweight stuff. I finished working out and there's something scratchy, high on my glute. It felt like a tag in my underwear. I had a toenail I picked up off the hotel room floor lodged in my underwear—disgusting! It's all fun and games until you pick up a toenail.

Young coaches buried in 12-hour-a-day training schedules will say, "I'd love to be doing what you're doing." I don't want to take the wind out of anyone's sails, but do you really? I really miss being in my gym. Most of my days are spent in a boardroom or talking to an attorney, accountant or business advisor. There are days when I feel like I'm selling widgets. I'm so detached from the great things the end product provides. I miss being able to put my hands on the people my product affects.

While sacrifice would be an odd word to use, I'm sacrificing what I personally want to do, which is hang out and be a gym guy. That's my favorite thing, for the greater good of helping more people.

I had to adopt new skill sets and learn about boring things. A day in the life of this is not nearly as exciting as it used to be. Be careful what you wish for. But it's so worth it when you can scale your business and help more people.

After I sold my gym at age 50, I got in the best shape of my life. I dropped weight and went to a low bodyfat. I had to sell my gym to get in shape. It's crazy.

If I am sacrificing anything, I've got to let go of my trainer identity and shift gears. I miss being in my gym; I miss seeing our clients and seeing the results of what we do because it's such an energetic and fun environment.

Anything gets old, but for those who are still in that environment, don't take it for granted. You might look at someone say, "I'd really like to do that." Maybe, but what you're doing is pretty damn incredible.

In terms of striving forward, give us three non fitness–related books everybody should read.

There are a million and one books. Outside of fitness is where a lot of us should spend our reading time, especially human behavior and business-related topics.

I talk about this book in every talk I do. I reread it every year and we give it to our customers: *The E-Myth Revisited* written by Michael Gerber. For trainers and anyone in the fitness business who's doing it from a place of passion, business systems sound like torture. They sound boring; they sound confining, like they're going to put you in a box.

The *E-Myth* is a great book to get you in the right mindset to start systemizing your business. It's this base that allows you to work your magic and do more of what you love. But you can't do it without systems. This book is for anyone who's an entrepreneur—even if you're an individual coach working in a gym, you're running your own business, so read *The E-Myth* first.

I like *Start with Why* by Simon Sinek, because I think the "whys" behind what people do, whether it's in business or fitness, are the most important part. If you understand those, you can change the way you align what you do and how you talk to people. You'll understand the motivations in doing what they're doing, which aren't always what we think they are.

And ultimately, as you and your business grow, there's a great book called *Rocket Fuel* by Gino Wickman and Mark Winters, written for anyone who's getting into hiring people or running a business. *Rocket Fuel* explains the need and the magic in the relationships between the entrepreneur, the thought provoker, the creative one and the implementer. If a creative person doesn't have an implementer or someone who can actually put those clever ideas into action, the business is never going go anywhere.

How many of us do that? We've got all these harebrained ideas and they never manifest themselves. You need to find an assistant, partner or employee—someone who can complement your weaknesses and get shit done. You might come up with wild and wonderful ideas, but if there's nobody to put them into play, it's never going to happen. *Rocket Fuel* does a great job of explaining how that should work.

***The E-Myth Revisited* should be a requirement. You shouldn't be allowed to open a business unless you read that book. *Start with Why* applies to so many things. I've been focused on that—with this idea of goals…why do I want that goal? It's a reminder; it really keeps us on track.**

What about a few people we should follow to help us in our development, whether it's fitness or otherwise?

I don't have specific people; I really don't. I wish I could give you a list to follow, but it's really hard. You have to find those people on your own. I know that's a terrible answer.

I'm in a group called Vistage, which is a business coaching group—there are people from different industries taking part in it. It's been impactful to learn how other people do business and how many things we have in common with other businesses.

We think fitness is unique and we spend all our time studying that, but there's a lot to learn from the person who has a pest control company or is a commercial roofer. There are general factors that apply across all businesses.

The guy who runs my Vistage group also has a business coaching group. His name is Tim Fulton. His business is called Small Business Matters and he's been in the profession forever. He's one of these guys who's made millions in tech. He's a consultant for big companies, but he's a real down-to-earth guy. He understands the entrepreneur. He's my guy; he's the guy I still meet with regularly in my group.

In this profession, there are so many rock stars, like all those in this book; I'd listen to any of them. My advice to anyone reading this: If you're not following the folks from the weekly *Strength Coach Podcast*, you should be. After that, look outside the field to see if you can find someone to mentor you on the business side.

Many of us are victims of information overload. It's too much to take in. You've got to pick somebody and just stay with that so you can take action, which is the most important part. Pick your favorite and figure out what works for you with that person.

Just pick someone and do something.

I find more anxiety and stress in reading and following too many people. They all have a lot to contribute, but I can't watch another Gary Vaynerchuk video. I don't want to work 75 hours a day or however many hours he works. People say, "He's a hustler." That's awesome, but I don't want to do that now.

We can't do all everything. Eventually, you're just taking in noise and not doing anything with it. Follow a few people you trust—maybe even locals—and just do stuff; get some shit done.

It's inspiring what you've done in this profession and how you continue to lead and help others. What you're doing with charity is amazing. Thanks so much for sharing your journey toward success.

BE LIKE RICK

"When I reached out for help, they were there to give it to me. Those people are in your life right now. You have to open your eyes and ask, 'I need some help. Can I buy you lunch and ask a few questions?' There's not a person on earth who if they care about you wouldn't offer you a bit of time."

LUNCH WITH MENTORS OUTSIDE OF BUSINESS

There are different levels of accountability.

You can do it though social media, by making what you're doing public.

You can do it with peers, by getting on the phone once every week or two.

You can do it with mentors who are in your life or who are clients.

You can get into a paid mastermind or accountability coaching group (see Frank Nash's Be Like).

We all have successful people in our lives. Most of the time, they're right under our noses: our clients!

Like Rick said, "Those people are in your life right now. Open your eyes to it and ask, 'I need some help. Can I buy you lunch and ask you a few questions?'"

Make a list of people in your life who are successful and who you respect.

For this action step, think of people who are not in the fitness business; we want a different perspective.

Ask if you can take the person to lunch or for coffee. This is similar to the Patrick Ward and Derek Hansen Be Likes, but those were with people within our profession.

Questions for the conversation:

> How did you get started?
>
> What were some early struggles and how did you overcome them?
>
> What do you think are the keys to your success?
>
> What failures have you had?
>
> What are some of the habits you attribute to your success?
>
> What would you do over again?

Try to listen more than you speak. Take notes. Record it if you can.

Make this a once a month event and cycle through the different mentors on your list.

Send a handwritten thank you card right after your meeting.

Bill is the founder and chairman of Parisi Speed School, a 95+ location franchise network with over 300 full-time performance coaches. He's the author of Success Patterns—Strategies to Building a Multimillion Dollar Training Business and Don't 'Should' On Your Kids: Build Their Mental Toughness. Bill is recognized as one of the most successful personal training entrepreneurs in the world with a 25-year successful track record of consistent growth. He built his original fitness business in 1992 from a $500 van and with $50,000 in debt and developed that into a globally recognized organization with yearly sales in excess of 20 million dollars. To explore his programs, visit parisischool.com.

Bill, you've been successful in several different areas—as an entrepreneur, as an athlete and more. How do you define success?

Success is pretty simple—I take this from my dad. My dad never made a lot of money. He worked for a utility company in the maintenance department; he worked three jobs. But my dad is very happy because he has great friends and a great family and for that reason, he's the most successful guy I know.

Success is about relationships, about enjoying what you have, being grateful and being fulfilled. That doesn't mean you don't reach for higher things. I know it's cliché, but does money really make you happy? No, money doesn't make you happy; money makes life more comfortable. That's not to say you can't reach for higher things. That's what keeps lots of people going. But that's not true for everybody.

Be happy with what you have, and if you're not happy, reach for higher things. Give it what you've got. If you put your mind to something and figure out the right strategies, you're going to get an outcome. It might not be the outcome you want, but that's when you adjust and move forward.

Sometimes when we're younger, we don't see these things. It takes a while to understand. You had success as a young man. You went to Iona College; you were a Division I All-American in track and field, and you competed in the Olympic trials in the javelin. When did you start feeling you were becoming successful?

I know this might sound a little odd: I've never fully realized it; I never look at myself as successful. I don't sit back and think, "I'm successful." I just ask, "What else do we need to do to get better?" As soon as you sit back and enjoy a success, you take your foot off the gas and lose a step. But that doesn't mean I haven't enjoyed some of the fruits of my labor.

I look at everyone around me as a part of this success. This is not me; this is an organization—it's an affiliation. My name's on the building because back in 1992 when I was thinking about doing this, someone told me to use my name, that people like a story. Here's the story: I not only started this with $500, but it was actually a $500 van. I was $50,000 in debt, living in my parents' basement at 25 years old.

When you come from humble beginnings, you value what you have…and you keep pressing.

We can see your work ethic: the 90 facilities, the franchising. You have a lot going on; you're speaking all the time. Many people don't feel they're a success because they're always striving for more. What do you strive for; what's that "it" from a business perspective? What gets you out of bed in the morning?

What pushes me is getting people to see the light—what this field is all about. I want people to understand we're not in the fitness business. We're not in the performance training business. We're not in the speed training business. We're in the inspiration business.

We're in the business of getting people to understand what it means to empower kids. My focus is youth from ages seven to eighteen. That's where we spend the majority of our energy, focus and business development systems. We empower kids, giving them the most important product on the planet to build higher self-esteem. We do that through fitness and performance and by helping coaches understand that. Content is important; training protocols are important, but you can get access to that. It's not hard.

We have great education; we make things simple and user-friendly. But what's important is how we deliver that education—not only how cue, but also how to build a relationship with an athlete, the parents and the coach.

You get personal satisfaction out of that, but how does that help grow your business? How do you develop it, monetize it in a way that you're getting paid a fair market value, and you're also getting emotionally paid from that experience?

Fair market value, plus getting paid emotionally—that's beautiful. You've mentored so many great coaches. You inspire fitness professionals through your speaking. Has your mentoring of coaches been a surprise?

It's like having kids. You have people who come through the system over the years, like Martin Rooney or Joe DeFranco, who were for years and have gone off to do remarkable work. Others have gone on to be coaches in the NFL or Division I head strength coaches. It's been great to be able to provide a platform, and I take pride in that.

I always keep good relationships with people and stay in contact. This field is big in one way, but it's also small. We all know each other; it's important to maintain good relationships, because we're in this together.

We want to gain more respect as a profession. We have to learn to work with one another more strategically. To a degree, we're competitors, but there's enough opportunity for everyone. We have 300 million people in this country and only about 19 percent of them work out. We need to make a bigger dent in that. We need to leverage each other more.

In view of your responsibility to young people and young coaches, what are some of the habits you try to instill? What are some of the habits you attribute to your success and are trying to instill in others?

The most important habit is having a routine. Science has shown that having a set routine helps condition the mind and sets up the daily tasks to be effective and consistent.

One of the most important habits I can suggest is to learn to engage. You have to learn to meet people, not just through email—I mean at conferences, at seminars, networking. Your network is directly related to your net worth. Networking is one of the most significant of success strategies.

Try to help as many people as you can by making connections. I've done that throughout my career, meeting people and seeing where we can make connections and help one another. It's never failed me.

One of the things that came out of that is that I probably have too much opportunity. More people can say that now because there's so much opportunity with the internet. There are new businesses you can start or things you can do; things have exploded with the advent of the internet. You have to be careful because you can lose focus. You can spin your wheels and have many non-starts; you start something and stop it. You have to be careful of that.

I don't want to get into a millennial discussion, but have you found it to be a harder because of texting and trying to get people to understand the value of relationships?

There's no doubt there are more introverts than ever, affecting their ability to engage, inspire and motivate. There are some gems and you have to find them to get them on the floor and engaged in your business.

Social skills are lacking compared to what I've experienced in the past. A lot of it has to do with their history and upbringing. But I believe you can modify behavior, which comes with your training and with the culture of your facility.

If you have the right environment and culture, you're going to bring people out of their shells. They realize it's fun to be outgoing, and that all comes with self-confidence. If you want to be successful in this business, you have to be engaging. You might not grow up with that personality or behavioral trait, but you can learn it.

Can you completely change your personality and change who you are? No, but you can modify behavior with enough motivation. If you want to grow and be successful, the number one trait you have to have is to be able to engage. You have to learn to inspire and get people off the dime to believe in what you're saying.

Being authentic, being who you are and not fabricating motivation, but truly coming from who you are is the key. You need to get uncomfortable and ask people what's going on in their lives and discover what's important to them. Have those conversations, get to their goals and identify if this is the right place for them.

Successful business relationships are personal relationships that are monetized. You can't have long-term successful business relationships in this field without personal connection.

You talked about goals. Let's go down that road. Do you have a formal process for setting goals?

At the end of every year, I evaluate my personal goals. This would be the amount of time I want to spend and the things I want to do with them. That's a priority; make sure you experience those moments.

Life is all about the experiences you create. The goals are to create as many or be around as many of those experiences as possible within reason. I still have to ring the register and work. I travel a lot; I'm not going to be at all the family events. But when I'm home, I make sure I'm present.

Those are goals. How many events I do want to attend? What does the sports calendar look like next year? How do I plan my schedule accordingly? What months am I out of town? This is how I'm effective in the planning phase.

It's the same with the business. How many facilities do we have? How many coaches are online? But more importantly, how many real success stories have we created in our network of growing coaches, stories we can share to inspire other people? We track those. We look at those in terms of the number of coaches we're impacting and getting them to understand what it takes to be successful.

You'll have the typical financial goals you track every year, but you have to have a roadmap.

Bill, we tell our athletes they have to recharge; they have to recover. How do you recharge on a daily, weekly and yearly basis?

My recharge is when I'm decompressing with the family, like spending time with the kids and just hanging out, whether that's going to their games or just chilling …doing things outside the box.

I also recharge by watching continuing education. I watch videos of people in the field to see what other people are working on. I enjoy gaining more information because there are so many different specialties.

I don't have any real hobbies but one: the financial sector. I have an undergraduate degree in finance and I got my Series 7. As a hobby and a recharge, I read about financial investing. That's been a hobby I took to the next level by getting a license. I wanted to see what it was like, so I did that a couple of years ago.

You value family and relationships. What sacrifices do you feel you've made to become successful?

Without a doubt, the level of travel and the time it takes to do what I do has been a family sacrifice. I traveled a lot more when my kids were younger. Now that I'm more established and a little older, I can get with them more. But I'm still doing a lot of traveling and am out at night at meetings.

Still, I don't think it's the amount of time you spend with your family that's most important; it's the quality of the time. It's powerful when you're with them at the important things, even if it's for a couple of hours a week. When you're not around that much and you've given up time, you learn to make the most of it when you do have the time.

How do you push through those times when you're thinking, "I just want to sell all this stuff and maybe I'll get into the financial field"? How do you push through your worst times?

Everybody has tough times. I don't care who you are, what you do, how big you are. There's the environment in our capitalistic society and with the internet and the opportunity that everyone has to start a business. It's a competitive environment with lots of opportunities, but also many ways to slip up.

It's not hard to figure out: Deliver a great product with enthusiasm and the right strategy. That's always going to work out in the end. There's a way to negotiate an opportunity to make something work as long as you're humble, honest and in it for the right reasons. If you're those three things and have a product or service that will help people, it's going to work out in the end. It always will, but if it doesn't, it's not the end. It's not over.

I've been around this business for 25 years. I've seen people lose businesses who had to close down and go into another line of work. In the fitness field, it happens every day. If the business isn't working out, you need to move on and sell or close. Or somebody has to take over and you might lose money.

But here's the point I want to make: I've had calls from people over the years, either competitors or friends saying, "We're not doing well. Can you take over? Or would you want to merge?" I get calls like that all the time, but you have to be smart enough to see the signs on the wall before things get that far. Your financials are lagging indicators of your business; they're *lagging*. Your revenue this month is a lagging indicator of how you were performing six months ago.

Your daily performance and customer experience are *leading* indicators of what your numbers are going to be like six months from now. You need to be tracking and managing daily engagement with customers and customer satisfaction.

If you do that and you have good scores and if you're doing surveys…if you're connected to your clientele and connected to your staff, if you're charging up your staff and they're giving great service and people are getting great results, then the lagging indicator, which are the financials, will be stronger. Your leading indicator—your service—tells you that.

In terms of development, can you give us three non-fitness books you feel could help?

There are so many of them, but I'll give you my three no-brainers in terms of the most impact I've seen. First is *How to Win Friends and Influence People*—I read that in college. I was in the cold tub reading that book one day and one of the other athletes came by, saw the title of it, and said, "*How to Win Friends and Influence People,* Dale Carnegie."

He looked at me and called me a loser. I was laughing. I tell everybody that story because that was probably one of the most impactful books I've ever read. Dale Carnegie helped people get what they want. You eventually get what you want, and that planted the seed for my free clinic idea where you go out and give free clinics…help people, help coaches. It's a very impactful book.

The Five Dysfunctions of a Team by Patrick Lencioni is a *New York Times* bestseller. That was a groundbreaking book.

It's a tough call for the third book because there are so many choices in business or personal development. It might be a toss-up between classics such as *Think and Grow Rich, The Power of Habit* and *Built to Last* by Jim Collins.

How to Win Friends was the perfect answer based on our conversation. Bill, name three people we should follow.

People in my inner circle here whom I've been connected to recently have been profound in their leadership. One is a guy by the name of Steve Leo; he came on as an intern, a young performance coach. He has been with me 23 years. He went on to open a number of Parisi facilities and now works with our corporate team. He's done a tremendous job leading our education team, and he's someone I look up to in many ways.

Another guy I learned a lot from—again, from my inner circle—is a guy named Richard Sadiv**.** Rich is a world-class powerlifter who worked for UPS for about 30 years. He got his job at UPS two days after his 18th birthday and learned a ton, worked there his whole career. He came to Parisi as a performance coach eight years ago. He eventually developed into one of our top performance coaches, training our NFL guys. Two years ago, he purchased our flagship location.

Now he owns the Parisi Speed School in Fair Lawn that does over a million dollars a year in youth training. When you talk about a strength coach, a performance coach or a trainer, not too many people have the motor Rich does.

UPS is a hell of an organization. They have to follow systems. In our field, we lack structure in our businesses. People fly by the seat of their pants. I've learned some great things about systems from Rich over the years.

Martin Rooney and I have been great friends for a long time. I brought Martin into the field as a guy who was working in physical therapy. The way he laughingly describes it is he was helping the older population recovering from hip replacements…but that wasn't him. He joined the Speed School, had a phenomenal 13-year run with us, and then went on to do his thing.

Martin has been great and is another terrific person to follow.

You're one of the truly authentic voices in our field. Your talks have inspired those of us in fitness, and you've helped so many people. Going over your journey into becoming successful has been great.

BE LIKE BILL

"If you want to grow and be successful, the number one trait you have to have is to be able to engage. You have to learn to inspire and get people off the dime and to believe in what you're saying."

LEARN TO ENGAGE

Before he became president, Bill Clinton took notes about everyone he spoke with, and he spoke to everyone he could. He was engaging, looked people in the eye and showed a genuine interest.

He had a box of alphabetical note cards listing the contact information of friends, teachers, political figures and other people he thought could be of help in his future career as a politician.

Unless you are running for office, you probably don't need to go that far.

Make it your goal next week to engage more with the people around you.

Start by trying to just saying, "Hi" or "Good morning" to as many people as you can.

Try to block out some "no smart phone" time each day (see Nick Winkelman's Be Like) and use that time to talk to people.

Pick three people with whom you are working and ask some deeper questions. Get to know them better. Find out their spouse's and kids' names. Find out if they have pets. Ask where they went to school, their hobbies or about places where they've been.

Try to talk less and listen more. Look them in the eye. Be present.

Keep building your network by being authentic and engaging.

Think quality over quantity.

BRIJESH PATEL

Brijesh joined Quinnipiac University in August 2008 as the athletic department's head strength and conditioning coach. He previously held the title of Assistant Strength and Conditioning Coach at the College of the Holy Cross in Worcester, Massachusetts. Brijesh primarily works with the men's and women's basketball and ice hockey teams at Quinnipiac, but also oversees the strength and conditioning development for all 21 varsity sports at the university. Brijesh is mostly active on Twitter at twitter.com/bpatel515.

I've seen you in action coaching and it's inspiring. The impact you have on these young men and women is incredible. You're making them not only successful in their sport, but also as human beings. How do you define success?

Success is a product of achievement. You may have accolades, championships, promotions, honors or even learning a new task or reading a book. Those are all ways to be successful.

You have the accolades, championships, promotions and honors. You moved up through the ranks pretty quickly and people were starting to ask you to speak at their conferences. When did you start feeling like you were becoming successful?

I don't know if I ever considered myself a success because I'm always trying to get better and achieve more. It's nice to be thought of as somebody who's achieved some level of success. But if I have to narrow it down, it was when people asked me to speak at conferences.

I feel successful when I see my student athletes and am able to get to work with them on a daily basis and when people who have graduated repeat some of the teachings I passed on to them. I may get a text or someone will post on social media and repeat something I said. Those interactions are when I feel a certain level of success, that I've impacted people. That's why I do what I do.

My perspective may be a little different, where strength and conditioning just happens to be my avenue to reach people—to help people see they can get better; they can improve and they can always try to find ways to better themselves.

Is that what gets you out of bed in the morning, that feeling that you're helping impact people?

I love to improve myself, whether that be learning something, reading or listening. There are always ways to improve and get better, but some people don't know how to get better. They want to and don't know how. I'm fortunate that I can sometimes fill that gap for people, primarily the student athletes I train.

What are some of the habits you try to teach your student athletes to help them become not only successful athletes but also better human beings?

Some of the non-negotiables we talk about with our student athletes are based on three things: Number one is accountability. The second is respect, and the last is work ethic.

If you can hold yourself accountable in every situation, you're going to teach yourself personal responsibility, and not only to yourself but to others. You're going to be accountable.

I'm accountable to my wife and to my family, but I'm also accountable to everybody I come in contact with and work with at the university. That's a big habit I take pride in and try to help our student athletes understand how this works.

The second element is respect. Respect everybody you come in contact with. Respect people you get to work with. Respect your superiors and the people below you in the hierarchy. That trait is important to me, and I also try teach that to our student athletes.

You can learn something from every single person you come in contact with. You can look people in the eye; you can say hello, you can shake their hands. You can ask them how their day's going and give them a friendly goodbye. Respect is a big thing I try to impart to our athletes.

The last bit is work ethic. I'm a firm believer that good things happen to people who work hard. The ability to stay positive comes along with work ethic. That's attributed to mindset and attention to detail—the relentlessness and urgency in valuing important things.

These are not only going to help the athletes in their sports, but it will also help them in their lives as they leave college. This education will make them better human beings.

Good things come with hard work, but you can't always have an undefeated season. How difficult is it to translate the message to keep working hard when things aren't going well in the season?

One big message we always use is to embrace the process. People say that, but they don't always understand what it means. Kids coming up in our society are very outcome-driven. We want to win a championship; we want to hang banners; we want to earn a promotion. We want things at the end of the road, and sometimes lose sight of the actual journey.

We try to help our athletes understand how to become more process-driven rather than outcome-driven, and to learn that today matters. We want them to see how this single workout matters, how going to sleep on time matters, how eating and doing their soft tissue work matters.

We live in an instant-gratification world where you can change everything at the drop of a dime. You can watch a whole series on Netflix; you don't have to wait from week to week. You can get whatever you want on Amazon…and you can get it the next day. There's no waiting for anything. We have to teach students how to delay gratification and get them to fall in love with the process.

When you do that, you can stay on a path of improving, regardless of whether you lost five games in a row. If you continue to work hard, continue to believe that focusing on the details will help you improve, you can get better. That's our mission and our task, each and every day to get a little bit better than we were the day before.

You have different goals for each team. Is there a formal process with your goals?

I wanted to be a head strength and conditioning coach and I am that. I don't have a future goal in terms of a job. My only goal is to build our strength and conditioning program and make it better. I started as the only full-time person and was the first strength coach at Quinnipiac. We're up two more full-time staff. We've built our internship program. We've built another facility. Consequently, I don't have personal goals; I have goals for our program and our department. I want to make this place as good as we can make it. Ideally, I'd like to have more staff and create bigger facilities. That will help us create a larger impact on our student athletes and the university community.

On this road to success, what sacrifices do you feel you've had to make to get where you are?

I definitely sacrificed my social life in college. I knew I wanted to be a strength coach when I was a senior in high school. I volunteered in a varsity weight room at University of Connecticut my second week on campus. By my sophomore year, I realized I couldn't go out and take the chance of seeing student athletes. If I told them to do something in the weight room, I wanted them to listen to me. If they saw me in a social setting the night before, they might not take me as seriously. That was a choice I made because of the goals I wanted to accomplish.

There were times post-college when I didn't make a family function because I had to work or I was doing something with the team. It was part of my process and part of my 10,000 hours. In my evolution as a coach, I felt I needed to do that. Looking back, I made the choice to sacrifice some time with family that probably helped me along my journey.

If I could go back, would I change it? I probably would because you never know when you may lose a loved one. You need to cherish those times as much as you can.

Staying consistent with your message and your non-negotiables must help you teach your athletes preparation and confidence.

If you're not prepared, if you didn't do the work or you took shortcuts, that's all you have to fall back on in times of adversity. You're not going to fall back on your confidence and your habits and what you've done. You're going to know you didn't do as much as you could have to be as prepared.

Preparation is so important. For example, presentations are one of the most feared things in the world. But you're talking about something you know! They don't ask you to present on something you don't know. If you know everything in and out, that's the preparation. You've already been there; you'll be fine.

You have to know your topic; you have to be confident in it. It's not enough just to know it, though. You have to also understand the information. I constantly try to educate our kids about why we do what we do, not only about the training, but also from a mindset standpoint. I have to be sure I understand the process of training, of recovery and of building their confidence, so they can understand that and get better from it too.

Coach, give us a three non-fitness books you feel everyone should read for their professional development.

I'm going to give you one I don't know if a lot of people have read. It's fairly new: *Chop Wood, Carry Water* by Joshua Medcalf. It's phenomenal because it uses principles from different types of books about mindset and power of habit and grit and puts those into the story. It's captivating. I've recommended it to athletes who later told me they've used it for games. I've bought it for my staff and interns; it's that good and that impactful.

Start with Why explains that you have to know what your "why" is so you can guide your "what" and "how." *Start with Why* is a fabulous book.

Probably the next book I think of is *Power of Habit.* It describes how habits are formed in response to stimulus. You think there's a cue, there's a stimulus and there's a reward and you may inherently have these habits that just form over time. If you want to break a habit, you have to change the cue—the thing you do in response to a certain stimulus.

The book offers many examples, like shopping and other types of habits that are interesting to understand. I'm in the business of changing habits: getting people to train hard, getting people to buy into things. That was a really good book to understand why people do some of the things they do.

Coach, what about three people we should follow to learn from?

Mike Boyle is the first I think of because I was fortunate enough to intern with him in 2001 and that was an impactful summer in so many ways. He changed the way I thought, program and how I look at things. As time has gone along, I've stayed in touch with him. Every now and then I'll shoot him a text just to thank him for everything he's done for me, but also for what he does for our profession. It's cool to see the impact he's had on people. His mind has shaped so much of what we do. I definitely recommend Mike.

Another person is Jon Gordon; his Twitter posts are fantastic. His books are awesome; one of the best books he's written is *Energy Bus.* Another good one is *Hard Hat,* which is really applicable to athletes. *Training Camp, The No Complaining Rule:* He has so many, but he also has really good posts on Twitter, so follow him there.

I don't know if people know of my third suggestion: Inky Johnson. He's a motivational speaker who played football at Tennessee. His story is terrific. You should watch some of his YouTube videos. He grew up in inner-city Atlanta—he came from nothing. He lived in a two-bedroom house with 14 people and never had his own bed.

He ended up going into a really bad public high school; he had an opportunity to go to a private school, but he didn't want to because, as he said, "I'm going to go to college. I'm going to go from the lowest level school because I believe I can do that." He ended up getting a scholarship to Tennessee, where he played football.

During his junior year, he was projected to be a top 30 NFL draft pick, but in the second game of the year he got hit and became paralyzed in his left arm. He can't use his left arm, so he couldn't play football anymore, but now he speaks to businesses, teams and universities. His message is so good—a lot about what I spoke of earlier. That's why what he says resonates within me.

Inky is a great guy we can all be inspired by, a guy who wanted to get an NFL contract to be able to provide for his family, but that was taken away in an instant. This is a guy who's not sitting around and complaining. He went back to practice and was there with his teammates even though he couldn't do everything. He was there because that's what he does, and that's a true testament of his character.

Those are three people we can all learn from.

Coach, it's been great going over some of your path to success. We appreciate you sharing about your journey.

BE LIKE BRIJESH

"Every now and then I'll shoot Mike Boyle a text just to thank him for everything he's done for me, and also for what he does for our profession. You can learn something from every single person you come in contact with."

GRATITUDE FOR THE LESSONS YOU'VE LEARNED

Write a list of at least three people who have made an impact on you. Under each name, write what that impact was and what you learned from them.

Do something for that person that shows your appreciation. Pick one from below that best fits your situation:

Get together and buy breakfast or lunch so you can express this in person.

Call the people up and tell them how much they impacted you and how much you appreciate them.

Send a gift. It doesn't have to be expensive, but should be meaningful. One of my podcast listeners, Ahmed Alumran, gave me a copy of *Tuesdays with Morrie* and wrote a beautiful message on the inside, thanking me for the impact I made on his life. He lives in Bahrain and handed it to me at the Perform Better Functional Training Summit in Long Beach last year. It was very touching.

Send a handwritten thank you card.

Send an email or text.

Don is one of the world's most in-demand and respected of exercise authorities. For years, he has helped actors, athletes and titans of business function at their full potential out of Drive 495, his gym in New York City. Catch up with Don at his site,donsaladino.com.

You've had great success in the personal training field, and it's skyrocketed over the last few years. Thinking of that, how do you define success?

My grandfather, who was my mentor, used to say success was peace of mind. It was different when I was growing up; I didn't understand him at a young age. We're kids—we're somewhat selfish and consumed in our own world. When you're young and someone passes the words "peace of mind," you don't really understand.

After going through struggles and ups and downs in business, in life, in everything else—from almost losing the business to losing loved ones—peace of mind has become inherent in how I define success.

Am I there yet? Sometimes. There are things I battle with, to be honest with you. But, all in all, I'm living a great life; I'm living my dream; I'm doing what I want to be doing and loving every day. But it's a grind. You get good days and bad days. However, with family and with the people around me, I've definitely nailed it.

When did you start feeling like you were on the right track?

That came probably a little later than it should have. Opening Drive 495 13 years ago was a huge accomplishment. I was a trainer who had a project self-funded through Angel Investors and that should have been something I patted myself on the back for at the time. But I didn't because I knew I had a lot of work to do.

Over the past five years I really got into social media and started learning about marketing and how to brand myself. For me, it really comes down to one word and that's "consistency." I saw things taking off and doors were opening to partner with different brands. I started getting involved with people who shared my beliefs and how I approach things.

I'm at the point in my career when I'm trying to minimize the distractions and focus on the bread and butter. The days of throwing balls in the air are ending; I'm starting to back off. I'm trying to focus on the task at hand and make sure I'm not getting too diluted and pulled in too many directions.

It's hard to stay undistracted.

I have an hour train ride in and out of the city. I'm not sitting there listening to music. I'm not sitting there reading a book. I'm prepping my social media; I'm setting up my posts. I'm doing everything I can so the day is as efficient as possible.

A lot of people don't want to do that work. But for me, it doesn't sleep. When I'm on vacation with my family and they're telling me to disconnect—I can't because this is what it takes. One day, when success is flying from every angle and the money's coming in to the point where we can't count it, God willing, then I get it. I can start establishing more of a team to do the social work. But for now, for me to put out what I want, this is the way I need to work.

It's effective—I doubled my social media in a short period. I was already at a decent number, but that doesn't come from just putting up ab shots. It comes from engaging with clients, customers and followers.

I respond to every person who passes a comment—every person. I get 50 direct messages a day. At some point during the week, I respond to each person. Right now, it comes down to a lot of engagement with the followers. That takes time.

You're authentic and people see that. They see the good and the bad with you. You don't just post, "I'm having an amazing day." You post about your struggles as well. That's a huge part of your appeal.

It's ridiculous for people to try to give the perception that things are always good. It's fake. Young people don't understand—you're making them think things are always like that. I can't stand people putting up posts where they always look their best.

The other day I was tired and made a rookie move. I came to the gym and my team and I were talking junk. I was going to hit 500 pounds in the deadlift for a couple of singles, which for me isn't a crazy weight, but it's heavy enough. The next thing you know, I have 565 on the bar and I'm pulling a max effort lift and I go into the lift thinking, "What am I doing?!" I barely moved the weight off the ground.

Afterward, I laughed, "That was just a total screw-up on my part, but big deal. I went forward." We posted it and it was funny.

You have to show the good with the bad. And I think anytime you're trying to paint a perfect picture, day in and day out, it's sending the wrong message.

What's that "it" that drives you? What's the motivation to get out of bed?

Being able to reach so many people and having more of an impact is a big part. What I love and am most proud about my brand is the authenticity. Am I the smartest guy? Am I the best looking guy? Am I the strongest guy? No, none of those.

But I think I have a way about myself that I can relate to anyone. No matter who you put me in front of, I can be relatable and make people feel comfortable.

It used to be that over 40 sessions a week, I was training 10 or 15 people, but now I can reach tens of thousands of people. It feels great to have people responding, saying I've changed their lives or sending before-and-after pictures or suggesting I'm the reason for the change. It's not an ego thing; it has nothing to do with that. I'm helping improve someone's quality of life. That's motivating.

Whether it's a good or bad day, I go home at night and assess what went well, what went wrong. It sounds corny, but I'm thankful. But often, I'm going home thinking, "That was something I can learn from to help me do better next time." The fact I can always improve is motivating and fun.

You spend a lot of time at work. What are some of the sacrifices you had to make to be successful?

Getting up early, I miss out on some of the things I enjoy. I love having dinner with people or having a drink with friends. For me to be optimal at work and with my family, if I go out to dinner on a weekday with friends and get in late, I have to fight through the next day. My training suffers and if my fitness and health suffers, it's not leading by example.

If I go to work and don't have resiliency and a certain level of energy, that's not something people want to be around. That's not going to enable me to be successful and to accomplish as much. For me to achieve what I want, it's a matter of living a clean life and picking my battles.

I'm not saying I don't ever go out and have drinks. Of course I do. Next week I'm going away for my parent's 50th and you know what? It's going to be my first week off of training in at least a year and I'm long overdue. I'm going to be on the water and will relax and have a couple drinks every night. I'm going to have fun and trust me, I'm not going to be eating clean. I'm going to give my body and mind a little rest and then it's back to it. I have to live a different lifestyle than most people.

There are sacrifices, but I'm really happy with them.

You've been doing this for nearly 20 years. Were there times when you were tired and wanted to give it up?

You've got your days when things just go wrong. You're sitting there and the sump pump blows in one club and then the air conditioning blows in the other and you're thinking, "I just lost $30 grand." Someone quits or does something stupid at work—you have those days. But my love for it has never changed.

You recharge your batteries and you're back at it. This is what I've been put on earth to do. The one thing I could pat myself on the back for is that I've meshed well with some great people in the profession. I've done really well with Drive's brand and my brand.

People sometimes try to devalue what you do. Those who are devaluing what you do aren't the ones who are doing what you're doing.

Most everyone has a high level of respect for each other. Those are the people I really enjoy hanging around with and learning from. I get around Boyle and I feel like I'm in school.

After I spoke at Perform Better, I asked him, "Mike, how was my talk?"

He said, "It was great."

I said, "Mike, really, how was my talk?"

"All right, this is what you need. You need more nuts and bolts."

And I said, "You're right; I was thinking that myself. I should go more in that direction."

It's great to be able to sit down with people who have turned into mentors to get their feedback. I remember meeting Mike and then later having him come into my talk; it was a star struck moment. I don't get star struck much, but seeing him sitting there was a special time. Becoming friends with him and being able to get feedback was icing on the cake.

But that guy—there's a reason he's so successful. You understand that when you meet him. He's a total winner and a great person.

Give us three other people we can follow to learn from. This is in general, for success and doesn't have to be people involved in fitness.

People don't give Tony Robbins enough credit. My brother and I went through with his Unleash the Power Within seminar and then my brother went through his business mastery class. There's an energy to him and an outlook on life everyone needs to look into—I don't care what line of work they're in.

I'm a big Charlie Weingroff fan; he's brought a lot to the profession. When I met him, I thought he was complex in his teaching and now I'm looking at it as a simplistic way of coaching other coaches and getting from point A to point B. He's someone I've always loved and it's fantastic to listen to him.

Mike Boyle, as I said, is another fitness person to follow. His work speaks for itself. He keeps things simple—we don't need to confuse training or make it more complex than it really is.

Everyone's trying to be the best trainer and I get that, but what bothers me is they're not focusing on other areas that it takes to be more successful. They're thinking, "Why am I not more successful?" You have to put the time in to be well rounded.

During my talk when I was in Rhode Island, I looked at a bunch of coaches and asked how many certifications they had.

And they yelled, "20!" "15!"

How many courses have you taken?

"100!"

How many courses have you taken on finance? How many courses have you taken on investing or how many books have you read on that?

"None."

"One."

I said, "That's why you suck at it. What do you expect? It's what you put into it."

This is one thing I tell coaches on how to be a great coach. Training is in your blood; that's not what I'm worried about. There are other things you need to start focusing on now.

Do you have three favorite non fitness–related books everyone should get to help in their development?

I like Tony Robbins' *Awaken the Giant Within*.

Tim Ferriss's *Tools of Titans*—I love that one.

And then a non fitness–related book and probably one of my favorite books because we can learn from biographies: Anthony Kiedis' *Scar Tissue*. I just love that story.

Don, it's so much fun to follow all you do and watch your brand explode. You help so many people throughout the world with your platform; it's an inspiration to us all. Thanks for sharing your journey.

BE LIKE DON

When I was speaking at Perform Better, I asked Mike Boyle, "How was my talk?"

He said, "It was great…"

I said, "Mike, really, how was my talk?"

He said, "All right, this is what you need: You need more nuts and bolts…"

PEER FEEDBACK

It's important to get honest feedback from people you know and trust. It can be hard to hear, but with certain people in our lives, we know they have our best interest at heart.

Pick at least five people to ask for some feedback.

You can use something as elaborate as Survey Monkey or something as easy as email.

Ask these questions:

> What three words would you use to describe me?

> What do you think are my biggest strengths?

> What do you think I can improve upon?

Look for commonalities among the answers and use those to start to improve upon some of your weaknesses.

PATRICK WARD

Patrick is the Director of Research and Development for the Seattle Seahawks, where his role centers around data analysis on a variety of different topics in the sport of American football. Before joining the Seahawks, Patrick worked as a sport scientist at the Nike Sports Research Lab. Patrick has PhD in Sports Science and is a Certified Strength and Conditioning Specialist through the National Strength and Conditioning Association (NSCA-CSCS). Patrick has published research across a variety of sports; his main research interests include training and competition analysis as they apply to athlete health, injury and performance. Patrick's website is optimumsportsperformance.com, although he's more active on Twitter at twitter.com/osppatrick.

You've had success in a few different domains, as a facility owner, trainer, massage therapist, and now with the Seattle Seahawks. How do you define success?

A lot of people attach monetary value to success. That's okay for some people, but to me, doing the things I want to do and having fun doing them is what it's all about.

When I was deciding what to do with my life coming out of high school, my mom said, "Don't study music. You can't make a living doing that; you should probably study sports medicine." That was kind of the motivation I needed to go study music.

My dad, who had a small trucking company his dad started, told me, "I never wanted to do this, but I had to work because I had a family. Don't listen to your mom. Whatever you decide, go and do it. Make sure two things: that you love doing it and that you're going to be the best in the world at it.

"Don't waste your time; every day I wake up and don't like my job. I wish I could have stayed in college and gone to law school and maybe gotten into politics—those are the things that interest me. Instead, I punch the time clock. Don't punch a time clock."

Maybe that's more indicative of the times in the 1970s. It's what people did; they just went to work. But what he said stuck with me. Find out what you want to do. Don't listen to anybody tell you what you should do just because it will make more money. Figure out what you want to do and then do it all the time and just be really darn good at it. If I can wake up every day and do whatever I want to do—work on cool projects, learn something new and have fun doing it, that's success.

So you went and studied music?

I was always interested in sports medicine and in high school, I was interested in nutrition, and training and exercise. I worked out a lot. I played sports, but I was also interested in music—I played jazz guitar. I didn't know what I wanted to do, and after talking to my parents, I decided to go Berkley College.

The time at Berkley taught me how to work because you have to practice so much at a full-on music school; it's nonstop grind. That taught me a lot about how to work. I'd practice seven, eight hours a day; aside from going to class, I'd be up all hours of the night practicing, writing and learning. It was a great experience, but of course, Mom was right. It's really tough to make a living in music. I moved to New York City; I played and did some gigs, but you can only play so many $20 gigs before you realize you can't play enough to pay the rent. That led me toward doing what I probably should have done from the start, but I have no regrets.

When did you start feeling like you were becoming successful?

My wife and I wanted to move out of New York City—I was working at an Equinox, training people. We picked Phoenix, not so much out of a hat, but sort of: "It's warm; it's cheap—let's go to Phoenix."

We went under the caveat that I no longer work in a big box gym or work for someone else. I wanted to start my own thing. At first it was a struggle. Of course it is, when you move to a city where you know no one. You have no one who can plug you into the scene.

We had no relationships with sports teams, coaches or people. We were forced to create, and it was hard. The last year of being there, after I got my facility going, was what I'd call successful. That was when I started to think, "This can work. I think I can do it."

Then Nike called, which was kind of weird. I worked hard to build a business in Phoenix and I'd have to shut it down. That was a hard decision, but it was the right one because it was a new path and a new challenge. I had been training people for a dozen years. That last year-and-a-half in Phoenix was sort of a domino effect from there. But during that time, I got to a point where I was comfortable saying I have a business and can do my thing.

You were a trainer, then went with Nike and are now with the Seahawks. All are different jobs within the profession. What motivates you to get out of bed in the morning? What is that "it" for you?

I have a hunger for knowledge. I like learning new things. I like reading. The main thing for me—my mantra—is always, what can I learn today and how can we apply it?

Sometimes I don't want to go to bed because my head is spinning with all these ideas. I can't wait to wake up and get into work to start pulling and looking at data…or maybe I need to do something else with some of the other work I've done or projects I'm working on. What wakes me up every day is the opportunity to learn something new.

What are some other habits you attribute to your success?

Reading, but also, getting out and meeting people to talk shop is really important.

I had a weird path. Most people get into this field, particularly in sports, by the conventional route of finishing an undergraduate, then going somewhere to get a graduate assistant job. They work under a coach at a university for two years and through that process, learn a system. They learn how to coach and if they work really hard and do a good job, the coach has a professional network to plug the assistants into. The coach calls up a friend at another university and says, "I've got a GA just finishing up—a really hard worker you're going to love. Do you have room on your staff?" That's the conventional route.

I didn't take that route. I went to music school then bummed around in New York City and figured things out. One of the other avenues for success, aside from reading and studying and learning, was that I used all of my money so I could attend every conference I could possibly go to. I'd buy people beers or dinner and sit and listen to what they had to say—not when they were on stage, but off camera. I'd go up and say, "Can I buy you a beer? I'd like to hear what you have to say. I'd like to learn something from you." And I'd sit there and just to absorb all I could.

And that's one thing I still do to this day: I go to conferences, meet with people and hear what they have to say. The internet has created a great opportunity for that because you can connect with people you otherwise would have had to fly out to a conference to visit. But there's something to be said for going out to a conference and meeting people on a personal level.

When I lived in Phoenix where there are four major sports teams, I'd contact the staff of the visiting teams. When a team came to town, I looked up the strength coach or the head athletic trainer and tried to get in touch through social media. Then, I'd try to meet them. That was one thing that helped plug me into the network while I got to listen and learn.

Were there people who, back in the early days, you reached out and were surprised when they said yes?

Before *strengthcoach.com* started in 2007—it was just a forum at *michaelboyle.biz*—I started connecting with people. That's where a lot of us "met" each other. Charlie Weingroff was one of the first I met, and now he's a good friend.

Dave Tenney was also on the forum at the time, and I ended up meeting with him. We had similar interests in training. We just emailed some exchanges back and forth, and then started talking. The next year, the Seattle Sounders were doing their preseason training camp in the Phoenix area, so he invited me to bum around with them for the two weeks they were there. We've had a good relationship going forward.

Sean Skahan was with the Anaheim Ducks then, and I knew his name through the forum. They came to town to play the Coyotes. I went to the stadium, met with him and had lunch. He had a lot of good ideas and wisdom after being around the business and having been in the NHL for a long time.

I met them all on that old forum. It was a cool place to meet people and plug into a network. Of course, it was Mike Boyle's forum and website, so he was another person I was able to connect with.

What's your process for goal setting?

In terms of the big goals—the broad stuff—I just go wherever the wind takes me. That's why my career had so many twists and turns from being a trainer to being a strength coach, a small business owner, then with Nike and starting SPARQ…and into the research lab.

The research lab led me down the avenue of pursuing a PhD, then going to a professional sports team as a stats guy, as a data analyst. Data collection has become a big part of sports and training, but we have to figure out how to analyze it.

I would never have been able to write that out in a notebook. I just like knowledge and learning new things, so when things come up to help me improve, I pursue them. When I was training people, all the trainers were talking about soft tissue work, so I pursued and got a massage license.

I'm a bad example of setting and going after goals; I don't have long-term goals. I guess if you pressed me for a long-term goal, I want to be the general manager of a sports franchise. That would be my some-day goal.

Cool. We heard it here first.

I don't know if I'll get there, but similar to the odd strength coach route I took, maybe I can take an unconventional path to blaze to that kind of role.

Theo Epstein started out in the PR department in San Diego, then started reviewing contracts; he started going to law school, and then suddenly, he's a GM. That's an unconventional path, and this would be as well—from strength coach to scientist to data analyst to GM would be a bizarre path.

It's not like I worked my way up through the scouting ranks and was going to universities and watching kids play. I'm a process-oriented person and I think that's what you need. If it happens, it'd be great; if it doesn't, again, as the wind blows, I'll do something else.

Let's talk about recharging and recovery. Being so busy all year, especially during football season, how do you recharge?

If you asked my wife, she'd probably tell you I don't recharge: I just keep working. It's tough during the season. The schedule is odd because during the season is the most busy time and we're kind of stuck in the day to day. When the season ends, instead of taking a break as some people can, we're prepping for the Combine and the Draft. I go from season end right into a different mode. After that, until the off-season training, things are a little more relaxed, and my days are more 9–5.

Once we hit mid-June when our off-season mini-camp ends, we have about five weeks off. I'll usually work for half of that. Then I'll do absolutely nothing and we'll go on vacation.

There are a high percentage of people who don't even take a vacation. It's crazy.

Honestly, if it weren't for my wife, Ivonne, I probably wouldn't. To me, a vacation would probably be sitting on the couch.

On a weekly basis, something like going to the movies is ideal. You spend all day with people talking at you and the last thing you want to do after that is go to a bar and hang out and have more people talk at you. I just want to go to the movies and turn my brain off.

Are there any sacrifices you've made along this journey?

Whenever you work in an environment like this, there are long days and sacrifices in terms of having a normal life. My wife is really into theater, so she'll go on the weekends when I have to work. Often, I'm not going to make dinner parties or social events with friends. There are sacrifices like that.

I grew up in Cleveland and I don't get home to see my family as much as I'd like because I go from the season to doing all the off-season work, and before you know it, the new season's starts. Those are the real sacrifices.

To be fair, football isn't as bad as other sports; our season is shorter. We play 16 games in 17 weeks with a five-and-a-half-week pre-season training camp ahead of that. It's not like baseball with 162 games and all the related travel, not including six weeks of training camp when they're not living at home unless they actually lived near the training camp. The divorce rate in baseball is high.

Football is better, but it is still hard and the family sacrifices. I'm amazed how my colleagues who have kids do it because they miss a lot. A good friend of mine, Keith D'Amilio, talks about working in the NBA: There are always games on Christmas Day. Sometimes he'd have to be at the stadium or 3,000 miles away on the road while his kids were opening gifts. They're not going to be three years old forever. You miss birthdays and soccer games and holidays. You miss some of those key times.

Was there a time you said to yourself, "What am I doing?" Did you ever feel like you wanted to give up?

Maybe work in a Starbucks? Yes, I did. We first moved to Phoenix in 2006 and were there until 2012. It wasn't until the final two years that I really got going. The first four years were a struggle. I didn't have enough money for a facility, so I rented space at a physical therapy clinic and a personal training studio and gave them a cut off the top.

I was trying to write blogs as free marketing to attract business. It was tough; we were living off my wife's paycheck and health benefits. I remember thinking, "This sucks. Maybe I'm not cut out to be a businessperson, and just need to go work for someone else. Maybe I should try to work for Athletes Performance; they're in town. Maybe this is the sign."

My dad would say, "Just keep going—just keep doing it." I'd make a little money and spend it on conferences and continuing education. People would say, "It sucks now, but keep pushing. It's going to happen. You're on the verge; don't stop now."

I hung in there, then one thing led to another, and things finally came together. But there were definitely times when it sucked and I wondered, "Am I going to be grinding like this forever and living week to week?" Those last two years in Phoenix, I just had to keep going. And that was it.

The hardest part about keeping going as a small business owner was that I didn't like being a business person. I like doing the work, but I don't like asking for money and doing the marketing and billing and business books. I don't like that side of being in business.

People get into doing something and they think they're going to be able to succeed because they love it. You can be passionate about being the operator, but that doesn't mean you're going to be a great business person.

It's different than being passionate about training people or making the cupcakes or whatever it is you enjoy. You're not necessarily passionate about doing the stuff that's going to make the money doing the things you're good at. That was the tough part with the small business. I had a lot of negativity and thoughts that I wasn't cut out for it. I just want to turn the lights on, do my work and turn the lights off and go home and do the things I love to do.

So here we've come full circle: That's success to me.

Give us three non fitness–related books that were important for your development.

I don't read too much outside of the sciences, but I love books like *Moneyball, Freakonomics, Super Crunchers* and *Outliers*. They always make fun of me at work because I call them "coffee table reads." It's not real science; they're just enjoyable.

They say success leaves clues. Who are three people to follow we can all learn from?

There are lots of people who have impacted me and I've learned from along the way. I mentioned two of them: Charlie Weingroff and Dave Tenney.

In science, a few of my PhD research professors have been really good. Aaron Coutts and Barry Drust are outstanding. They sit atop the Mount Rushmore of sports science in terms of things how they do things.

Matt Weston is a really good statistician and I've learned a ton from him. Luke Bornn at the Sacramento Kings is a really good mathematics guy. They're really useful people to tap into and learn from and watch what they're doing.

Patrick, you are someone whom so many in strength and conditioning look to for information. Your constant pursuit of excellence has been such a great example for everyone to follow. Thanks for sharing your journey.

BE LIKE PATRICK

"I used all my money so I could attend every conference I could possibly go to. I'd buy people beers or dinner and sit and listen to what they had to say—not when they were on stage giving their message, but off camera. I'd go up to them and say, 'Can I buy you a beer? I'd like to hear what you have to say. I'd like to learn something from you.'"

CONNECTING WITH COACHES AT A CONFERENCE OR WORKSHOP

If you bought this book, there's a good chance you already go to workshops and seminars.

An ideal seminar is the Perform Better Functional Training Summit because they have multiple presenters over three days and that will give you the best odds of connecting with someone.

Pick three presenters you would love to connect with. You need to do this ahead of time, at least one month.

Connect with them through social media or email if you can—send a message.

"Hi, Coach, my name is Anthony Renna and I am a trainer at a gym in White Plains, NY. I love the information you put out and I would like to buy you breakfast, lunch or a coffee at the Perform Better Summit in Providence to learn more about your career. If this is possible, let me know what works best for you and I'll arrange it. Thanks for your time and I'm looking forward to your lecture and meeting you."

Don't just talk about training; make sure you find out about who they are—try to connect with on a personal level. You want to leave the meeting making them say, "What a great person I'd like to hang out with anytime."

A lot of these coaches are busy. That's why you need to pick three, in case the first two fall through.

In the very least, make sure you go up to them during the social hour on Friday night to introduce yourself.

David believes fitness is a common thread for humanity to connect through, is pretty certain of the power of play and recognizes the unique nature of individuals and the sense that there's a "fitness ID" that works for them. David has a partnership with Arizona Grand Resort in Phoenix and has helped create a fitness community known as ACTIVEIGHT, where the mission is to magnify the good in fitness and the people it serves. He welcomes new enthusiasts; find him at facebook.com/davidjackfitness.

Years back, you spoke at Perform Better about building success in this profession. You're somebody who has had success in a lot of areas. You're leading people now— your mission is always about others. I want to take a step back and talk about this idea of success and see how you define it.

There are common threads, common truths that unite us in our definitions of success. Success has the freedom to be different for every person, which makes it interesting and exciting. My definition of success has evolved over the years, much like how I approach and coach fitness and the way I use it in my life. Success is how I can help others become successful; how I can help others grow; how I can help others be inspired about the things that matter to them.

Leadership is tied to success in a way, but when you think about leadership, often you get caught thinking you're the person on the stage—you're the person in the front of the room. You're the one coaching; you're the one getting in the magazines. What I've come to believe is it's a form of servant leadership. Am I leading well so others can follow? Am I listening to others and genuinely wanting to step into their lives in ways that matter and help serve them and help them serve others. Am I willing to become less so others can become more?

In the past, it might have been the idea that I have to deny myself from being successful or I have to be less than so other people can be more. But it's not like that. It's a genuine joy from helping activate the best in others.

Success is kind of like sport—what's your metric? Because our metric of success will ultimately dictate how we view what we do, what others do, who we are, our identities and how we view what matters in our lives. We gauge the things we think, the things we do with our time, our talents, inspiration and goals.

If success in sport is about winning and losing—the score on the board—we've already lost. If that's the only metric that matters, we miss the learning process and all the nuances of athletics.

Success in sport means doing what we need to do now, together, for a common goal that's greater than ourselves, continuing to stay in that process, enjoying it, being committed and working together. The scoreboard will take care of itself.

It's the process that matters; the journey matters to me. Is it nice to win? Sure. Is it nice to put more numbers on the board? Of course. But if they become my end-all, be-all, then it's all about winning or losing—it can't be winning or learning.

When it all comes down to it, faith is my foundation. My success will be this: When I stand before my God, before my higher power, and He looks me and says, "Well done.

You did what I put you there to do. And you know it wasn't about what you could do for yourself or what you could acquire. It was what you did for me when I asked, for those I asked you to do it for."

If that day comes, I will have had success. If I've honored the things I've put my hands toward to get to that bigger measure of success, I've had success. If I screwed up fitness, but I treated people right, I've got a success on one side, but I didn't honor the thing I was acting on, on the other side.

That's my diatribe on how I look at success and how I'm trying to make it fit for myself and where I orient myself tomorrow or even the next hour.

The "what matters" piece is important. That's part of the reason the idea of success has evolved. You have to go through a journey to learn what matters to you.

And you start where you start. I'll use a fitness analogy. If people have never worked on movement patterns, don't have any pattern recognition, can't understand the body in space or don't have any movement economy, it would be ridiculous to have them do a complex or a hybrid with Olympic lifts. Their first success might be setting their feet right, tying their shoelaces tight enough, and doing a bodyweight squat with good form… feeling it where they should feel it and not feeling it where they shouldn't.

That level of success is enough, especially when they know there's more coming. But when you start coaching, you can't see all of this. You start by having a heart to serve people, to meet them where they are, giving them what they want so you can earn the right to provide them what they need, that thing you're passionate about delivering.

Do your best to honor the thing you're feeding them. Feed them good food; that might be just enough when you're first starting out. Get that right. Honor your craft. And do your best, with an open heart, to deliver it in a way that makes people healthier and fitter, serves and doesn't steal from them.

I love what you just said: "Earn the right to provide them what they need." Too often, we think we have the answers—we're trying to provide something that's more about us. We do things because we think our peers or mentors are watching.

I trained a guy who never brought the intensity or focus I thought was needed for training. But in his mind, it was good enough. According to him, I was saving his life. When he walked in, he'd tell me about his issues, but he always added, "You know what, Ant? At least I'm here."

He thanked me every time because he felt better walking out than he did walking in. He loved it and it was enough for him, but in the beginning, it wasn't enough for me. Eventually, I understood it was good enough because that time was about him.

We're thinking, what can I show this person? What can I teach? But you're receiving as much as you're giving. Our clients are the sharpening block for our knife. They're the only way we grow our craft.

Try to do the right thing—and maybe in the beginning, you've got to follow a plan, to have some structure until you don't need it anymore.

Then, we understand why when someone is sweating and smiling, when they feel things where they should feel things, when they don't feel pain that day, they say things like, "I can't believe an hour has already gone by."

That has been the foundation of one of my marks of successes, when a person loves coming to see me and loses sight of the world during that hour. This can't happen all the time, but I try show that fitness is the outcome, not always the goal. That helps change the way fitness appears, serves and appeals to people—when it's the outcome, not always the goal.

Too often, especially when starting out, we don't realize the impact we're having. When you don't understand the value you're bringing, you won't see yourself as a success. When did you feel like you were getting this right and were having an impact?

The true story is, I still don't know that I am. There are days when I wonder if I'm doing anything. Am I making a difference? I'm still working on it. I don't know if I'll ever arrive at that place.

On the other hand, I've received messages, letters and phone calls from people I've never met, who said wonderful things about something I was able to provide, that something I did made a difference in their lives. That's so encouraging—it keeps me going.

It's a tough profession. It's a profession where you don't get to punch a clock and leave everything at work and go home. It brings in the mental, emotional and spiritual sides of life. You're serving people. There's so much dynamism in that. There are so many moving parts. It takes its toll.

Two metrics of success that meant something to me are being able to provide for my family; that's a sign of success and there's nothing wrong with that. And second, having people tell me how I've helped them is another marker.

The money piece is not important enough and is still a challenge, charging people for what I do—feeling comfortable making money by serving people. A lot of us deal with that; I still need to work through that.

But there are two big metrics of success if I have to spin them out. One is when I enjoy what I'm doing…and not that it's easy. I have my moments where I wonder why I'm doing this. I've had hundreds of those moments over my career. But when I'm grateful, joyful and at peace with what I'm doing and I feel good about it and invested in people, I'm moving toward a metric of success.

To the second piece, it's a story in my mind. It's an insane story, how I got to work with *Men's Health*. I was a fan of the magazine when I was younger; I read it and knew the brand. I got a phone call about 10 years ago that started my working relationship with them. It's insane how I got connected with them; it's a total God story. The person on the phone said, "We got your name from so-and-so. This is the project we're working on. We have 25 or 30 people we're considering to be on the National Leadership Committee for this project, and heard your name; we want to pick your brain."

I gave them everything I could think about as it related to youth, youth wellness, coaching and leading youth. I hung up the phone thinking how awesome it would be if I got to work on the project.

It's great to want to be a part of something because you're passionate about it. But in that moment, my faith took over and I thought, "But if it's not for me, God, it's not for me," and I let it go. I literally took my hand off that phone and severed my heart from it. That has become a sign of success for me.

And, thank God, that's been one of my greatest marks of success. I've been able to take opportunities and sever my heart from having them matter, although it's still not easy.

I want to talk about what gets you out of bed in the morning. What excites you about your mission?

I'm in a season of transition now, so I'm not 100 percent sure about the mission. In the past, there were things I thought were "it" until I got there and realized…that's not it. It was a cool piece, but it's not it.

And that's part of maturity and growth. It's like someone who says, "I've got to bench 225; that's my goal." This person does all the work, gets to 225, stays there for a bit and then, "This isn't really it; it didn't make me happier. What's next?"

I've come to a place where I've surrendered my life to whatever I'm supposed to do. Many times in my career, there have been stretches of time when I woke up and didn't love what I was doing. That's a clue there are things I have to let go of and be open to receiving other things. Sometimes you're in a valley; sometimes you're walking in the wilderness and just have to show up. You do your best when you don't know where you're going and don't know how things are going to turn out.

And that's not easy. Walking by faith—not by sight—is not easy. And I'm in that season right now. I've been through it before, so I have a foundation to manage the discomfort.

When I find people who have a common interest, I'm in a zone. With ACTIVEIGHT, we've come to a place with a group of fitness professionals around the world with different talents and experiences. We have a fitness profession that needs people working together to make things better. It started with a phone call to people I knew and has evolved into a mission among peers who want to magnify the good in fitness.

That became our true north mission. It's a two-part mission: How do we identify and find the things that are really good in fitness…foods and products and programming and coaches and anything related to these, finding the pillars of fitness. And when we find them, how do we vet that? How do we magnify and share those with the world?

It's a "Together We Rise" model. How do we help you step into the things you're passionate about? How do we help you get better at your craft, at why you do what you do, overcoming the challenges of what you do? When you get better, we all get better. And when we all get better, rising tides raise all ships. When we go back to our communities, everybody we serve gets the best of us.

That's a way we can all continue to help one another raise the standard of care and leave something behind we can all be proud of.

At the same time, it's not all champagne and roses. There have been times when I wanted to get out of this field. When you're having a tough time, how do you get through it?

The foundation for me is prayer. That's always first. It always has been for everything I do.

I remember the reason I started the work and I remember the mission. Sometimes it's going to be hard, but that's when we've got to dedicate our best—even when it doesn't make sense, when it's mundane and when no one's looking.

That's the greatest form of inspired action. That's the greatest form of legacy: what happens when no one's watching, when there are no articles, no fanfare, when your arm's not going to be raised across the finish line.

This is where I build character. This is where I step through and remind myself why I'm doing this work. And I've got to buckle down. The other side is, sometimes I need to uncover what I need to let go of. If I have to grind it out, something's missing. There are clues telling me something needs to be changed. Where do I need to reorient; what might I need to let go of? What conversation do I need to have with somebody or myself?

I have an amazing group of peers who are good friends—some of them are partners in my faith and hold me accountable, but also speak life to me. We're always going to be challenged; that's the story of life. Who's with you and who's behind you? Who's in front of you, leading you somewhere better and genuinely invested in you doing that? Who are the people with you when you bump into the obstacle, when things are hard, when your kids are sick and you're exhausted and your clients are going bonkers and the money's not coming in? Who can you reach out to?

You need people who are there for you. That's hugely valuable.

Whom am I mentoring? Whom am I trying to raise up? Whom am I trying to leave something better for? If I don't have someone in front or if I'm not reaching out to the people with me, or if I'm not pouring into someone behind me, that gets me in a place where I'm stuck and challenged.

What's the fundamental challenge in our profession? Most people don't value themselves. That's why our identity work is so important in what we do. The proof of it is this: people who have to buy another car or house to prove to the world they've made it.

Our statistics prove we don't put ourselves first; we don't invest in our fitness as human beings. When someone doesn't value that, it's really hard as a profession to sell it. People won't eat organic eggs for an extra two bucks because of the cost, but they'll stand in line at Starbucks for $5 coffee. They think they don't have the money to buy better food or don't have the time to do something about their fitness.

But they have the time and the money; they just don't see the value. That's what we as fitness professionals step up against. The public doesn't see fitness as we see it. We've have to remind ourselves, "This is what I've been called to; this is what I've chosen."

What an important point about people not valuing themselves. The concept of who's in front of you and who's behind you is important. We should actively, consciously figure that out. When you do that, you'll start to understand your value. Until you realize you're helping people, you might not understand that value.

Dave, what are some habits you feel contributed to your success?

I'm probably a little different than most people in this book who knew what they wanted to do. I didn't; I was headed in a different direction. I was called into this field; I didn't choose it. It's been a journey of favoring grace and stumbling as I go, but I had a passion for movement—being active, free play, being involved with other people and working out. I started with a foundation of and an appreciation for physicality, human movement and physical development.

Because I didn't know anything, I had the blessing of the naive where you can't get caught up in what you think you know; I didn't know *anything*. I was open to listening, learning, exploring, discovering and collaborating. Ironically, that's my motivational core. I know that about myself now and I can use it with more wisdom.

I had two phenomenal mentors who came into my life when I was trying to learn more about fitness. B.J. Baker was with the Boston Red Sox and is a certified trainer and an NSCA strength coach; he became a mentor of mine. Mike Morris at the time was the assistant strength coach and head speed coach of the New England Patriots—two good men wanted to share their knowledge with me. Their doors were always open; they didn't have anything to hide.

Having people like that in your life is critical.

I stepped into a phase of my career where I was in the trenches, all day every day, learning things, throwing things out, collaborating. I was surrounded by good coaches who made me better.

You see this places like Mike Boyle's, with all of the coaches who come through and work on the floor together. They're coaching, but they're also sharing ideas. It's unbelievable how fast you rise when you get in a group of peers who are passionate about the same thing.

In churches, we call this a "strong church." You can see churches where people have been coming to the same church for 15 years, sitting in the same seat, walking out before the last service song is done. This is like a fitness professional being in fitness for 15 years, but staying at the same level.

In a strong church, people are doing small group and service work, coming together, sharing ideas and the place is on fire. With coaches, who are you tapping into and who are you coaching with? How are they making you better?

About five years ago, I had a conversation with myself coming off a presentation at Perform Better. I had some quiet time and spent that time thinking about how I'd found some success in this profession.

And this was the right-sizing truth I wrote about myself: I'm not the most technical coach…truth. I don't know anatomy, kinesiology and the human body nearly as well as most of my peers…truth. I don't have tons of certifications…truth. I went down the list. I don't have some crazy, super IQ…truth.

The only thing I had done, ever, consistently, in my whole life—the one thing, every single session I've ever done, every single camera I've ever been in front of, every single program I've ever written: *I prayed about it.*

And it hit me like a ton of bricks.

That's the one thing I consistently did because I thought I needed that: "God, when I walk into this space today, even if I don't want to—and there are many times when I've said that—help me see this person like she was the last person I'm going to see. Help me see this person the way you see her. Give me new eyes, different ears and a heart to feel differently. Let me move where I need to move, help me do what I need to do. And protect her; keep her safe and help me remember why I'm here."

And I turn it over and walk in. And that has been the foundation of what has served me well and helped me do what I do to the best of my ability. It's foundational.

People who aren't religious would see this as being present. It's an important point we often miss in this profession.

If you're not of faith, it doesn't matter—here's the common thread: Don't rush into a room at the last minute and not think about what you're doing, why you're doing it and who's behind the door. Take a moment to be intentional. Think about who's coming in and how you're going to act in a way that honors the client, serves and gives the best you can give right now. Your best doesn't mean killing yourself. I love to ask people their definition of "best" because it shows how they're wired, which provides a ton of information.

I was working with a young coach who had a young man coming in who's a friend of his—he was just going to take him through a workout. I said, "I'll stick around in case you want to ask me anything."

He was kind of roaming around. I said, "Set the stage."

He said, "What do you mean?"

I said, "Now's the time to see this in your mind, to see him walking through the door, to prepare your mind and heart, to get ready for what you're about to do. Set the stage."

I saw him take some time—he's looking around and has gotten quiet. He's focused; he's present. I saw him writing something on the wall, like a workout, but he's never trained with this guy. I asked, "What'd you write?"

He said, "Just some stuff I want to take him through."

I asked, "How do you know?"

He said, "I don't know. It's stuff I like to do. I asked him a couple of questions and it's stuff I think he might like to do."

I said, "That's good, but how do you know if that's what you're going to do with him? He hasn't walked through the door yet. You haven't asked him the questions you want to ask. Would you be willing to depart from that?"

"Absolutely."

And I said, "You're on the right track. You started with the information you had. You started by wanting to honor him, wanting to deliver something you know and that you're good at. But you're also willing to erase that whole board when he walks in the door because of the way you're present, you realize what you wrote isn't going to serve him today."

That's so powerful. Set the stage.

What about goals? Do you have formal process of goal setting?

Because I'm such a go-by-the-spirit guy, sometimes I don't get really concrete with goals. It starts at the top, knowing this is where I should be going and where I want to go, and this is the work. Sometimes I won't take the first step because it sort of steals from the big picture. It almost poisons the art. That's a challenge area I have to work on.

There's a sweet spot in it for me, which is knowing my true north mission. And in the end, I've found the power of compounding. It's the least thing I am wired to do every day, but it's the most valuable. Little things, done consistently; keeping track of them, keeping them in my mind, using them as guide posts—that really helps me stay the course and not drift too far.

But at the same time, if I'm too structured and think I have to do things a certain way— sometimes I miss the mission when I'm on the mission. I'm still finding balance there.

Let's finish up with three non fitness–related books everybody should read for their development. Could you give us your book suggestions?

The book I read the most is the Bible. That's by far the book I read the most.

Give us reasons why somebody would read that, even someone who isn't religious.

For example, let's take the Book of Proverbs in the Bible—it doesn't have anything to do with a God you have to believe in. It's a book of wisdom. And there are cool one-liners and thoughts that will wow you. It's good as a moral compass toward high-level humanity.

Throughout the Bible, you'll find common themes of the miracle of creation, the miracle of being human, the fact there's someone who loved us enough to give us a chance to be alive and to be in this place.

We don't know how to breathe; we didn't make oxygen to breathe. We don't know how to make water; we'd die without it, but it showed up.

It gives you an opportunity to see yourself differently than the way the world tries to peg you—to see yourself as not good enough. It gives a different picture of what it means to be human and how it might give you a blueprint to see life differently.

And do you have a couple other books for us?

The World's Greatest Miracle by Og Mandino to start with. It's not really faith based, but it will go there if that's how you're wired. It's a little dated and some of it's science, but he used it to help us see how valuable we are.

I like the book by Brené Brown called *Rising Strong* for fitness professionals because of the mindset it explores. I see it with fitness enthusiasts when I ask, "How do you know you got a good workout?" People now, especially getting into the 30s or 40s, still have an athletic desire and a warrior mindset. And they're chasing it at work and it's a grind. They have to walk out of training feeling crushed. If they're not crushed, it wasn't a good workout.

We're in scary territory here. That tells us so much we need to know about what they think fitness is and what it has to do for them to be effective. The grind—this "kill yourself" mentality—it's a badge of honor for them.

In the beginning of the book, Brené Brown says, "I hear this term thrown around everywhere about being a badass." She's a person of faith, but still spicy. She notes how interesting it is that the people who call themselves badasses or grinders usually aren't people who get what that means.

Real badasses are people who can fall flat on their faces and aren't afraid to do it. They hurt and they feel their hurt, and they feel the pain of it. They don't try to shrug things off. They feel their feelings, their pain, and they find a way to stand back up.

You have to be able to fall hard and feel it to truly rise strong and help others do the same. I love that. That's a really cool book when it comes to emotional fitness and emotional and mental wellness.

We'll finish up with the three people you think we can all learn from.

In our profession, I'll just going to bang out a few: Dan John, Mike Boyle, Mark Verstegen and Martin Rooney. The list goes on—there are so many. And there are many peers I've learned from—it's insane how many terrific people we can follow in our profession.

Michael Port is a guy who has some really brilliant work when it comes to stage craft, communicating and speaking more efficiently. Darren Hardy always has interesting ideas when it comes to mindset and motivation. John Maxwell is a great person to look into some of his principles on leadership. Pat Rigsby—when you talk about fitness business stuff—here's a guy who's written a kajillion words on fitness businesses.

Again, when I look at trying to coach, when I look at trying to be a human being, I'm going to go back to the Bible—I'm going back to my faith. Two of the greatest examples for me were Jesus and the Apostle Paul. I'm not talking about them from a faith perspective; I'm talking about how they taught people. Look at the way they taught, the way they raised up and empowered leaders, the way they told stories. They were some of the greatest teachers to ever walk the face of the earth.

I still feel like I know less today than I ever have, like I'm still trying to find my way. I'm doing the best I can with what's in front of me. There's no measure of me that feels successful or that I should be leading. I step into where I'm called and do the best I can with awe and wonder and fear and trembling.

Thanks for letting us take a look at your journey; this has been so insightful. Keep leading people the way you're leading because so many of us have become better because of you.

BE LIKE DAVE

"Who's with you and who's behind you?

"Who's in front of you, leading you somewhere better than where you are and genuinely invested in you doing that?

"Who are the people with you when you bump up to the obstacle, when things are hard, when your kids are sick and you're exhausted and your clients are going bonkers and the money's not coming in? Who can you reach out to? That's hugely valuable.

"Whom am I mentoring? Whom am I trying to raise up?
Whom am I trying to leave something better for?"

BUILD A "STRONG CHURCH"

Make a list of people in each of the categories in the table below. Building relationships is so important; we have heard it from so many people in this book (see Jay Ferruggia's Be Like).

Do you have at least three people in each block of the table? If not, actively try to fill those holes.

Are you in contact with these people on a regular basis? For mentors, take them to lunch periodically (see Rick Mayo's Be Like) and pick their brains. Make sure you thank them! (See Brijesh Patel's Be Like.)

For peers, go visit in their workplaces and talk shop (see Derek Hansen's Be Like). Start an accountability call (see Frank Nash's Be Like) and get feedback from them (see Don Saladino's Be Like).

For those you're mentoring, help them with accountability. Help them with their goals (see the Be Likes of Todd Durkin, Brett Bartholomew and Ron McKeefery) and take an active role in what they're doing.

Who is in front of you? Who are your mentors?	Who is with you? Who are your peers?	Who is behind you? Whom are you mentoring?

Staying active and current with all three of these groups will help you realize you've got people by your side; you are not alone in this journey.

Helping other people, not just your clients,
will help you appreciate the value you have in this world.

Gray is the co-founder of the Functional Movement Screen and the author of the bestseller, Movement. He's a consultant for many universities and pro sports teams in all four major sports and lectures internationally in the fields of physical therapy, sports medicine and performance enhancement. Gray is a Board Certified Orthopedic Clinical Specialist with American Physical Therapy Association who practices physical therapy in Virginia and continues to publish in all areas relating to rehab and exercise. His personal writing is at graycook.com, while FMS is at functionalmovement.com.

You've been successful in a lot of different areas: as a clinician, therapist, educator and author. How do you define success?

You're asking the 52-year-old's version of success; if you'd gotten the 20-year-old version, it was a number in my bank account. The 30-year-old version was saying, "You need to have things together in both your home and professional life." But the 30-year-old version of me was way more articulate in my professional life than in my personal life. Forty was a huge conflict. You get opportunities you hoped for, but you have to turn down some of them, where sometimes you feel it's almost a disservice to those dreams and goals you set earlier.

You get to 50, and you're saying, "What?" I think it was best stated in the *Crocodile Dundee* movie from a billion years ago: "We're all like two fleas fighting over who owns the dog." My answer from the 52-year-old version of myself is being able to achieve some degree of balance in my personal and professional life, like the yin and yang symbol.

The one thing about a cloudy day is you know there's a sunny day coming. Many times we get two or three things that don't go our way. We start projecting that our entire future is going to turn out that way. I try to keep myself from those projections by applying the serenity prayer, "Please let me be completely aware of the things I cannot change."

But also, to understand all the different opportunities, I have to change things. Success is being comfortable with where you are, still trying to do your best, but in a way that doesn't seem so anxious. It has a lot of poise, grace and wisdom to it, not just intelligence. That's what we try to do on the lecture tours. We try to wow you with our intelligence, but the way to thump a crowd is with wisdom. You don't just know your subject matter; you know the practicality and the application.

Most of healthcare and fitness currently exists in a state of complexity for profit. We've made getting healthy and fit so hard or conflicted, people almost feel obligated to seek professional help.

A hundred years ago, professional help wasn't accessible. If you wanted to lose weight, you just kept experimenting with what and how to eat until you lost weight. The lessons you learned were more authentic and sustainable than if you just read a blog. We used to have to live out every mistake we made. Now we're trying to hack them in advance. The black belt you can get online is different from the black belt you have to stand in front of your guru and earn.

The definition of success evolving is a common theme, and that makes the next question pretty hard: When did you begin to feel you were becoming successful? Do you remember a point when you began to feel like things were beginning to work?

I guess I did, but there's a little voice in the back of my head that at least attempted to keep it from being about me. My dad switched careers when I was 10 years old. He went from being a pretty successful businessman to a minister. At the time—in the mid-'70s—being a minister wasn't that popular of a job. He was called to it.

The Methodist Church stuck him in Dry Fork, Virginia, and gave him two churches to preach at every Sunday morning. His yearly income put our family a little below the poverty level. I was one of the kids in the school lunch line on free lunch. My dad took a hit, but he knew we could do it. He was following his heart.

He always told me, "Be a leader, not a follower." I thought that meant being the captain of the football team, the captain of the track team. I did that by trying to be friendly, open and humorous; I was a bit of a class clown. I was able to position myself in leadership roles, but I don't know if I was a good leader.

When I got to physical therapy school at the University of Miami, I was so blown away by everything I was learning and doing that I sat on the back row and didn't say a word for about three years. Socially, I said a lot of crap. But professionally, I sat in the back row with my sleeveless shirt and Umbro shorts and just absorbed it all.

There were a lot of places where I was conflicted—for example, between orthopedics and neurology. Out of that came the thought that we should be looking at movement in a different way. I started giving that message to the people in our clinic: Let's do this differently.

We wound up being inventive because we had fewer resources than everyone else. The central message in the Functional Movement Screen and our original screening family born out of the little clinic in Danville, Virginia, was that we knew we weren't going to get more resources.

We weren't in Atlanta or LA or Chicago. We weren't working with a pro sports team. We didn't have a shoe contract…and universities were way too ivory tower to listen to a bunch of rednecks. We decided, "We're going to take what's in front of us and learn to make cleaner and more accurate decisions. We're going to be snipers. We're not going to shoot as much, but we're going to aim better than anybody else."

I met Bill Foran in Miami, and we had some mutual connections; he was a strength coach for the Miami Heat. He gave me an opportunity to do a chapter in his book High-Performance Sports Conditioning, and I thought, "Let me write about the movement screen."

Reebok heard me lecturing at a regional conference and some of the VIPs at Reebok said, "We like the way this guy's talking about fitness." At the time, they had the Core Board and wanted me to talk about it. I said, "I'll only talk about the Core Board if you let me talk about movement."

I just kept sticking to my guns saying, "It's not me; it's the way I'm talking about movement. It's not the messenger; it's the message."

I've had situations where I let my head get puffed up, but I quickly get back to my home zip code. I go for a hike, do some work, hang out with people who don't know what I do on the road and remember that I get to deliver this cool message. When I get to speak at a big event, I tell myself in the hotel room, "It's not you, but you get to carry a good message, and that's an awesome responsibility. Don't screw it up."

I get to be treated as a successful person. But if I can pat myself on the back, I think part of my success is trying not to let my ego get blown up just because I have an opportunity to carry a good message. That's where it rests for me, and it took it a while to get there. When I see younger people, I want to tell them, "It's the message, not the person."

One thing I've respected about you over the years is your ability to reinvent yourself without really reinventing yourself. For example, you immersed yourself in kettle-bells or with MovNat. You're a voracious learner.

A lot of the books we gravitated toward in the fitness field have been based on your recommendations, and that message of movement has always been underlying. Is that what gets you up in the morning? What is that it that drives you?

Part of it's the fact that I get to pick where I live. I live in the hometown that adopted me when I was 10. My two oldest daughters went to the same high school I did. My parents live very close. I get to work with my brother every day—we pulled him into FMS when the team realized I'm a good writer and idea man, but I suck as an editor. He's way smarter at that than I am.

The only bad thing you can say about the area where I live is that I have a long drive to the airport…which is not so bad either because it helps me mentally switch compartments.

But taking this message of movement and creating more independence and sustainability is a bad business statement. If you're a personal trainer or a physical therapist or an athletic trainer, the purpose of your professional life should almost be that of the Chinese physician a thousand years ago.

Waking up and helping the people who need not to need you—that puts you out of business before you know it. But actually, it doesn't…because your waiting room is always full with new people with new issues who have been positively referred by somebody you helped put on a different path.

When I wake up, I'm wondering, "Does everything that my professional life is focused on help somebody who has a movement issue get more independent with movement?" Then I want to make that more sustainable. That sucks as a business statement because you don't know where your next paycheck is coming from. But if you give back independence and don't create unnecessary dependence or complexity, it helps them adjust their relationships, their professional lives and their time management.

One of the things that gets me up is the fact that I can pretty much wake up and do anything I want. I have a few responsibilities, but I could easily get my responsibilities down to about 15 hours a week. The rest of the time I can do what I want and it doesn't mess with my income that much.

I started getting into this path thinking, "If I can help take this movement message to the masses, we can make a true impact." Who would have ever thought a couple of rednecks could add a station to the NFL Combine that a good number of the people value?

We didn't even try; we weren't working with a shoe company, jamming our methodology down their throats. Does that help the U.S. military? Does that help the fire service? Does that help physical education get out of its own way as we can help kids become more physically relevant?

The movement message is the purest message because we have movement before we have language. We have movement before we have organized thought. We have movement before we have anything else. If you get those lessons right and remember them the next time you have another obstacle—even though it may not be a physical obstacle—you can apply the same methodology you did to the physical one.

I have those 15 hours a week I have to serve my company and some of my other work responsibilities. The rest of the time, I write what I want to write. I talk about what I want to talk about. I invent what I want to invent. But I do it in a way that looks like an ADHD kid.

My wife and I volunteer—I'm a PE teacher once a week at a school that doesn't have a physical education program. I called Chris Poirier at Perform Better and said, "I have $2,500 I want to lose right away. How much can I get at the Gray Cook discount to jam into this little gym?" We wound up with some plyo boxes and balance beams and a bunch of fitness education tools.

I wanted to measure these kids like I teach trainers to do, but I'm not going to use the FMS prescriptive. I give the kids physical obstacles and challenges and in the last five to 10 minutes of every class, I ask them to talk to each other about what they could do differently next time.

It looks like American Ninja Warrior, but there are some lessons in there. They don't know they're learning to balance better, but they are. They don't know they're learning four different transitions in climbing, but they are.

Getting people more fit, more balanced and more into a mind-body connection without them asking for it or without turning it into sets and reps—it's almost like a magic trick or somebody going off on a guitar riff and making it a little more like art. This makes things stick better.

I'm very aware of what I going to do with that other 15 hours a week that I'll be proud of five years from now and that I can go back and say that was a good decision that day.

You mentioned obstacles and the idea of staying true to the message. It's a struggle, especially being out there and seeing your message 10 years ago when you had a smaller company and you were taking the brunt of the criticism.

How do you push through those times when you're feeling like, "I'm just trying to do some good work; I'm not making the money I should be making and I'm still getting criticized?"

Everybody starts wiggling when we're in the hot seat. But when you're in the hot seat, maybe that's the spotlight and if you crack now, you'll never get another time in the light. If you hold true, perhaps you'll get another chance.

If you have 20 clients singing your praises and you have one client who's pissed off, that one client will talk more about the disappointment than the other 20 will hold you up. You have to have about 50 satisfied customers to wash the bad one.

I need to have so much success that if we let that one guy chirp long enough, everybody will realize he's just an asshole. Some people have an axe to grind. They don't have a good principle-based philosophical, strategic argument. Once I realized I was consuming negative comments in the same way I consume a philosophical book or a scientific text, I recognized my problem.

Now, I never read course evaluation. If I do, it's because somebody jammed it under my nose. But for the most part, when the NSCA or others sent me reports saying, "This is how many people liked you, and this is how many people didn't," I say, "You don't need to send me that. If you invite me back, I know that even though there were negative comments, you put those in perspective. Even though there were some positive comments, you put those in perspective too, and you think I can put more butts in the seats than somebody else on your list. If you ask me back, it's not even because you liked my message. It's simply because you got the ratio of positive to negative you're looking for."

I try to never consume a ratio of negative information that overlays positive information. Which positive information? Things that stood the test of time. Media, the news, the constant "What's the next thing we can all be offended by?" has to go away if we're going to think clearly. I try to study as much philosophy as I do science because philosophy guides science. Just because we can do something, doesn't mean we should. Science says anything is possible, but there are some things we probably shouldn't be doing from an ecologically, sustainable, independent standpoint.

I try not to consume much negative information and I don't allow a lot of negative people in the company or in my relationships. My partner, Lee Burton, will criticize any idea I have, but he's just helping me make my case. Greg Rose does the same thing—I could wring their necks, but they force me to make my case; they make me pin up my argument. They make me stick to logic and systems.

I'm not saying I avoid criticism, but I avoid negative chatter. I avoid documents written by unqualified people and try to consume information that stands the test of time—way more than I do things in wet ink by somebody with a new diploma.

Did you envision Functional Movement Systems would be where it is right now? Give us an idea of how you thought about what you wanted to do with your goals.

I didn't do this intentionally, but when I first read Simon Sinek's book *Start with Why,* it helped me develop the language. If you don't know why you're doing something, you should back up and figure that out before you worry about how or what you're doing.

I've always been on a mission to realize what most of us debate about methodology. My goal has been to uncover principles that are operational in my profession, which is health, fitness and performance, and discover how movement plays into that.

There are many ways we get information—you could tell us something or we could observe you. I wanted to get back to the principles of realizing that completely different approaches can get us fit—like those of Pavel Tsatsouline and Erwan Le Corre. Moreover, there's a good chance if you sit with them long enough, you become a healthier and probably a more evolved person. But yet, one uses natural obstacles and the other uses human-made obstacles.

The path they put you on is complete. I didn't want to study those paths from the ivory tower; I wanted full immersion.

How do I get full immersion? I do it by contact and study. My goals sit internally in me as a crock pot saying, "That seems like a contrasting view of fitness and function and movement. Let me go full immersion and see if I can understand that common thread."

There was a point when my marriage was breaking up—I was getting ready to be a single parent of two little girls and I had no idea what to do. I started listening to Anthony Robbins and getting proactive in my steps. But I've never been someone who's going to make 38 bullet points—because I know that if I cover the first three, I'm a smarter person. Then I should probably invent three more and I'm going to be an even smarter person.

Many times, we stack up way too many goals, but as long as the goals aren't dependent on each other, stack as many as you want. If you have a few goals and one is dependent on the other going to fruition, don't even plan that because underpinning that may change your perspective.

I set goals, but I don't consider the goal vetted until I've gone full immersion. Then I back up and entertain conversations with respected colleagues to refine my thinking. Then I try to teach it because you don't fully know something until you teach it.

My goal-setting processes are to find something I'm interested in and see if the same principles I'm trying to convey hold up with it. They got here with a different methodology—can I add value not just by introducing my system? My system is simply a parallel test I run in the background to see if something's warranted.

Many people asked me about Tom Brady's *The TB12 Method* when it came out. Instead of going chapter by chapter saying what we agree and disagree with, if Tom Brady is healthy for a 40-something guy and has a great Functional Movement Screen, is generally fit by fitness standards and if he's accomplished all those goals, that's the way he did it. I don't know if we need to question his effectiveness; he's effective.

Could we have done this more efficiently? Not all of us have Tom Brady's resources. The argument is, can we do things more efficiently once they're effective? Seek out the effective elements and then chip away, doing a dissection, but doing it in a hierarchical and elegant way so you don't throw out something that needs to be observed.

I don't actually have a goal-setting process other than to see out that thing that interests me. Let me see if it's got integrity; let me go full immersion. Let me come back out of it and see if there's a systematic way with which to consume and think about it. It makes me better somehow.

What are some of your habits or personality traits that you attribute to your success?

I grew up listening to my dad preach. It was never boring; he made it relevant. He wasn't teaching gloom and doom. He was giving us a spiritual journey that was more about the opportunities than the punishments. That inspired me to try to speak in an eloquent way to not turn people off.

If somebody walks in the room already turned off, I don't try to engage them to try to flip the mood. I let the crowd do it. I try to speak from the heart. After a lecture people sometimes say, "I've never heard you say that before," and my answer is, "I never know what I'm going to say." I have the basic architecture, but I bounce things off the audience in different ways and watch how people respond.

I like getting into deep conversations. I like it when I'm speaking to a group that's more specialized or focused. General groups are probably the worst groups to work with because if we have a PhD researcher in the front row and a person who's a recently certified trainer three rows back, the questions are so random that we under-serve most people. We're forced to lecture at the poles from the most remedial aspect to the most complex.

When I've got a group that's at least functioning at the same level, I get into a flow state. It's like we're skiing down a slope and we get this riff going. I've always been able to do that; probably the good side of ADHD is hyper-focus as opposed to the inability to focus.

Another habit is that I always try to re-center myself. I'm naturally one of those people who gets out of balance when I start burning the candle at both ends; I go way too far. When I've got an idea in my head, I sleep way too little. When I'm coming off a five-day fast, I gorge way too much. I'm constantly pulling myself out of balance.

I've never had a practice of meditation, but I always find myself in nature. You could put me in the middle of Chicago and I'll find a park or a nature trail if I have a little time. I don't care if it's 10 degrees or 95, I'll be out there as far as possible away from other people, just trying to get some energy back.

I studied personality—and even though I'm an extrovert, I'm about as close to the line as you can be. An introvert gets more of an energy recharge from pulling away. An extrovert gets energy from performing or engaging. I'm right on that line where I love to go inside and re-center myself, then come back out and tell people what I figured out; I love bouncing back and forth.

But when I get pulled on the road too much or into performing too much, I get a little bitter. It's not because I don't like the opportunity; it's because I'm not able to center myself.

You can start to resent some of the things that have made you successful because you feel tied to them if they pull you out of your routine and it takes you off track. Speaking of routines, do you have a specific routine you follow in the morning?

When my wife and I had two teenage daughters six years ago, we got a surprise with my youngest daughter, Xena. There's a 16-year gap between the oldest and Xena. We have two girls going through the boyfriend, high school, college, sports, driver's ed, blah, blah, blah. Then we have a newborn with colic in the house.

My mornings are less structured than most people in my house. Right now, my oldest daughter is out of college, trying to get into PT school, working full time at a clinic. Danielle is managing Xena, doing some nutritional work and managing me, and Kayla is in college. I have four women in the house who have to be out by 8:00AM. My job is to facilitate that their exits.

I'm up, cooking the free-range eggs; I have the Bulletproof Coffee going. One likes turkey sausage, another likes sautéed spinach. I've got the whole kitchen thing going; I'm like Bobby Flay in the morning, and then I shut it down and take an hour to organize my day.

Even if I can't get in a workout, I have two properties—one is a timber farm and one is a cabin up on the lake. On both of them, I can walk for two or three miles and never come off the property.

Whether I jog or decide to carry a sandbag, whether I go split some wood, whether I cut some trees or make a trail or take a walk while I'm doing one of my phone calls—that's my routine.

Even though the meetings and phone calls occur at different times, the breakfast is always consistent. I get up and serve the family because that's my job.

It reminds me of my mom, although the opposite genders: three boys and a husband, even a male dog. She didn't see a toilet seat put down in 20 years. But she used to yell at us, "I'm not a diner cook!" That reminds me of Gray's early morning diner.

When people come to town, there aren't that many hotels or motels in Chatham, Virginia; we have a few BnBs. When people visit, maybe for us to shoot a video or when I have somebody coming to the clinic for a consult, they mostly stay at the house. They're amazed to see me up in the morning; I've got a French press going over here, yerba mate tea going over there. I'm doing my thing.

There's a new book out called *The Captain's Class* that talks about some of the best sports dynasties of all times. It mentions captains we've never heard of, not the Wayne Gretzkys or the Michael Jordans. It's the captain of the team, usually the guy who doesn't need to pick up the locker room, but will do it if nobody else does.

It's good to serve; we have to do that.

Gray, you've talked about some of the walks you take where you're recharging. Are there any other ways you recharge?

During the winter and fall, there are a lot of hikes. I'm managing a hunting property, so between doing some hunting and upkeep, I get plenty of activity. I don't try to have a structured exercise program other than sometimes Indian clubs as a formal discipline.

I'm into defragging in a sauna at night. In the mornings, I'm up serving, but at night while everybody's doing their routines, I move away. I have a sauna in the house. I turn on Netflix or a video I've been planning to watch; I put the iPad on the floor of the sauna and sweat for an hour.

In the summertime, I'll usually cycle between trail running, stand-up paddle boarding and some basic kettlebell exercises. The constants I currently have are jogging, walking or Indian clubs. Seasonally, I'll add the paddle board and usually I'll participate in a few races in the summer. I'll plan a 20-mile canoe race or stand-up paddleboard race to give myself something to train for.

Most people would be blown away by how little I train—how little formal exercise. I'm a very active person and if I find a deficit in myself, I use exercise as a supplement to get myself out of that hole. But most of the time, I structure my life so I'm active enough where I don't have problems.

One of the things people don't understand about the movement screen is that it's not an indicator of fitness; it's an indicator of variety. If you're a healthy person who doesn't need many supplements, there's a good chance you've got a colorful variety in your diet. It's not myopic in any way; it looks like a rainbow.

I think that way about activity. The best way to have a good movement screen isn't to focus directly on the movement screen. When many of us have a fitness goal, we get so focused on it that we can't help but have imbalances.

These kids I'm working with in the PE class get a better movement screen, but it's because of the variety I'm jamming into their lives. If something in that variety inspired them, I'd say, "Get on that path and run with that. Just don't go so far that you take yourself out of balance. If you're getting paid for it or getting a gold medal, then go out of balance as far as you want. You'll probably be able to afford the time and energy to get back in balance when the time is right."

Gray, we'll finish up with two more questions. First, give us three non-fitness books everyone should read to help in their development.

The first is a personal book, but it helps in a professional life and to stay balanced; it's called *The Four Agreements* by Don Miguel Ruiz. It's great as an audio book to meditate to, read by the actor Peter Coyote. *The Four Agreements* is like spiritual weight lifting. It's an easy thing to listen to and a hard thing to do. It's as much of a mental, philosophical and spiritual challenge as adopting a new full-immersion exercise practice.

Once or twice a year, I'll work through *The Four Agreements* just to make sure that my compass is right.

The Simon Sinek book *Start with Why* makes sure your professional principles are in check. If you don't have professional principles—you just have professional interests—it will force you to start seeking principles. That will build a better foundation.

I'll pick two more authors—they're both philosophers, Bruce Lee and Alan Watts. I read a lot of Bruce Lee's work, not just because of the martial arts, but because Bruce Lee, a formally, classically trained martial artist, gave himself the authority to say, "Don't do it that way; do it this way." That's a huge conflict of interest.

It's elegant if you give yourself permission to think outside the box once you're considered by your peers to be good within the box. I didn't start talking about movement until I was a certified strength coach, an Olympic weightlifting coach, a Pilates mat instructor, a physical therapist—and I already had a board certification as an orthopedic specialist.

I didn't start talking until I had every corner of the box painted. Then I started sticking a toe out and realized, "Nobody chopped my foot off. Maybe I'll stick my neck out."

Bruce Lee did that; if you look in his philosophical writings, he said, "You need structure, but at some point, if that structure doesn't lead to fluidity or flow, what's the point?" He was right.

Alan Watts was an Anglican priest who introduced Zen Buddhism to the West. He has a bunch of his writing on audio. But the one I like is a set of CDs called *Out of Your Mind,* mostly from the late '60s, early '70s. What he said back then about balance, professionalism, the environment and getting out of our head sounds pretty timely today.

Those are non-fitness books you can easily use to make yourself a better fitness or healthcare professional. Those books will force you into a balanced perspective when the profession is trying to pull you into a polar place.

Bruce Lee and Alan Watts are good people to follow even though they're no longer with us. Are there other people you recommend we follow?

Tim Ferriss is great to follow. I read *The 4-Hour Work Week* and was getting ready to go back through it—I go through an audiobook and sometimes I'll immediately start over again. I was in the process of doing that when my phone rang: Tim. I thought, "That's pretty freaking cool."

He was in South Africa writing *The 4-Hour Body,* and through a common connection, he wanted to interview me for one of the chapters in the new book. I knew he was trying to hack the movement screen when he said, "What's the best workout, even if you don't have time to do a movement screen."

I was thinking, "That's against my platform, but he's doing what he's supposed to do in scrutinizing a topic, so let's do this."

I like the way he dissects successful performances and talks to successful people—his podcast absolutely blows me away. Many times if I'm going to for a long bike ride or a two-hour paddle or hike, I'll find one of his podcasts that will last about that long, regardless of who he's interviewing—just to listen to the art of the interview, sort of like studying Larry King.

If most of us had an opportunity to talk to the people he's talking to, I don't know if we could carry it for that long. He does that in an elegant way and makes you wonder, "How would I answer that question?"

Tim scratches the surface well. You can't be a master of everything. If he interviews somebody who piques your interest, go full immersion there.

I recently listened to an interview of Tim's with Ray Dalio, the guy who wrote the book *Principles,* and then I went full immersion, listening to every TED talk Ray's done—I got his book and went through it. I listened to what Anthony Robbins said about him in his financial books.

I sometimes let Tim Ferriss decide who I'm going to investigate. I know very well I won't investigate every person he introduces me to, but I like the exposure to people who otherwise wouldn't have crossed my path.

I'm very interested in seeing some of the information you uncover in your interviews for the book. I think you're going to find more common threads than controversy. But it's okay if we disagree because that's when the reader will realize, "I get to make a choice. Which one fits me better?"

We're all at different stages in life—someone's going to have advice that's going to fit you now. When you see the common thread, own it. When you encounter controversy or contrasting opinions, figure out which suits you better at this point in your life.

But make sure you bring honor to it. Don't short-sell it. If you see something that interests you, investigate it. You'll either adopt a new practice or decide that, "A fool who persists in his folly, will soon become wise."

You'll figure out, "That's what's at the end of that and I'm going to go somewhere else now." Either way, it's good.

Embrace the controversy and pick a side. Get good enough at it to know if you're in the right or if you need to expand your mind. Otherwise, the common thread is probably a no-brainer. If 80 percent of the people interviewed have a common thread, that's one you don't need to worry about investigating; you just need to do it.

Gray, thank you. You've been somebody all of us in the fitness profession have looked to as a leader. We appreciate you talking about your journey to success.

BE LIKE GRAY

"Make sure you bring honor to it.
Don't just short-sell it; if you see something that interests you, investigate it."

FULL IMMERSION

Pick an area of study to fully immerse yourself. It could be powerlifting, weight-lifting, kettlebells, a certification, nutrition…it doesn't matter.

Commit to making it the only thing you will investigate for one month.

Imagine that after the one month, you will have to teach the subject at a major conference.

Discover everything you can on the subject—videos, articles, books and pod-casts learn everything you can. Make a goal to spend at least one hour each day learning about it.

Find an expert on the subject and if you can't study with them, get on the phone. Try to find someone you can spend some time with on the subject. If it's a fitness topic, find a trainer to work with you.

At the end of each week, find a willing "student" to teach everything you learned that week. One of the best ways to retain knowledge is to teach it.

Think about writing an article on what you learned or making it into a presen-tation (see Mike Boyle's Be Like). That will put the pressure on to really learn everything you can.

ACKNOWLEDGMENTS

"No one gets there alone."

A huge thank you to the 50 contributors in this book who took the time to get on the phone for the interviews, answering all the email and dealing with my numerous requests. You did it without hesitation and I am grateful.

A special thanks to Mike Boyle, Don Saladino, Ron McKeefery, Geralyn Coopersmith and Alwyn Cosgrove for being part of the original Success Series that led to the book idea. You made this happen.

Michael Hyatt, I would not have thought I could be an author if it wasn't for your coaching, lessons and accountability. You helped me overcome so many self-limiting beliefs. I would have never met Ellie, Rene, Sheila, Steve, Debbie, Matt, Mary, Scott and Cynthia, who have been there with me through this whole process. You all rock.

To Frank Daniels, my accountability partner, thanks for all the pushing you did, always keeping me on my toes and calling me out when needed.

Thanks to Chris Poirier and Perform Better for being part of *The Strength Coach Podcast* from Day One. So many amazing things have come from the podcast and none would have been possible without you.

To Betty Gerstein, my first client in the fitness profession, thanks for the constant support and for the first edits after some brutal transcriptions.

Thanks to Laree Draper for always supporting *The Strength Coach Podcast*, for believing in me and making this process as easy as it could be.

Thanks to my parents for always being there and for being more excited about this than me. You're the BEST.

Thanks to my Bee (and Emma) for always, always, always supporting me and believing in me. This doesn't happen without your love, patience and support.

INDEX OF BE LIKES

BOOKS RECOMMENDED BY THE BEST

INDEX OF PEOPLE REFERENCED

ABOUT THE AUTHOR

Anthony Renna has been a personal trainer since 2004, first working with Equinox, then on his own at different facilities before opening his own gym, Five Iron Fitness, in 2008.

He sold Five Iron in 2016 so he could focus on his true passion of providing educational resources for fitness professionals to excel in the profession. His mission is to help them find success and make an impact in the world by sharing all he has learned from the best of the best.

As the founder and host of both the *Strength Coach Podcast* and *Strength Coach TV,* he has interviewed hundreds of strength coaches, fitness professionals, physical therapists and gym owners. He applies what he learned by helping fitness professionals in his personal coaching and accountability group. You can learn more about the group via the page *CONTINUEfit.com/Propel.*

Anthony continues to train clients a few hours a week and is a partner with Mike Boyle in *StrengthCoach.com* and *BodyByBoyleOnline.com.*